MW01079716

INTRODUCTION TO PRENATAL PSYCHOLOGY

Stephen M. Maret, PhD

**To Courtney Lauren
and Brandon Kent,
my two favorite fetuses.**

Life is tough. It takes up much of your time, all your weekends, and what do you get in the end of it? I think that the life cycle is all backward. You should die first, get that out of the way. Then you live 20 years in an old-age home. You get kicked out when you're too young. You get a gold watch, you go to work. You work 40 years until you're young enough to enjoy your retirement. You go to college; you party until you're ready for high school; you go to grade school; you become a little kid; you play. You have no responsibilities. You become a little baby; you go back to the womb; you spend your last 9 months floating; and you finish up as a gleam in somebody's eye.

**Anonymous
Quoted in Mike Yaconelli's *Dangerous Wonder* (1998)**

January 2009
Copyright Church Gate Books
churchgatebooks@hotmail.com
New Providence, NJ

Cover designed by Courtney L. Maret

CONTENTS

6   EMBRYONIC DEVELOPMENT

Introduction
Embryo Support Structures
     The Placenta
     The Umbilical Cord
     The Amniotic Sac
Embryonic Growth
     The Gastrula
     Patterns of Development
     Organogenesis
     Physical and Structural Growth
Conclusion

7   FETAL DEVELOPMENT

Introduction
The Third Month (Weeks 9-12)
     Sexual Differentiation
     Physical Development
     Chorionic Villus Sampling
The Fourth Month (Weeks 13-16)
     Fetal Breathing
     Lanugo
     Mecomium
     "Quickening"
     Physical Development
     Amniocentesis
The Fifth Month (Weeks 17-20)
     Vernix
     REM Sleep
     Physical Development
     Fetoscopy
The Sixth Month (Weeks 21-24)
     Sensory Capabilities
     Fetal Viability
     Ultrasound
The Seventh Month (Weeks 25-28)
     Fetal Development
     Fetal Surgery
The Eighth Month (Weeks 29-32)
The Ninth Month (Weeks 33 to Birth)
Conclusion

8   MATERNAL DEVELOPMENT

1

INTRODUCTION AND HISTORICAL CONTEXT OF PRENATAL PSYCHOLOGY

Men have existed – before they are born.

Ambrose of Milan

INTRODUCTION

Prenatal psychology at its very core is the simple extension of commonly held and accepted developmental psychological principles into the period prior to birth. Like child psychology or adolescent psychology, prenatal psychology is the study of the human organism within a particular period of time, with specific attention given to the unique capabilities, limitations, and environmental factors typical of development at that stage.

Among the factors making prenatal psychology different from any other developmental stage is the unique environment of the womb, and the almost complete dependence that this environment implies for the embryo and the fetus. Dependence, however, does not mean a lack of development, or imply the absence of a unique and developing personality. Infants remain relatively dependent on others to insure their survival, and yet, the evidence is overwhelming that infant development and personality exists.

This understanding of infancy as a psychologically significant stage of life is relatively recent. Prior to the 1960's, the neonate was regarded almost exclusively as a physiological being (Rau, 1982). The introduction of Brazelton's Neonatal Behavioral Assessment Scale in 1970 had a profound effect of changing attitudes towards the newborn (Schindler, 1988). By 1973, William James' infamous description of the infant's perception of the world as "blooming, buzzing confusion" was being replaced by the concept of the "competent newborn" (Stone, Smith & Murphy, 1973). This change in perception was slow, and was forced by the accumulating research evidence. More than 30 years later, this notion is now widely accepted and taken for granted.

Rau, writing in 1983, described the change in perceptions of the neonate that had occurred:

And so arose the picture of a baby that incorporates the essential and psychologically important characteristics-- even if they are still only rudimentary-- which also form the older child and adult, respectively. It is the picture of an active organism, one which contributes to its own development in interaction with the world around it. As a result, it can now even be described in terms of subject, not only in objective terms which are already well-known. (Rau 1983, p. 83)

Rau's description applies equally well to the fetus, who, like the baby, is also an "active organism" with "essential and psychologically important characteristics", who also "contributes to its own development in interaction with the world around it". This is the subject and content of this book. We will be examining each facet of prenatal development, beginning with conception, and continuing into the embryonic and fetal periods, culminating with birth. We will describe the prenate's "world", and include discussion of his mother, her behavior and environment, the placenta, the womb, and the umbilical sac. Finally, we will examine how development of the prenate within his environment is clearly psychological. The prenate is our subject, and not just the object of study, for this book.

The notion of the "competent fetus", however, is still not widely accepted. Similar to the perception of the newborn in the 1960's, the prevailing view of prenatal life continues to be one of viewing the fetus as relatively passive and inert physiologically and devoid of meaning psychologically. Even in the face of large amounts of accumulating evidence to the contrary, the physiological and psychological capabilities of the fetus continue to be minimized and disregarded.

There are several reasons why general perceptions of prenatal life have not yet "caught up" with the research data and evidence. One explanation may be the fact that interest in embryology extending as far back as the middle ages and before, has been primarily oriented towards anatomy and the "mechanics" of pregnancy and birth and not towards a fetal perspective. Thus, the legacy of this outlook has been to view the fetus, "apart from some aimless kicking which began in the fifth month . . . [as] as placid, fragile vegetable who developed quietly in preparation for a life which started at birth" (Liley, 1973, p. 192).

Although interest in the dynamics of intrauterine life continues to slowly change, there is still the tendency to begin with adult functioning and work backwards, eventually arriving at the prenatal period. Intentional or not, this "comparative" mentality has contributed toward the regard of the preborn and newborn as inadequately functioning adults rather than well functioning fetuses and neonates.

An additional factor which continues to influence perceptions of fetal capabilities may be a much-cited study by Langeworthy in 1933 titled *Development of Behavior Patterns and Mylenization of the Nervous System in the Human Fetus and Infant.* This study made the assertion that "incomplete myelinization of sensory tracts" resulted in the inability of the fetus to receive neural messages from its specialized sense receptors. However, research subsequent to Langeworthy's study has clearly shown that full myelinization, which occurs only after birth, is not essential for sensory functioning. While full myelinization does increase the rapidity of conduction, well-organized neural activity and sense receptivity is possible long before the nerve fibers are completely myelinated (Bekoff & Fox, 1972). DeMause has noted that Langeworthy's "incomplete myelinization" misstatement "continues to be used to deny the ability of the fetus and the newborn to feel pain in many areas of medicine, from the use of aborted fetuses as subjects in painful medical experiments to the denial of anesthesia during circumcision and surgery of the newborn" (DeMause, 1982, p. 253).

Further, the modern discussion of the notion of "consciousness" as it relates to adults, and the difficulty in defining the term adequately, has lead to the view that the term itself is taboo. Chamberlain points out that "it is unfortunate that for all concerned that these specialties [obstetrics and pediatrics] came to prominence in during as era of psychology when the subject of consciousness was taboo and neonates were considered essentially decorticate. Therefore, virtually all the routines of modern obstetrics and pediatrics presuppose an infant who is without personal thought, feeling, or memory-- a position which, I think, can no longer be reconciled with the facts" (Chamberlain, 1983, p. 3).

Various ethical issues related to human embryological and fetal research have rightly prevented certain types of investigations. Thus, particular data regarding fetal life was simply unavailable. The result was an over-reliance on comparative animal studies, which ultimately has proved to be inadequate. This is due to the great variation between human and animal, even human and mammalian, reproductive physiology, psychology and embryology. While still important, especially in research on teratogens, animal studies prove less than satisfactory when seeking data on specifically and uniquely human characteristics.

Previous lack of technology has also contributed toward a faulty understanding of fetal functioning. As technology (including sonography, photography, sound spectrography, electroencephalography) has become more and more sophisticated, a "window" on the embryological and fetal life of human beings has been opened which was previously unavailable. Various forms of medical technology has also pushed the threshold of "viability" earlier and earlier, in a sense allowing external observation of the entire "third trimester." These technological advances have served to provide a huge opportunity to study fetal life, and consequently correct previous faulty assumptions.

Commenting on the confluence of these variables, Davies has written that perhaps study of fetal life has been lacking due to the fact that the fetus itself was so "inconveniently tucked away in a most inaccessible situation. This area of medicine offered little opportunity for discovery, and did not attract much talent. Why study a creature so passive, so dull, so small, and technically so difficult?" (Davies, 1973, p. 965).

Finally, and perhaps most importantly, attitudes toward legal abortion and its acceptability have implicitly influenced the acceptability of the idea of the "competent fetus". The notion of a fetal personality with unique and distinct character traits and behavioral competencies implies a conceptualization of fetal personhood not unlike infant personhood. Abortion of a fetal "person" is thus indistinguishable from infanticide. Consequently, there has been resistance to the idea of "prenatal psychology", predominantly among those who affirm the acceptability of abortion, particularly the late-term variety (also called partial-birth abortion) of the practice.

But the research evidence is now substantial and overwhelming enough that denying the physiological and psychological sophistication of prenates is to ignore reality. As will hopefully be evident from the remainder of this book, the confirmation is overwhelming that the fetus is indeed amazingly competent.

HISTORY OF PRENATAL THOUGHT

Early Western Thought

The idea that the prenatal environment affects the developing organism is certainly not new or unique to the last century. Many early thinkers speculated, some accurately and others mistakenly, regarding fetal behavior and psychology as well as the influence of maternal and/or environmental determinants of fetal outcomes. Democritus and Epicurius both surmised that the embryo ate and drank *per os*. Plutarch later compared these views to that of the earlier Alcmaeon who postulated a "sponge" theory of prenatal nourishment. Plutarch wrote that "Democritus and Epicurius hold that this imperfect fruit of the womb receiveth nourishment at the mouth. . . . But Alcmaeon affirmeth that the infant within the mother's wombe, feedeth by the whole body throughout for that it sucketh to it and draweth in a manner of a sponge" (Plutarch in Gupta & Datta, 1988, p. 514).

Writing about the same time as Alcmaeon, Empedocles theorized regarding the origin of twins and affirmed the profound influence of the maternal imagination upon the fetus, to the point that it could be guided and interfered with at will.

With the work of Hippocrates and those associated with him, namely his son-in-law Polybus, embryology takes a great leap forward, particularly with his treatise *On Semen and on the Development of the Child*. Hippocrates rightly surmised that it is the maternal blood flow which nourishes the embryo. Further, he argued that the umbilical cord allowed for fetal respiration (Ellinger, 1922).

During the next century (4th century, BCE), Diocles of Carystus extended embryological thought through his examinations and dissections of fetal remains. He reported that he had found traces of the head and spinal cord in a 27-day-old embryo and was able to clearly distinguish the human form at 40 days (Allbutt, 1921).

With the possible exception of Hippocrates, Aristotle stands out among the early Western thinkers as the most important advancer of embryological science. Due to his extensive dissections of various animals and animal embryos, his observations filled several major works of general and comparative biology and embryology, among them *On the Generation of Animals, The History of Animals, On the Parts of Animals, On Respiration,* and *On the Motion of Animals*. He correctly understood the nature of fetal nutrition and he anticipated several important aspects of embryology, among them genetics and enzyme actions. Interestingly Aristotle also speculated that sensation is first acquired during pregnancy.

Following Aristotle, embryological understanding in the western tradition stagnates, and even regresses. But exceptions to this trend also stand out. For instance, Herophilus of Chalcedon, a member of the Alexandrian School and writing in the 3rd century BCE made many dissections of embryos and described in some detail the ovaries, Fallopian tubes, and the umbilical cord (Gupta & Datta, 1988).

In addition to the Greek thinkers, two Romans also made contributions toward the understanding of embryology that lasted well into the Middle Ages. In the 1st century AD, Sorenus of Ephesus wrote a book titled *On the Disease of Women*, which, although largely obstetrical, also showed an advanced understanding of embryology. Tertullian, writing in the following century and arguing that the fetus is already a living being in the uterus, stated that "Soranus . . . [was] sure that a living creature had been conceived" (Jackson, 1988, p. 109), thus implying at least a rudimentary acknowledgement of the separate life of the fetus.

The second Roman of note was Galen, who lived in the 2nd century AD and wrote three works touching on embryology with the intriguing titles of *On the Anatomy of the Uterus, On the Formation of the Fetus*, and *On the Question as to whether the Embryo is an Animal*. Galen called the processes of intrauterine life "genesis" and while much of his descriptions of it are inaccurate, he alludes to the processes histogenesis (tissue-production) and organogenesis (differentiation of tissue into organs) as "alteration" and "shaping" or "molding." The period of "genesis", according to Galen, includes four distinct stages (Gupta & Datta, 1988): (1) an unformed seminal stage; (2) a stage in which the *tria principia*"are engendered (the heart, liver and brain); (3) a stage when all the other parts of the body are mapped out; and (4) a stage when all the other parts have become clearly visible

There are also historical accounts that Cleopatra, the prominent Ptolemaic queen, supervised her own somewhat gruesome embryological research studies in 1st century BCE. However, most experts note that the original source of this cannot be traced and so the account must remain in the category of "legend". It was said that Cleopatra dissected live female slaves "… impregnated by prison guards at known intervals of time from conception-- following the procedure of Hippocrates with regard to hen's eggs. This Alexandrian experiment established that the male fetus was complete in 41 days and the female in 81" (Gupta & Datta, 1988, p. 531).

Early Non-Western Thought

Preceding and parallel to the early Greek and Roman embryological advances was an active tradition of speculation regarding embryological and fetal processes in places outside of the traditional "west". Most prominent are a group of Indian writers, the earliest being Susruta, around the late 6th or early 5th century BCE.

Similar to the early Greek and Roman thinkers, much of their speculation was faulty, but much also anticipated later discoveries. For instance, modern genetics is prefigured with Susruta's affirmation that "the bodily and mental characteristics of the future child, whether manifest or latent, are pre-determined" (Gupta & Datta, 1988, p. 521). He divided the "genetic" contributions of each parent according to sex, with the father contributing the "stable and firm components" of the body (the hair, nails, bones, nerves, arteries, veins, teeth, tendons and semen) while the "soft components" (blood, fat, muscles, heart, bone-marrow, liver, spleen, intestines, umbilicus, rectal parts, and sex organs) result from the mother's "genetic" contribution. Emerging from the "physiological and spiritual harmony" of the parents are the "genetic" characteristics of intellect, health, valour, constitution, and "brightness of complexion." (Susruta, 1954).

Susruta also clearly articulated a sophisticated understanding of the interdependency of the feto-placental unit, both physiologically and psychologically. He noted that nourishment from the mother's body begins by means of the umbilical cord as soon as the fetus is "endowed with life" and advocated a variable diet for mother and child depending upon the needs of the growing fetus. In addition, Susruta maintained an understanding of the impact of the mother's psychological state upon the emerging fetus. Following the third month when all the major limbs and organs are present in their rudimentary forms, Susruta states that the fetus acquires a consciousness of its surroundings and begins to "long for" sense objects. These "longings" are imparted to the mother and are expressed externally through the mothers "desires." If the exchange is short-circuited and these desires are denied, suppressed or remain unfulfilled, then the effect on the fetus can be profound. According to Susruta, various congenital defects such as paralysis, dwarfism, blindness, various sense organ defects and lameness can be the result.

That Susruta maintained some sort of fetal psychology was clear. Along with the above stated affirmations of consciousness and sense perception, he noted that the fifth month resulted in the acquisition by the fetus of a "mind of its own" and is said to "awaken". This was quickly followed by the realization of an "intellect" in the 6th month.

A second prominent early Indian thinker in the area of embryology is Caraka, who shared similar theoretical notions with Susruta regarding the "genetic" contributions of the mother and father to the developing fetus. From the mother come the "skin, blood, flesh, fat, navel, heart, liver, spleen, kidneys, urinary bladder, colon, stomach, intestine, rectum, anus, small intestines, large intestines, and mesentery", while the father contributes the "head-hairs, beards-mustaches, nails, body hairs, teeth, bones, ligaments, and semen" (Caraka, 1982, p. 421). The fetus' appetite, vitality, clarity of senses, and quality of voice all arise out of parental harmony while the qualities of life-span, self knowledge, mind, sense organs, respiration, impulse, sustenance, characteristic physiognomy, voice and complexion, happiness, misery, desire-aversion, consciousness, restraint, intellect, memory, ego and will are cause by the fetus' self, known as jiva.

Caraka also shared with Susruta an understanding of the importance of fetal nourishment. He maintained that the child's shape, vigor, energy and sense of contentment all arise as a result of proper nourishment. According to Caraka, the physiological process of embryonic and fetal development proceeds from that of "shapeless jelly" the first month to being "tumor-like" or fleshy the second to limb and sex-organ differentiation the third month and so on. He believed the fetus' and mother's hearts to be connected through the umbilical cord and placenta, transmitting nourishment through the blood, as well as "vitality and complexion." Caraka assumed that the fetus could be destroyed, deformed, or suffer psychologically due to physical or emotional disturbances of the mother. Indeed, Caraka was very aware of the possible prenatal psychological influences on the emerging child's psyche and listed a comprehensive catalogue of possible mental stress, shocks, and maternal habits which might cause psychological damage to the fetus. He writes:

> The woman sleeping in open places and moving out in the night gives birth to an insane; if she indulges in quarrels and fights, the progeny will be epileptic. One indulged in sexual intercourse to ill-physiqued, shameless, and devoted to women; one always under grief to timid, undeveloped or short-lived; one thinking ill of others to harmful, envious, or devoted to women; the thief to exerting, wrathful or inactive; the intolerant to fierce, deceitful and jealous; one who sleeps constantly to drowsy, unwise and deficient in digestive power; one who takes wine constantly to thirsty, poor in memory and unstable in mind. . . . The pregnant woman gives birth to a child suffering mostly from the respective disorders the etiological factors of which are used by her. Thus the facts causing damage to the fetus are said. Hence the woman desiring excellent progeny should particularly abstain from the unwholesome diet and behavior. Observing good conduct, she should manage herself with the wholesome diet and behavior (Caraka, 1982, p. 468).

In addition to Susruta and Caraka, other Indian thinkers also made various embryological speculations. Most concurred with Susruta and Caraka, indicating a striking congruity on the subject of a fetal psychology, especially as it relates to sense perception and consciousness. One example is from a man named Parasara, who wrote that "during the sixth month, holes appear in the ears of the embryo. During the seventh month vessels, ligaments, bones, phalanges, hair on the head, nails and skin appear on the embryo. The embryo becomes more conscious during this month" (Parasara, 1968).

Medieval and Early Modern Thought

Following Galen, the advance of embryology and fetology was, at least in the Western tradition, arrested for almost 13 centuries. While several works do occur, they are essentially composed of restatements or compilations of Hippocrates, Aristotle, Sorenus and Galen. For instance, Albertus Magnus' *De animalibus* from the 13th century was essentially a close restatement of Aristotle and Galen, especially as it relates to areas of embryological interest.

Perhaps one exception to this is Trotula's 11th century text on various gynecological ailments and their cures (Trotula, 1981). Trotula, thought to be a woman, was associated with the medical school in Salerno, Italy. Her work was not available in an English translation until the middle of the 15th century but still preceded by almost a century what was at one time thought to be the earliest obstetrical text to appear in English, *The Byrth of Mankynde*, translated from Eucharius Rosslin's *Der Swangern Frawen und Hebammen Rosegarten,* first published in 1513 and first appearing in English in 1540.

Similar to the medieval period, various derivative works continued to appear in the 15th and 16th centuries. However, several small advances began to appear, including Leonardo da Vinci's embryological and fetological statements, drawings and illustrations. With the publication in 1604 of Hieronymus Fabricius' *De formato Feotu*, the description and illustration of the physiological dimension of embryology and fetology takes a great leap (Cunning-ham, 1985). But this publication, and the ones preceding and it, contain little if any speculation regarding the existence of a fetal psychology.

Up until the 16th century, the prevailing view of embryological development was the epigenetic, that the various components of the developing creation occurred sequentially. The historic weakness to this conceptualization is that it did not adequately account or the complex mechanism of the "creation" of life itself (McLaren, 1985). A less dominant but plausible rival view was the preformation theory, which argued that embryonic life in miniature already existed within the parent and thus development consisted simply in growth, not creation. Such an argument, postulated early on by Plato and Aeschylus among others, came into vogue during the late 16th century. But because of the inability to locate an ovum or sperm in the uterus, the epigenetic line of reasoning was revived by some. William Harvey, for instance, in his important 1651 work *De generatione animalium*, took this view (McLaren, 1985).

The period of the end of the 17th through the end of the 19th century brought about significant technical and "physical" advances in embryology and fetology. With the availability of the microscope at the close of the 17th century, the sperm was first seen by Hamm and Leeuwenhoek in 1677 following by five years the observation of the ovarian follicles by de Graff. Thus, the preformation theory again begins to prevail, but is split between two camps, the "animalculists" and the "ovists", the latter holding that the miniature offspring was to found in the ovum and the former that it was to be found in the sperm. The preformationist view in its various manifestations predominated until at least the middle of the 18th century.

It was also during this period that some speculation regarding fetal cognition and understanding takes place. John Locke, writing in his *Essay Concerning Human Understanding* speculated that the capacity to form ideas may be characteristic of fetal life. Jean-Jacques Rousseau, writing in the next century, regarded the fetus as a "witless tadpole" (Hepper, 1989).

The late 18th century brought some important advances, including Spallanzani's application of the experimental method to embryology which finally demonstrates that both the ovum and sperm are necessary for conception to occur (Patten, 1946). This discovery, along with a general lack of evidence for the preformation theories resulted in a switch back to the epigenetic argument, this time permanently, although the change was quite gradual. The preformationist theory was permanently laid to rest in 1900 by Driesch who showed that forms of the cells of a fertilized egg, can, when separated, develop into complete embryos. The present view is that "development is strictly preformational as regards the genes and their hereditary influences, but rigorously epigenetic in actual constructional activities" (Arey, 1954, p. 4).

The late 18th and 19th centuries brought many technical advances. For instance, William Hunter's *Treatise on the Human Gravid Uterus* was published in 1774 and was an important advance in embryological and fetal observation and illustration. Von Bauer finally clearly identified the mammalian ovum in 1827 (Arey, 1954) while Schleiden and Schwann lay the foundations of modern embryology with the formation of cell theory (Patten, 1946). Wilhelm His' book *The Anatomy of Human Embryos*, published in 1880, stands as the first great modern work dealing with specifically human embryology.

Twentieth Century Thought

With the biochemistry, biology, anatomy and neurology of embryology and fetology gradually becoming clearer through much of the early to middle part of the 20th century, the groundwork was laid for a return to substantial speculation about the psychological sophistication of the fetus. Certainly crucial to this debate was the thought of Sigmund Freud. His impact upon the subsequent psychodynamic understanding of fetal life was profound and undeniable. Addressing Freud's negative influence on prenatal psychology, deMause writes that ". . .virtually all contemporary psychoanalytic theory denies the possibility of mental life before or during birth. The newborn is believed to be without memory, ego, objects, or mental structure" (deMause, 1982, p. 247).

But whether intentional or not, Freud "opened the door" (Lake, 1978) to a consideration of the psychodynamics of intrauterine life. Freud himself appears to be inconsistent. For instance, Freud wrote in *Inhibitions, Symptoms and Anxiety* (1936) that "birth still has no psychic content" and "birth is not experienced subjectively as a separation from the mother since the foetus, being a completely narcissistic creature, is totally unaware of her existence as an object". However, in the same work he also referred to birth as the "earliest anxiety of all" and the "primal anxiety." Frank Lake cites Freud as writing that "there is much more continuity between intra-uterine life and the earliest infancy the impressive caesura of the act of birth allows us to believe" (Freud in Lake, 1978, p. 5).

Phyllis Greenacre, writing regarding Freud's position notes that even though "he doubts the importance of the individual birth experience in influencing the quantum of the anxiety response, largely because the birth experience is without psychological meaning, at the same time, nevertheless, he emphasizes the continuity of the intrauterine and the postnatal life" (Greenacre, 1952, p. 52). D.W. Winnicott noted that Freud held to his view of birth being psychologically inconsequential most of the time. However, he also writes that "the only time when he was said to have deviated from this view was once when he was heard to have wondered if an infant born by Caesarian section might have a different pattern of anxiety" (Winnicott, 1958, p. 175).

Freud's schizophrenic attitude toward birth is perhaps illustrated by his initial embrace of Otto Rank's book *The Trauma of Birth* as "the most important progress since the discovery of psychoanalysis" (Freud in Lake, 1981, p. 3). However, he apparently turned against Rank at the behest of Abraham, Jones and some of the others of his inner group who warned that Rank's book would eclipse Freud's work (Taft, 1958). Later, in writing to Abraham, Freud alluded that he was "getting further and further away from birth trauma. I believe it will 'fall flat' if one doesn't criticize it too sharply, and then Rank, who I valued for his gifts and the great services he has rendered, will have learned a useful lesson" (Fodor, 1971, p. 39).

Otto Rank began his study of the possible effect of birth experiences in 1904, finally publishing *The Trauma of Birth* in 1923. This work, which clearly laid the groundwork for an understanding of the effect of pre-natal events on subsequent functioning, described Rank's contention that not only was birth the first experienced anxiety, but that it was the prime source material for all the neuroses and character disorders. It was the "original emotional shock underlying all personality dysfunction." Rank wrote that "we believe that we have discovered in the trauma of birth the primal trauma," and that "we are led to recognize in the birth trauma the ultimate biological basis of the psychical." He continued: "We have recognized the neuroses in all their manifold forms as reproductions of, and reactions to, the birth trauma" (Rank, 1952, p. xiii).

While Rank did not articulate a fetal psychology *per se*, he alluded to the significance of the prenatal:

> All symptoms ultimately relate to this "primal fixation" and the place of fixation is "in the maternal body" and in peri-natal experiences." He continues by writing that "we believe that we have succeeded in recognizing all forms and symptoms of neuroses as expressions of a regression from the stage of sexual adjustment to the pre-natal primal state, or to the birth situation, which must thereby by overcome". (Rank, 1952, pp. 78-79)

Building on Rank's work, Donald W. Winnicott (1957; 1958; 1972), a British pediatrician and psychoanalyst, continued to push the "primal" influence back earlier, alluding more strongly to the importance of pre-natal life. Although, like Rank, his primary emphasis was still on birth as an event "etched on the memory" that manifested itself in the stresses of later life, he also alludes strongly to the possible effect of the prenatal period, extending back as far as conception, upon the developing psyche. He writes that "there is certainly before birth the beginning of an emotional development, and it is likely that there is before birth a capacity for false and unhealthy forward movement in emotional development" (Winnicott in Lake, 1987, p. 169).

An American contemporary of Winnicott's was Phyllis Greenacre, who, in her book *Trauma, Growth, and Personality* also makes allusions to the possible impact of the prenatal environment, but subsequently seems to back away from the implications. She writes "The fetus moves, kicks, turns around, reacts to some external stimuli by increased motion"(Greenacre, 1952, p. 54). Indeed, research showing the increase of fetal heart rate and fetal movements to such stimuli as loud noises and maternal nervousness would indicate that these are signs of anxiety, as they would be in the child or adult. While Greenacre retreats from any kind of affirmation of a distinctly "fetal anxiety", probably due to persuasion by Freud (Ridgeway, 1987), she did affirm that anxiety-like responses in the fetus give rise to a predisposition to anxiety in the child and adult. She summarizes her own ambivalence to birth and pre-birth anxiety when she wrote that "perhaps the struggle of birth is at once too terrifying and too inspiring for us to regard it readily with scientific dispassion" (Greenacre, 1945, p. 40).

While Freud, Rank, Winnicott, Greenacre and others all made allusions to the possible importance of the prenatal, it is in the work of Nandor Fodor and his follower, Francis Mott, that the prenatal is specifically emphasized. It is Fodor's work *The Search for the Beloved: A Clinical Investigation of the Trauma of Birth and Pre-Natal Conditioning*, which was published in 1949, that really marks the beginning of the modern "prenatal psychology" movement. As is clear with the title of the book, the first part of the book was devoted to birth trauma, while the second part is devoted to the "Traumata of the Unborn." Fodor affirmed the importance of birth for later development, the therapeutic effect of re-experiencing birth and prenatal life, the specific problems raised by particular maternal habits and behavior such as rejection of the fetus and attempted abortion. He wrote:

> The life of the unborn is not necessarily one of unbroken bliss. The unborn child is dependent on his mother's blood-stream for oxygen, for food, and for the elimination of its waste products. There are many maternal afflictions that affect and perhaps weaken the child before birth. Many children seem to start post-natal life with a handicap. (Fodor, 1949, p. 396)

In the same book several pages later, Fodor affirmed that the prenatal period was more crucial than birth for subsequent functioning. He writes that "the release of the trauma of birth is the introductory phase of the integration of pre-natal trauma. The more vital phase concerns the shocks suffered prior to birth. In order to release these shocks, the mind must take cognizance of their existence and nature" (Fodor, 1949, p. 400). Fodor approvingly quotes an earlier writer named Sadger to indicate his position. Sadger wrote that he believed "that which all my patients assert, that the embryo already feels plainly whether its mother loves it or not, whether she gives it much love, little love, or none at all, in many instances in fact in place of love, sheer hate" (Sadger, 1941, p. 336).

Francis Mott's work was primarily based upon the analysis of various case histories, particularly dreams. He was as explicit in his emphasis upon intrauterine life as Fodor was. His fundamental principle was that "every psychological feeling derives from an older physical feeling." For instance, the very basic psychological sense of "I" is originally derived from the physical sensation of contact between the fetal skin and its environment. Thus, the bi-directional flow of blood from mother to fetus as mediated by the placenta through the umbilical cord, gives rise to the physical "feelings" of aggression, submission, emptiness, fullness, giving and taking that is the basis for subsequent psychological "feelings". Mott utilized the term "umbilical affect" to designate this exchange, defining it as the "feeling state of the fetus as brought about by blood reaching him through the umbilical vein" (Mott in Moss, 1987, p. 203). As Mott envisaged it, the umbilical vein not only conveys nutritive resources and as such could be experienced as a "life-giving flow, bringing . . . renewal and restoration" but could also "be the bearer of an aggressive thrust of bad feelings into the foetus if the mother herself was distressed and 'feeling bad.'" If the mother felt emotionally unsupported , then "this feeling of deficiency, lack of recognition and the failure of looked-for support, would be just a specifically felt by the fetus. It became distressed by the failure of its immediate environment to provide the expected acceptance and sustenance, not so much at the level of metabolic input . . . but to nourish the earliest beginnings of the person in relationship" (Mott in Lake, 1987, p. 1).

Stanislav Grof's work is contemporaneous with that of Mott's. His analysis, however, was less dependent upon dreams as the content for his theories and very dependent upon LSD-assisted abreactions. Beginning in 1953, Grof began utilizing LSD as a psycholeptic agent in therapy. On the basis of an analysis of over 3000 LSD-therapy sessions, Grof (Grof, 1975; Grof & Halifax, 1977) found that patients described feelings and experiences, some of transmarginal stress, relating to their pre- and peri-natal experiences. Many of these experiences were later confirmed both by hospital records as well as by those who had been present at the birth of the patient.

On the basis of his research, Grof divided up the perinatal experience into four "basic perinatal matrices" and described the phenomenology of each. The first, called "Life in the Womb", was composed of the recollections of fetal life and involves the summation of experiences with which the baby faces the impending experience of birth. This summation tends to be either the positive "experiences of an undisturbed intrauterine environment where the basic needs of the embryo/fetus/baby are met" (Lake, 1981d, C56), or the negative recollections of the "bad womb" situation such as fetal crises, emotional upheavals in the mother and attempted abortions.

The second matrix, called "No Exit", and occurs at the beginning of labor but before the cervix opens. The "good womb" experience, where it has occurred, is inexplicably terminated and the supporter of the fetus for the last nine months becomes the aggressor. There is relentless force to "push out" the constricted fetus which can seem destructive or even murderous. Those that have suffered a "bad womb" experience are having their earlier traumas recapitulated and reconfirmed. Regardless of the experience of the first matrix, the still-closed cervix, combined with the contractions of the uterus, temporarily creates a trapped, hopeless feeling of "no exit".

The third phase involves the actual process of birth. The cervix opens and the fetus and womb begin to elongate. The fetus' head is pushed and molded to fit into the inlet to the pelvis. The reaction to this third matrix is variable. Some are active and some passive; some sense a maternal synergy and others maternal opposition; some are excited about the possibility of a new environment and others want to remain in the womb.

Lastly, Grof described the immediate post-birth experience as variable. There is the ideal of close, physical, and prolonged contact with the mother to "soothe away all the foul tensions that have arisen to perplex them, which they cannot understand" (Lake, 1978b). Along with the sense of confusion and bewilderment, there is the possibility of the sense of abandonment, loneliness, separation anxiety, and in the extreme, a sense of nothingness and dread.

CONCLUSION

As this very brief historical survey makes clear, the idea of a conscious prenatal experience and the notion that what happens to us in the first 9 months of life is critically important for the remainder of our days has been around for thousands of years. As the rest of the book will attempt to make clear, the prenatal period may be the most important and influential period of time in our lives. The research evidence continues to mount that the prenatal period can no longer be ignored as psychologically insignificant.

A hugely important theorist in prenatal psychology is the focus of our next chapter. Frank Lake was a British psychiatrist who wrote several books and many articles addressing prenatal psychology. Along with several other key individuals, he is a theoretical pioneer.

2

FRANK LAKE'S THEORETICAL APPROACH

For Thou mine embryo-form didst view,
Ere her own babe my mother knew.

James Montgomery

INTRODUCTION

Several years prior to his death in 1982, Frank Lake referred to "a new paradigm for psychodynamics with revolutionary implications" (Lake, 1978a, 3). What Frank Lake was describing was his formulation of a "maternal-fetal distress syndrome" (hereafter "M-FDS"). At the core of this "new perspective" was the simple, commonly-made observation that the environment of an organism shapes and molds that organism. The developmental interaction between nature and nurture, between the organism itself and the immediate environment produces a particular individual with particular characteristics (Anastasi, 1958). What made this essentially "old perspective" revolutionary for Lake was his application of it to early pre-natal life.

While some of his predecessors had emphasized the importance of the early postnatal environment (Freud), perinatal experiences (Otto Rank) and prenatal influences (F.J. Mott, Nandor Fodor and M.L. Peerbolte), Lake focused upon the first trimester of intrauterine life. He affirmed that the developmental process, not only in the physiological dimension, but also the psychological, emotional, cognitive, and spiritual dimensions, originates not in early infancy or at birth or even in the second or third trimesters of fetal life. Rather, Lake asserted that "we must begin at conception, through the blastocystic stage, to implantation and the events of the first trimester. It is here, in the first three months or so in the womb, that we have encountered the origins of the main personality disorders and the psychosomatic stress conditions" (Lake, 1981g, ix). Thus, while the developmental process begins at conception, this process is manifested both positively and negatively, both in adaptive and maladaptive learning, both in psychologically healthy response patterns as well as psychopathological ones.

THE MATERNAL-FETAL DISTRESS SYNDROME

Definition of the Paradigm

The mechanism underlying Lake's formulation of the M FDS is the pivotal assertion that "powerfully impressive experiences from the mother and her inner and outer world . . . reach the foetus, defining its relation to the intra-uterine reality in ways that persist into adult life" (Lake, 1981c, 5). Describing two extreme "environments" to illustrate his point, Lake wrote:

> The foetus in the womb is not inert, not insensitive, not so primitive and unsophisticated an organism that it cannot differentiate between . . . the womb of a gloriously happy and fulfilled wife and mother-to-be and . . . the uterus of a desperate, dissipated or dishonored woman whose hatred of life may take her own in suicide or that of the foetus in an attempted abortion which didn't quite come off. (Lake, 1981f, 65)

It is the uterine environment of the latter which is most likely to cause "the maternal-fetal *distress* syndrome". But underlying Lake's approach is his general contention that "the behavioral reactions of a pregnant mother affect her fetus in ways that contribute to its perceptions of itself and of its environment in the womb; and these perceptions persist into adult life" (Moss, 1987, 204).

While this definition contains the essence of Lake's M-FDS, it does not encompass the totality of the paradigm. What it does describe is the "point of exchange" between mother and fetus. However, prior to this exchange is a mother's experience of her environment. These experiences are in turn mediated by her pre-existing attitudes and emotions. Contingent upon the quality of this interaction, her response is expressed neurohormonally. It is this placental exchange of neurohormones which constitutes the point of "umbilical exchange". Following this exchange is the re-translation of the received "umbilical affect" by the fetus from neurohormones into a perceived experiential environment and finally, into an "interpretation" of that environment. According to Lake, this constant and continual process begins at implantation and only ends with the severing of the umbilical cord. The effects of the process, however, whether positive or negative, conscious or unconscious, are indelible.

The final formulation of the M-FDS came relatively late in Lake's thinking and can only be found in his later works encompassing the final four years of his life. Writing during this period, Lake stated that most of his professional psychiatric career had been spent working "in a half-light, oblivious to the earliest and severest forms of human pain" (Lake, 1981g, vii). This "half-light" was caused by the assumption that "the nine months of foetal development in the womb were free of significant incident, a blank without possibility of psychodynamic content" (Lake, 1982b, 57-58). Lake was to eventually conclude the opposite, that fetal life is as "eventful as the nine months that come after birth. The foetus is not unaware of itself, or of the emotional response of the mother to its presence, but acutely conscious of both and their interaction" (Lake, 1982b, 58). While Lake was not dismissive of the potential suffering of the post-natal experience, he affirmed that the "first three months after conception hold more ups and downs, more ecstasies and devastations than we had ever imagined" (Lake, 1981g, viii).

Development of the Paradigm

Lake's final conclusions with regard to the M-FDS resulted from a process of gradual development. The component, if incomplete, parts of the theory can be readily discerned early on. An evolution of sorts takes place, particularly with regard to the definition of the critical period of maternal-embryo/fetal/child interaction. What remained essentially static throughout this evolution was the central assertion stated above; namely that a mother's behavior and emotional state and the environment which this creates for the emerging child, are determinative of that child's later emotional and behavioral state. Given this constant, there are at least four "phases" or steps in the process that eventually gave birth to the final formulation of the M-FDS.

"Womb of the Spirit": As a classically trained psychiatrist, Lake early on affirmed the importance of early infancy, the "first half of the first year of life" (Lake, 1982c, 42). However, looking back on this early period, Lake later wrote that he stuck his "neck out 23 years ago in affirming birth and the early months as powerfully relevant occasions of stress" (Lake, 1981g, ix).

During this first phase, Lake still held the assumption that "the nine months of foetal development in the womb were free of significant incident, a blank without possibility of psychodynamic content" (Lake, 1982b, 57-58). But here we already observe the major components of the later formulation of M-FDS: the primacy of the mother-embryo/fetus/child dyad, the existence of repressed memories from early life, the effect of these experiences on the adult personality and his/her present functioning, the ability to "relive" these experiences, and the existence of transmarginal states. Indeed, at this early point, the later definition of the M-FDS could be slightly modified and still hold true: the behavioral reactions of a mother affect her child in ways that contribute to its perceptions of itself and of its environment and these perceptions persist into adult life.

In the introduction of a pamphlet on personal identity written in the latter part of the 1960's, Lake wrote that "the very earliest experiences which can lead to disturbed feelings of identity . . . take their origins in the distresses of babyhood" (Lake, 1991b, 43). This is illustrated clearly in a schematic representation found in his early book *Clinical Theology* titled "The Womb of the Spirit", in which he writes that "the analogy of the growth of the baby in the womb is an apt one" (Lake, 1964, chart N.b.).

This chart illustrates what Lake calls a "dynamic cycle" as the paradigmatic basis for making an "ontological analysis of the normal Mother-Child relationship" (Lake, 1964, chart N.b.). Lake describes the dynamics of each phase, two input and two output, in terms of a sequential effect upon the emerging infant, with each phase influencing and shaping the next in turn. A cyclical pattern emerges in which each phase either receives input from the outside "world" or imparts output to the outside "world", while simultaneously influencing the form of the next phase. Lake's analogy of fetal life, and indeed, his use of the term "womb of the spirit" prefigures his later theoretical emphases.

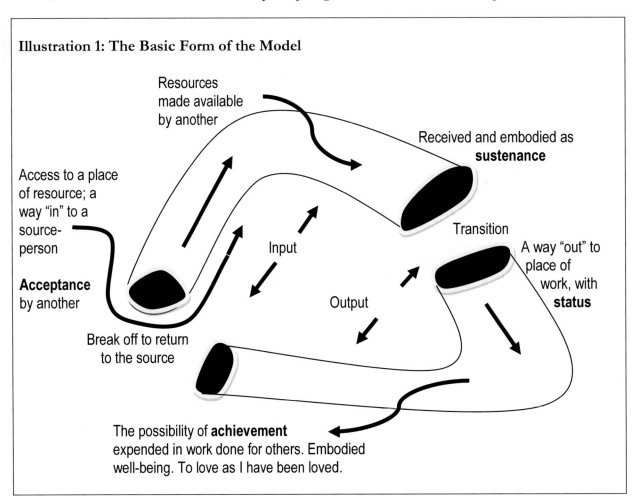

Illustration 1: The Basic Form of the Model

The first input phase in the cycle, which Lake called "being", is compared with biological actuality: just as "physical being is the result of nine months response by the fetus to the supplies of the Physical Being from the Mother" so "personal and spiritual being is the result of nine months (more or less) response of the baby to supplies of Personal and Spiritual Being from the mother" (Lake, 1964, chart N.b.). Whereas the placenta and umbilical cord serve as the conduits for nourishment during the period of the "womb of the physical", so there is the "umbilical cord of sight" by which spiritual being passes from the mother to the child during the period of the "womb of the spirit." If all goes well, this relational element allows the baby to "come into being as a person, gaining self-hood and the sense of identity by responding to the light of her [his mother] countenance" (Lake, 1964, chart N.b.), just as consistent physical nourishment during the prenatal period will allow the fetus to be born physically healthy. There is a similar parallel with the constriction of supplies. If the supplies of "physical being from the mother are constricted, the foetus will be distressed; if blocked, it dies" (Lake, 1964, chart

N.b.). If "being" supplies are constricted, there is a diminishment of personal and spiritual "being" of the infant leading first to panic and then to dread; if all supplies of "being" are removed", "non-being" results.

The second input phase is what Lake refers to as "well-being", resulting from the ongoing sustenance of being. Here the communication of "well-being" is achieved simultaneously in both its physical and spiritual dimensions. Lake writes that "not only is there the obvious inflow of physical sustenance in the form of milk when the child is at the breast, there is an equally important flow of sustenance from the mother to the baby on every level of personality" (Lake, 1964, chart N.b.). Lake specifically mentions satisfaction, joy, fullness, and graciousness.

The two output stages, designated by Lake as "status" and "achievement", are directly dependent upon the events of the input phases. Lack of "being" and "well-being" ultimately results in adults who manifest these "lacks" in the form of various neurotic and psychotic maladaptive dysfunctions. These characterizations remained valid even after Lake's thinking about the M-FDS was formulated. All that changed was the timing of the etiological experiences. Writing immediately prior to his death in 1982, and referring back to the nine month period of early infancy, namely the "womb of the spirit", Lake noted:

> There is one statement . . . which obviously now demands correction [and it is this]: "The roots of all the major neuroses-- hysterical, phobic, conversion, schizoid, anxiety-depressive and obsessional-- derive from separation anxiety in this phase." Some cases of each do . . . but the evidence . . . indicates that, if we are talking about the main roots of personality disorders . . . , it is [to the first trimester that] we must look and not later. (Lake, 1982b, 25)

During this period of Lake's intellectual evolution, he clearly was significantly influenced by several thinkers, including Guntrip (1952, 1957, 1961, 1968) and Fairbairn (1952a, 1952b), particularly in his conceptualization and understanding of the schizoid personality type. Also important were both Sigmund Freud and Melanie Klein (Klein, 1975a, 1975b). Both emphasized the primacy of the events of early childhood for later psychodynamic functioning. But when it came to an investigation beyond this period, Lake contends that the orthodoxy of both rendered the "investigation of life, distress and near-death in the womb . . . a 'no-go' area. The obvious distress of much intra-uterine existence has been assumed to have no emotional consequences. By definition, nothing could happen there to interest the analyst" (Lake, 1976b, S3). However, Lake saw both Freudian and Kleinian theory pointing beyond itself to indicate the importance of prenatal life for later psychodynamics. For instance, Lake noted that Freud's death instinct (*thanatos*) is present, by definition, at conception and thus must be functioning in opposition to the life-instinct (*eros*) wish both pre- and post-natally. Lake saw Freud himself "opening the door" to this thinking when he wrote in *Inhibitions, Symptoms and Anxiety* that "there is much more continuity between intra-uterine life and the earliest infancy than the impressive caesura of the act of birth allows us to believe" (Freud, 1936, 109).

Birth: Lake early on parted ways with classic Freudian and Kleinian interpretive schemes relating to the non-importance of birth. But there is no clear delineation between Lake's emphasis upon the first months of post-natal life vs. birth as the crucial period for subsequent functioning. In fact, in *Clinical Theology*, Lake emphasizes the importance of both infancy and birth. However, in the extensive chapters and the summary charts of the various disorders in *Clinical Theology*, he treats birth trauma as a part of the process of infancy. In the etiology of the various neuroses and psychoses, it becomes one factor of many in the possible cause of later psychological maladjustment.

Sometime after the publication of *Clinical Theology* in 1966, Lake's thinking subtly changes. He begins to place a much greater emphasis upon perinatal events than before, and speaks much less of the cruciality of the events of early infancy. While Lake never denies that post-natal experiences are not eventful or even momentous, they tend to be less so than earlier events, often being a recapitulation of previous experiences. Illustrative of his de-emphasis of the relative importance of the "womb of the spirit" period of infancy, he makes a comparison between two choices:

> If I were presented with a hard alternative, that in the case of a woman about to become pregnant, she had to undergo nine months distress during the next year and a half, but could choose whether the bad half came first, to be inextricably shared with the unborn baby, or came second, when her baby was already born, I would unhesitatingly urge her to choose to keep the months of pregnancy undisturbed, and face the task of coping with big trouble after the foetus had left her womb. Then she could cry or rage, grieve or despair, while the baby was sleeping, apart from her tumultuous reactions, protected to a significant extent from them". (Lake, 1981a, 3)

For much of Lake's professional psychiatric career, birth and birth trauma were held to be *the* pivotal and crucial events for later "being" and "well-being." In 1977, referring to the previous 20 years of his professional life, Lake wrote: "I had happily taught and theorized on the basis of birth as the first significant psychodynamic event for twenty years [from the age of 43 to 63]" (Lake, 1977a, 5). This emphasis upon the cruciality of perinatal experiences, which includes "events round about the birth; before, during and after birth" (Lake 1976a, 1), was not widely accepted at the time. There were, however, those who concurred with Lake on the importance of the perinatal.

As discussed in the previous chapter, Otto Rank's 1923 book *The Trauma of Birth,* and the work of D.W. Winnicott and Stanislav Grof all were highly influential, and were highly influential on Lake's thinking regarding the potential psychological significance of birth and the prenatal. Because both Grof and Lake had begun their investigation into prenatal trauma via the use of LSD as an abreactive agent, it is not surprising that Grof's organization of the pre and perinatal experience was consonant in several ways with Lake's subsequent delineation of the M-FDS. For Grof as for Lake, early experiences become "patterns or principles of perceptual organization for later experiences" and serve as underlying prototypes for later complex reaction patterns (Lake, 1978b, 230). Likewise, both Lake and Grof stressed that biological stress experiences are at the root of later psychopathology.

Both men found that under the influence of LSD, numerous patients described feelings and experiences, some of transmarginal stress, relating to their pre- and peri-natal experiences. Some of these experiences were later confirmed both by hospital records as well as by those who had been present at the birth of the patient. Lake's LSD research continued from 1953 to 1970 (Lake, 1981g, 7), but beginning in 1969 he started to utilize Reichian (Reich, 1972) and bio-energetic deep-breathing techniques, which he actually found to work just as well or better than LSD-25.

The work of Ivan Pavlov, particularly his research and formulations of "trans-marginal" stress, is also influential on Lake's thinking in this period. In Pavlov's research with dogs, he found that the "paradox of transmarginal stress" results when emotional pain is pushed beyond the threshold of tolerance, thus producing a paradoxical longing and identification with oblivion and death. Lake discovered that Pavlov's formulations were in accordance with the findings of his ongoing research utilizing LSD as an abreactive agent. Many of the research subjects who abreacted to the pre-, peri, and early post-natal periods reported paradoxical experiences entirely consonant with Pavlov's descriptions. Lake wrote that "so far as I know, no one has hitherto used Pavlov's concept of transmarginal stress as the main interpretive hypothesis by which to unify those phenomena of discontinuous responses conceptually" (Lake, 1964, 2).

The Prenatal Period: While in 1976 Lake could say that "pre-natal events are quite important" (Lake, 1976a, 17), sometime in the period between 1977 and 1978, there was a gradual and discernible shift in Lake's emphasis towards the prenatal period as the *most* influential for subsequent functioning. Toward the beginning of 1978, Lake wrote that "even in the nine months growing in the womb there may be unimaginable sufferings and catastrophes" (Lake, 1978c, 46). In a Research Report from December 1978, Lake wrote:

> Some of you have followed our research into what looked like the earliest recallable experiences of human beings, namely, the sensations and emotions accompanying one's birth. . . . Increasingly over recent years we have been invaded by evidence that the foetus in the mother's womb is picking up all sorts of messages about itself (Lake, 1978a, 2).

Lake continues to describe the rudiments of a M-FDS:

> The catecholamines which convey the "messages" to do with emotions round the mother's circulation, gearing all her organs and cells to feeling joy or sorrow, love or loathing, vitality or exhaustion, pass through the placental barrier (which to these substances is no barrier) into the foetal blood stream via the umbilical vein. In this context the foetus does its own emotional homework and responds, either passively accepting the mother's bad feelings as its own, as if true for itself, or by being protestingly overwhelmed by them. It can aggressively fight them back, in resolute opposition to sharing the mother's sickness. Others become "foetal therapists", trying to bolster up a debilitated and debilitating mother from their own feelings of relative strength. Sensitivity to "poisonous" feelings coming from a rejecting mother is very great. . . . To be the focus of mother's love imprints a confidence that "sets you up for life". (Lake, 1978a, 2)

The evidence that Lake cited to give credence to this shift in thinking came from the ongoing workshops in which deep-breathing techniques were being used to abreact early perinatal and increasingly pre-natal "memories." Lake likewise found support for his findings in the orthodox psychoanalytic dream and association analysis work of Nandor Fodor and Francis Mott, particularly Mott's utilization of a term first used centuries earlier-- "umbilical affect" (Moss, 1987, 203). Both Mott and Lake used this term to describe the "feeling state of the fetus as brought about by blood reaching him through the umbilical vein" (Moss, 1987, 203). As Mott envisioned it, the umbilical vein not only conveys nutritive resources and as such could be experienced as a "life-giving flow, bringing... renewal and restoration" but could also "be the bearer of an aggressive thrust of bad feelings into the foetus if the mother herself was distressed and 'feeling bad.'" If the mother felt emotionally unsupported, then "this feeling of deficiency, lack of recognition and the failure of looked-for support, would be just as specifically felt by the fetus. It became distressed by the failure of its immediate environment to provide the expected acceptance and sustenance, not so much at the level of metabolic input . . . but to nourish the earliest beginnings of the person in relationship" (Lake, 1978d, S1).

Thus, Lake's formulations are highly similar to Mott's. Where Mott's research primarily focused on dream analysis, Lake's ideas took shape following the results occurring from over 1200 LSD and deep-breathing assisted re-experiences of peri- and pre-natal events. That the two were so highly corroborated encouraged Lake that his findings were not unique. Where Lake differs from Mott is in his final emphasis upon the first trimester as the MOST determinative phase of development.

Thus, with emphasis upon the prenatal stage, the M-FDS is essentially the affirmation that a maternal-fetal "affect flow" exists and consequently the emotional state of the mother is transmitted by way of the umbilical cord to the fetus. This "affect flow" is determinative of subsequent psychological and emotional functioning and perception.

The First Trimester: The fourth and final phase of Lake's thinking with regard to what constitutes the critical period of maternal-fetal affect flow is also the most controversial. That there was a distinction between his emphasis upon the prenatal period in general and the first semester in particular can be determined from a later paper he wrote:

We thought initially that the pervasive traumatic influence of maternal distress on the foetus would be spread (if it occurred at all) throughout the nine months of pregnancy. We have now modified our thinking in the wake of the evidence that the first trimester is the locus for most of the catastrophes, for most of the sufferers from the M-FDS (Lake, 1977a, 3).

In a second research Report written in 1980, Lake implied the evolution of his thinking:

We find that it is not sufficient to look back, to find the origins of significant trauma, of consequent fixated pain, and therefore of the personality reactions that represent flight from that pain, only so far as the first year of life, or even to the traumas of birth. Things go wrong -or go well- much earlier than that (Lake, 1980b, 1).

Referring to these earlier sources of pain, Lake writes that it is the fetus who is vulnerable to "all that is going on in the mother, particularly in the first trimester, that is in the first three months after conception" (Lake, 1976a, 2-3). Thus, it is on the first trimester as the primary and crucial period of life that Lake finally settles. Although he continued to affirm that later pre-natal, peri-natal, and post-natal experiences all powerfully affect the post-natal functioning of the child and later the adult, it is the first trimester of intra-uterine life that is most determinative for all subsequent psychological, cosmological and ontological functioning.

Research Leading to the Paradigm

Within the evolution of the overall theoretical process that Lake was thinking through there were two specific research phases that gave him the "evidence" to conclude that the first trimester was determinative for later functioning: the LSD research (1954-1969/70) and the primal integration workshops (1975-1982).

LSD Research: In a speech given in September of 1976, Lake described his initial introduction to LSD research:

My chief sent me down to work with Sandison at Powick in 1954 because we were making no headway with alcoholics at all and he'd heard that LSD helped alcoholics to come to some awareness of what it was that made them go on drinking. So I went down . . . [and on return] I was given full time for two years, no other job [but] to pick out patients, [give them LSD,] and sit with them for four hours, six hours, as long as was necessary. (Lake, 1976a, 2-3)

He quickly discovered that when used in the presence of a trustworthy therapist, LSD-25 seemed to serve effectively to de-repress the "forgotten" memories of the patient. As he began to take note of "whatever the patients said as the thick crust of repression crumbled under the impact of the drug and the contents of the unconscious mind emerged into consciousness" (Lake, 1964, xix), he noted several striking similarities among what seemed to be a re-experiencing of repressed infantile memories. First of all, "the situation of the baby at the breast, for better or worse" and "the loss of the countenance of the mother, as a significant source of primal anxiety, occurred with painful frequency" (Lake, 1964, xx). Secondly, he wrote:

I was not prepared for the frequent abreaction of birth trauma. I was assured by neurologists that the nervous system of the baby was such that it was out of the question that any memory to do with birth could be reliably recorded as fact. I relayed my incredulity to my patients, and, as always happens in such cases, they tended thereafter to suppress what I was evidently unprepared, for so-called scientific reasons, to believe. But then a number of cases emerged in which the reliving of specific birth injuries, of forceps delivery, of the cord round the neck, of the stretched brachial plexus, and various other dramatic episodes were so vivid, so unmistakable in their origin, and afterwards confirmed by the mother or other reliable informants, that my suspicion was shaken. (Lake, 1964, xix)

A third commonality from the LSD-assisted abreactions of birth and early infancy was the occurrence of discontinuous reactions to severe stress. With regard to both birth and events in the first year there seemed to be a normal reaction to mounting stress, but then suddenly, "dramatically and dreadfully, the struggle to live, reaching a certain margin of tolerable pain, seemed to switch, automatically, into a struggle to die, of equal intensity with the previous struggle to live" (Lake, 1964, xxi). Lake found that Ivan Pavlov had observed this same paradoxical phenomena in dogs. This "transmarginal stress" (Pavlov, 1928; 1957; 1960) seemed to produce autistic, withdrawn, and classically schizoid children and adults. It was in this discovery that Lake saw the root of schizophrenia and the schizoid personality disorder as occurring in the first 6 months of post-natal life.

Related to this observation was a fourth, that the reaction to early emotional stress tended to set up a pattern of similar reacting that is life-long. Persons who early on reacted "hysterically" tended to react hysterically as adults. Persons who adopted the typical "depressive" defense patterns early on, tended to utilize them as adults.

These observations served as "evidence" to spur Lake on to what would eventually result in the M-FDS. Towards the end of his research with LSD in 1969, Lake did a follow-up study on 68 patients, 57 of whom responded. Half of these persons claimed to have experienced events of early childhood or birth *as if* they were reliving them (Moss, 1983; 1987). Of the 57, 37 reported that they remembered experiencing being born and 21 that they had relived some aspect of intra-uterine life.

In his book *Tight Corners in Pastoral Counselling* (1981), Lake reported that there was a period of overlap between the residential workshops and the LSD phases of his research. He writes that "only at the very end of the period in which I was using LSD-25 in the therapy of neuroses and personality disorders, that is, at the end of the sixties, did I invite those who wanted to work at primal depth, using LSD, to come to residential conferences with spouse and friends. I soon found how greatly this group work helped the process, and wished that I had realized that earlier." He continued, "At the same time the value of Reichian and bio-energetic techniques broke upon us, and we discovered that deep breathing alone was a sufficient catalyst for primal recapitulation and assimilation. Nothing more 'chemical' than that was necessary, so we stopped using LSD" (Lake, 1981g, 7).

The Lingdale Workshops: With the discovery of the importance of a facilitative group for primal work noted above, the second phase of Lake's research began. In 1958, Lake began running "clinical theology" seminars. Each seminar lasted for 3 hours and met 12 times, approximately once every three weeks for one year. They gradually evolved into the residential workshops that were inaugurated in 1975 at Lingdale, the headquarters of the Clinical Theology Association in Nottingham. They were initially three days in length, later expanding to as long as 6 days in duration, and were offered on various themes and topics. As these conferences developed and evolved, and as the theory underpinning the M-FDS was beginning to coalesce, Lake introduced an integrative seminar called "Primal Therapy in Christian Pastoral Care" (Moss, 1990, 3). Towards the conclusion of 1978, these seminars evolved to the point that some were centered upon personal growth, some explored prayer and healing, and still others focused on primal therapy. Lake brought all three of these elements together into a workshop titled "Personal Growth and Primal Integration in the Small Group" (Moss, 1990, 3). It was in these seminars, along with the primal integration workshops that followed them, that much of the "evidence" for the M-FDS emerged.

Primal Integration Workshops: The Lingdale workshops were conducted during this period at a residential facility immediately adjacent to Lingdale. Located near the center of Nottingham, but on a quite cul-de-sac surrounded by gardens and enclosed by a fairly high stone wall, Lingdale provided an ideal place for a residential retreat-like seminar. The house was quite large, able to accommodate between 14 and 18 persons, with sufficient space to allow for several "primals" to be occurring simultaneously. During the period between 1979 and 1982, over 500 persons attended these seminars at Lingdale, some lasting as long as 7 days.

The seminars, whether at Lingdale or elsewhere, usually began with some brief introductions and the presentation of an itinerary of the days to follow. During the first two days of the seminar, the focus centered on getting the participants emotionally comfortable both with each other and the facilitators. A certain degree of comfort was required in order to feel a "sense of safety" and was facilitated by a supportive sharing process whereby each person spoke "of the aspects of their own personality functioning on which they hoped to work" (Lake, 1981c, 7). This process, not unlike conventional group therapy, included probing not only into their current emotional functioning, but also into the history of their lives. Especially noted and emphasized would be any information and memories associated with the circumstances of their conception, prenatal period and birth.

A second component of the first few days of the seminar was some teaching with regard to the biological and physiological facts of embryology. In order to understand better the prenatal environment at each successive stage, a workshop facilitator would give a 2-hour lecture, usually accompanied by slides and other illustrations of embryonic and fetal life, although not always. While this lecture was primarily designed as presentation of the basic scientific facts of embryology, very often either the lecturer or a participant would begin to "resonate with aspects of the story that were particularly applicable to them" (Moss, 1990, 3:6) and communicate this with the other participants. Following this review of embryology and building upon it, the facilitators, often very informally and as a function of other activities, then began to communicate the various principles and practice of primal integration.

After several days of preparation, very often several of the participants would begin with the "work" of primal integration. At Lingdale this was done in a room large enough for four persons to be "working" at a time, each with three or four persons immediately around them. The room was usually carpeted and comfortable with dim lighting. Each "session" lasted from 2 to 3 hours and would be followed up by a feedback-session with the larger group. The "session" would begin with the "subject" relaxed in a supine position on the floor being guided in a "conception-to-womb talkdown". The facilitator, usually Lake, would simultaneously speak to all four "primalers". This address would begin with a simple relaxation routine, sometimes by way of guided fantasy but always with the use of deep-breathing. The facilitator would then remind the participants of the facts of early life. Lake states that he would rehearse, "in a neutral, emotionally unbiased voice, the undisputed facts of human development, the anatomy and physiology of the meeting of the sperm with the ovum recently released from the ovary whose lifetime it has shared, to conception and cell division to the morula and its hollowing out to form the blastocyst" (Lake, 1981c, 9). As this occurred, very often the participant would curl up in the fetal position and become totally oblivious to the other participants, "genuinely creating 'a womb' out of the small group and experience within it an authentic transcript of intra-uterine experience" (Lake, 1981g, 27).

In addition to the reiteration of the "anatomico-physiological facts" the "talkdown" included repeated promptings to recall certain forgotten or ignored data related to the participants' mother and father and the entire environment in which conception and early pre-natal life occurred. Along with this recall, the participants were also encouraged to give voice to the emotional memories.

The "talkdown" would proceed in a chronological manner, beginning with an identification with the ovum *as* part of the mother and the sperm *as* part of the father. This was followed by a recapitulation of the emotions and sensations of sexual intercourse and then conception, followed in turn by the zygotic and blastocystic stages and then implantation. Lake wrote that he would seek to lead participants to "tune in" on the emotional state of the mother and father. He would ask them:

Reflect on their mother's feelings as she joins the father on the night of the conception. How does she feel about herself? How does she feel about having her first child, or adding to the family, or trying again after one or more miscarriages or fatal birth accidents? How does she feel about the man-probably her husband alongside her? Is she full of joyful anticipation at being aroused by him, open to him and being entered by him? (Lake, 1982, 67)

The "talkdown" would temporarily conclude at the sixth week, with the crucial suggested awareness of the umbilical flow returning from the mother. Lake, in a transcript of a talkdown from a workshop at Lingdale dated 10/2/80, concluded with these words:

And breathe up deeply into your strength, and make any kind of neutral noise as you breathe out. Ah. But reach down into contact with any feelings in the belly. What is it that comes in from mother? Because she's in contact with all that world outside, the world of men and women, and all that goes on. (pause) So breathe deeply, and explore what it is that comes through from mother into you, and give a voice to it as you breathe out. A-ah. Take your time, and just be aware in your own space of what it was like for you to be in the womb. . . . Breathe strongly and give yourself plenty of air to get into contact with this child as the end of the cord. (Lake, 1980a, 4)

Following this phase of discourse by the facilitator, the participants were left to work through the remainder of the third trimester without the aid of a verbalized facilitation. At this point in the seminar, contingent upon the prenatal experience of each participant, the reactions would vary significantly. Lake wrote:

Each became so totally different, and were discovering their own pace and intrinsic direction of retrieval and re-living. I, as conductor, would 'go off the air', leaving them to explore, for the next couple of hours, the unique features of their own record of the first trimester. (Lake, 1982b, 65)

Following this period, Lake writes that "at a point usually clear to the long experience of the facilitator" (Lake, 1982b, 65), he would then begin to rehearse the remainder of the fetal experience, moving through the months of the middle and finally third trimesters, to finally conclude at birth. Depending upon the retrieved memories of birth, the session often ended at this point, was prolonged, or needed to be taken up at a second session. Lake continues that "at all points in the journey, from conception to bonding, the subject is in adult contact with their facilitator and small group. They will go out to the toilet and return, immediately in contact again with the foetal world at the point where they left it" (Lake, 1982b, 66).

At the conclusion of the session, following a brief break, a feedback session would ensue in which a greater exploration of what happened would be encouraged. Assisted by the written and recorded records of each "primal", the participant evaluated the experience in light of their present life. What insights have been made? Lake writes that a typical question put forth might be "How far do they recognize, in the foetal states now fully and clearly relived, the source of life-long attitudes and decisions, fixed perception and rooted character stance and posture" (Lake, 1982b, 68-69). If a second session was needed, the participant would return in order to finish out the chronological process of the experience. The entire seminar would conclude with some preparation for "re-entry", and for some of the participants, follow-up weekends at Lingdale were encouraged.

The recorded tapes and written transcripts of the sessions provided much of the evidence for Lakes' formulations of the M-FDS. In addition, Roger Moss, a co-researcher of Lake's during this period, completed a follow-up postal survey of those who had attended the residential workshops at Lingdale between October 1979 and April 1982. The survey, consisting of 52 main sections covering

11 sides of paper, was sent out to 500 of the total of 516. A return rate of 56.2% (N=281) was achieved and these were analyzed in light of the data and evidence already at hand. These results, as well as the data from the Lingdale sessions, provided the grist for Lake's theoretical mill. Based on this evidence, Lake formulated a theory with specific elements.

Components of the Paradigm

Following conception and prior to the process of implantation is the short preliminary stage of the "blastocyst." Lake affirmed that this period is "often felt to be a good experience of non-attachment, even of unitive and quite 'transcendent bliss'" (Lake, 1981g, 15). "There may be a sense of continuity with the monistic sense of 'union with the Absolute' experienced by some in the first week after conception, a kind of blastocystic bliss" (Lake, 1981d, C41). This stage is immediately succeeded by implantation in the lining of the maternal womb, gradually resulting in umbilical circulation through the umbilical cord and placenta. Lake writes:

> As this begins to function, the foetus is evidently put into direct contact with all that is being transmitted round the mother's own body as an expression of her emotional ups and downs. The foetus feels acutely the feelings which are the product of the mother's life situation, for better or for worse, and her personal reactions to it. (Lake, 1981g, 15)

According to Lake, the establishment of umbilical circulation allows every woman to have a profound impact upon an emerging fetus within her. This occurs through the phenomenon that Lake called "umbilical affect". This term is defined as the "feeling state of the fetus as brought about by blood reaching him through the umbilical vein" (Moss, 1986, 203). This maternal-fetal "affect flow" transmits the emotional state of the mother to the fetus by way of the umbilical cord in a manner similar to the transmission of nutrients and various teratogens such as viruses and chemical agents. Lake wrote:

> Before birth, the foetus may be seriously damaged if the mother is dependent upon alcohol, nicotine or other drugs. It is also damaged by the less readily identifiable changes that transmit to the baby a mother's rejection of a particular pregnancy and of the life growing within her. Any severe maternal distress, whatever its cause, imprints itself on the foetus. (Lake, 1981g, 16)

The effects of this "affect flow" are mediated by the interaction between the mother's emotional state and the fetal response to it. The maternal "affect flow" spans the full range of emotional possibilities. At one polarity, stands the ideal of total joy and acceptance resulting in an "emotive flow" that communicates recognition, affirmation, and acceptance to the fetus. The other extreme represents maternal rejection and distress that results in the "invasion of the fetus in the form of a bitter, black flood" (Lake 1981g, 16). Either way, this "invasion" is usually the result of often very complex and mixed emotions. Lake describes these mixed messages:

> She may have been full of anger internally, while fear, compliance or compassion prevented its ever being shown externally. she may have loved the man by whom she became pregnant, while hating the resultant fetus, or loved the prospect of having a baby, while hating, fearing or feeling deeply disappointed and neglected by its father. The fetus receives all such messages but has difficulty in distinguishing what relates specifically to it and what belongs to the mother's feelings about her own life in general. (Lake, 1981g, 21)

Similarly, the fetal response varies from "'taking it all to heart' as a judgment against itself, to be passively endured, or strongly to oppose it, or 'to get right out of it' by splitting off the ego, the experiencing 'I' taking leave of the too-badly hurt foetal body" (Lake, 1981g, 21). Whatever it is, the foetal response to the maternal "affect flow" is contingent upon it's own constitutional factors as well as the intensity and duration of the emotive flow (Lake, 1981g, 21-22). "The tendency is to feel identified with all of these invading maternal emotions in turn and to react to each" (Lake, 1981g, 21). It is this response, according to Lake, that is so determinative for subsequent functioning, especially when the fetus is responding to an emotive flow of severe distress. The result, depending upon the specific intrapsychic dynamics, is the appearance of a particular group of symptoms and signs that characterize a particular psychopathology. Thus, "this intra-uterine interaction is the source of images, perceptions, meanings, values and personality defenses to cope with them" (Lake, 1981f, 65).

Lake organized the occurrence of "umbilical affect" and its effects on the fetus into three general manifestations and four consequent graded response patterns. The former is primarily based upon the quality and quantity of the "affect-flow" from mother to fetus, while the latter is based upon the response of the fetus to this "affect-flow". Both the response of a woman to her pregnancy and the reaction of the fetus within her to her response are events that actually exist along a continuum of possible responses ranging from absolute and joyous acceptance to horrendous and cataclysmic rejection. In the most general terms, the three main anchors along this continuum include joyful acceptance of the fetus by his mother, conscious or unconscious ignorance and/or disregard of the fetus by the mother, and finally, conscious or unconscious rejection of the fetus by the mother. The four "graded responses to increasing degrees of pain due to un-met intra-uterine and peri-natal needs" (Lake, 1981d, C68) are also somewhat continuous.

Changes in the mother's environment may occur in the course of the pregnancy that may drastically alter the fetal environment. The beginning of the pregnancy may be perceived by the fetus as positive and "ideal", while later changing to a negative perception due to some stressor in the maternal environment. An opposite experience is just as likely, with an initial negative environment, due perhaps to a crisis pregnancy, with a later adjustment and acceptance resulting in a much more positive environment.

The Manifestations of "Umbilical Affect"

Positive: One possible manifestation of maternal affect is what Lake termed "positive". This pattern is characterized by joy and acceptance. The mother, upon discovery of her pregnancy, exults with joy and happiness, giving rise to a "flow of the mother's positive, aware, attention-giving emotional regard to the developing foetus within her. The development of a positive Foetal Skin Feeling, as the ground of 'the excellent self' may be perceptible" (Lake, 1981d, C41). Elsewhere Lake writes that the mother's joy and "recognition of her changed state leads to foetal joy in being recognized, accepted, and indeed, welcomed" (Lake, 1981g, x).

Negative: The second general pattern resulting from the maternal-fetal affect flow is what Lake termed "negative". While this manifestation is disconcerting and distressing to the fetus, it is not so because of any perceived attack. Rather, the fetus "wants to feel its presence recognized" and "this is often denied. There is a puzzled, then distressed sense of being disregarded, unnoticed, of no interest or account in the cosmos" (Lake, 1981d, C41). The fetus is frustrated by his mother's "non-recognition of her own body as she works on furiously before and after she knows she is pregnant. It is deeply disturbed by her lack of recognition of herself as pregnant and the fetus as a growing human being inside her when she does know" (Lake, 1981d, C41). As such, the fetus cannot thrive because it's yearning is fixated. There is often fetal distress in the awareness of the mother's emotional need and at times a response of "trying to help", of attempting to somehow palliate, ease or prevent the mother's distress. This gives rise to what Lake called the "fetal therapist."

Strongly Negative: The third and final pattern of manifestation and response from the maternal-fetal affect flow is what Lake called "strongly negative". This pattern is what gives this entire paradigm it's designation as the "maternal-fetal distress syndrome". As such, and because of it's dire and myriad consequences, it's discussion comprises by far the most material in Lake's thought and works.

When the "umbilical affect" is strongly negative, the fetal distress that results comes directly as a result of an "influx of maternal distress" (Lake, 1981d, C41), to her distress in relation to the world:

> It may be due to her marriage, to her husband's withdrawal rather than more intimate supporting when he is asked urgently for more than his personality can easily give. It may be due to the family's economic or social distress in a distressed neighborhood . . . If she is grieving the loss of, or nursing a still dying parent, the sorrow overwhelms her and overwhelms her fetus. (Lake, 1981f, 66)

Whatever the cause, "the pain of the world, picked up by the family, is funneled by the mother into the fetus" (Lake, 1981f, 66). Included in this dynamic then, is "both the registering of the intrusion of the mother's condition, of yearning, anxiety, fear, anger, disgust, bitterness, jealousy, etc. into the fetus, and its own emotional response to this distressed and distressing invasion" (Lake, 1981d, C41). Particularly distressing, because they give rise to the "fear of being killed by maternal hatred" (Lake, 1981d, C41), are failed abortions and near miscarriages.

When the fetus is invaded by a "black, bitter flood" of "incompatible . . . and alien emotions" (Lake, 1981g, x), this transfusion leads to an assortment of possible reactions. The fetus may attempt to utilize various coping mechanisms or may seek to actively oppose this "invasion". The mode of contravention varies with "constitutional factors, intensities and duration of stress, as well as previous experiences severe enough to cause conditioned responses" (Lake, 1981g, x). Thus, the "strongly negative" pattern of manifestation and response, of the "foetus being 'marinated' in his mother's miseries" (Lake, 1981g, 141) and reacting in a variety of ways, results in a variety of serious disorders.

The Graded Levels of Fetal Response: Corresponding somewhat to the three variations of maternal "umbilical affect" are the four variations of fetal response.

Ideal: The first such response is the "Ideal". This condition exists when, from implantation onwards, "the fetus in the womb is well-supplied in every way," it's physical, emotional, and spiritual "shopping list" being satisfied by the "hopes of a well-stocked maternal shop" (Lake, 1981d, C68). There is a sense of "warm and contented happiness, even of a deeply embodied bliss. . . . The umbilical connection with the mother from the placenta is wholly satisfactory" (Lake, 1982b, 13). There is the communication of peacefulness, tenderness, love; the mother is said to "keep a warm womb" (Lake, 1982b, 13). Contingent upon her reaction to her life situation is her ability "to meet the emotional needs of the foetus, and fulfill the archetypal 'blessed mother' image" (Lake, 1981d, C68). Ideally, "all the warmth and tenderness of the love she is receiving from her husband, family and neighbors, . . . fortified, perhaps by a spiritual sense that God the Father's exchanges of love are just like this, and as she opens to him too, all her loves mix and are made available to the foetus within her, though she may as yet have only an inkling that she is pregnant" (Lake, 1982b, 14).

Coping: When the maternal affect flow is less than "ideal" but is still "good-enough" to prevent a loss of trust, the second response level is manifested by the fetus. The "Coping Response" results when there is a "discrepancy between need and proper fulfillment . . . but the main conditions of satisfactory interaction are being more or less met" (Lake, 1981d, C68). There is either a maternal failure to meet perfectly the "essential need for recognition and caring attention" or an "influx of maternal distress" (Lake, 1982b, 21), or both. While the fetus has "lost hope of the 'ideal,'" it attempts to "cope with the deficit or the distress" (Lake, 1982b, 21) by accepting the "ongoing exchange with the source person, out of sheer need" (Lake, 1982b, 21). These interactive conditions, although not perfect, are "good enough" to permit the fetus to cope adequately with the disparity. It is only when the emotional supplies of the "maternal shop" are less than ideal and there is the recognition of this lack or "badness", that what has preceded, if "ideal" in some sense of the term, is now defined as having been "good". Thus "fetal coping is really saying 'However hard it is to hang on to the acceptance of the mixed good/bad, rough/smooth stuff that comes in the navel, the alternative, to refuse the good because the bad is so bad, is to cut oneself off from life itself'" (Lake, 1982b, 22).

The consequences of the "coping level" for later functioning are determined by the severity of the deficit and the consequent reaction. However, since the world is not an "ideal" place where one's needs are always met fully and immediately, the coping level is more predictive of future interaction and thus can serve as a kind of vaccination against future deficits and disappointments. Lake states that "those who in the first trimester were well able to cope with a mixed bag of maternal emotional inputs are better placed for dealing with later troubles than those for whom it was so 'ideal' as to have escaped their notice" (Lake, 1981d, C68). Indeed, this level can serve to "flex the muscles of faith" with the spirit expanding "to include the negative aspects of relationships with increasing and justifiable hope and trust" (Lake, 1981d, C68).

A second possible consequence, this time definitively negative and shared with the third and fourth "levels", results from the economy of the exchange between the fetus and his mother. The "good" and "bad" of the "affect-flow" are accepted "with the corollary that the 'badness' must not be fired back at the placenta/mother via the excretory umbilical arteries, but 'loaded up' in the foetus' own body structures" (Lake, 1982b, 21).

Thus the "badness" is displaced and contained within a body part and may include muscle groupings, or any one of the alimentary, respiratory, or uro-genital tracts. Thus the "ostensible ongoing acceptance of the way of exchange is riddled with ambivalence" (Lake, 1982b, 21).

The third possible result of the coping response may be that of the fetal therapist". This result occurs when a constitutionally strong fetus receives an ambivalent or clearly negative affect flow from a weak, inadequate mother. The fetus accepts the burden, often life-long, of doing everything possible to prevent and palliate the mother's stress and resultant distress. This necessitates a denial of and refusal to meet one's own needs.

Opposition: When the "emotional store" of the mother is judged by the fetus to be "not good enough" for trustful coping, total opposition results. Between the previous level and this third one something shocking has happened; "distress has shattered the erstwhile trust between the ego and its world" (Lake, 1981d, C68). Depending upon the constitutional style and strength of the fetus, the oppositional attitude will vary between being aggressively active to passively non-cooperative. What is sought is the immediate termination of a "significant margin of pain" (Lake, 1981d, C68). There is no longer an ability to cope, as was true with the previous level. "In the face of too severe, too prolonged, unremitting deficiency of maternal recognition of the fetal presence" (Lake, 1982b, 22) "the organism stops being its trusting self, open at the interface" (Lake, 1981d, C68) with the mother. Perhaps the fetus has a sense that the "negative umbilical affect" is like "a great nail of affliction or skewer transfixing the foetus at the navel, with an overwhelming invasion of bitter, black maternal emotions" (Lake, 1982d, 22).

The fetal reaction to this umbilical exchange varies. Sometimes the fetus can use the "down time" of the night, when the affect flows ceases or is reduced to a trickle, to "regather its incredibly renewable faith, hope, and love, to reaffirm what ought to be, and wait like Prometheus for the day when the carrion birds return to attack" (Lake, 1982d, 23). A concomitant reaction may be the willing of the death of the source person, which is often repressed because of its "unacceptability." The pain itself must be repressed and "split-off"; "the catastrophic sensations are dissociated from the memory of the hurtful environment. Stable 'character' is based on maintaining this" (Lake, 1981d, C68). Life goes on, but with the unconscious scar remaining.

As with the earlier level of coping, these repressed memories are displaced symbolically, either onto some body system or part, or onto an representative "image." Thus, the "disposal of invasive maternal distress and deficiency . . ." is achieved by "displacement and containment within the foetal organism" (Lake, 1981e, w11), and serves to "contain the badness" (Lake, 1982b, 23).

In extreme cases of level 3 opposition, and yet not extreme enough for the transmarginal stress of level 4, there is successive retreat from the umbilical badness to the point where the fetus is symbolically consigned to one small part of the body or compelled to "leave" totally. The remaining good of the fetus itself is "imaged as taking refuge in the head, or as retreating to just the centre of it" (Lake, 1982b, 23). When this "good" is compelled to leave the body entirely, it is felt to exist "only outside the body, floating in the space above the head" (Lake, 1982b, 23).

Transmarginal Stress: When and if the "affect flow" from the mother to the fetus reaches the point where the fetus perceives a "sheer impossibility of keeping up the opposition to the invasive evil which seems interminable and relentless" (Lake, 1982b, 30), then the fourth level has been reached. When the absolute margin of tolerable pain has been reached and passed, paradoxical and supra-paradoxical response patterns result in which "the self turns against itself, willing its own destruction and death" (Lake, 1981d, C68). The stance of the fetus switches from being life-affirming to death-affirming. Beyond the margin of tolerable pain, of transmarginal pain, the "foetus longs, not for life, but for death. The plea is not for a relief of the weight, but that it may be crushed out of existence" (Lake, 1982b, 30). "There is a loss of 'being' at the center, replaced by a [paradoxical] desire for 'nonbeing'" (Lake, 1981d, C41).

The Effects of the Paradigm

The existence of a "positive umbilical affect" and "ideal" fetal response because of a prenatal sojourn in the "womb of a gloriously happy and fulfilled wife and mother-to-be" (Lake, 1981f, 65) is somewhat rare. That during fetal life this person was well-supplied in every way, that the birth process went smoothly, that the maternal bonding was immediate and strong, and that the environment of infancy and early childhood was affirming, in all likelihood results in an adult whose psychological and emotional adaptation is, while not perfect, near ideal. They have the psychic tools to cope well with the exigencies that dynamic existence gives rise to. They, as Lake describes them, are those with "more robust natures, nurtured in kinder wombs, [and therefore] can shrug off . . . disappointments, or bear them, finding no antecedent pattern of neglect to latch on to" (Lake, 1981e, 2). They, in turn, visit the benefits of their "history" on their progeny to the "third and fourth generation."

That the great majority of persons do not share this ideal "history" gives rise to two other major categories of adults, the "normal" and the "abnormal". The former includes those who cope with life by "murdering the truth" successfully, those who "go along with it" and by the dynamics of repression succeed in keeping the truth of the early trauma and tragedies of fetal life safely at bay. Lake described this dynamic:

> As soon as the tragedy of human life impinges upon the infant, indeed upon the fetus still within the womb, the truth of what has happened is immediately murdered by repression and turned into a lie which denies that it ever happened. (Lake, 1978c, 65)

Lake continues to describe this "average man":

His is a life lived over the top of the tissue of closely woven lies, a fabric of falsehood. . . . Therefore, the line between the 'normal' person and the 'neurotic' is not that the normal personality can function without the intrinsic falsehood whereas the neurotic person cannot. Quite the contrary. We call a person 'normal' if the self-deception that he uses to repress, deny, displace, and rationalize those basic wounds that are ubiquitous in human beings from babyhood works quite well. He is 'normal' in so far as his defenses against too much painful reality are as successful as (all unbeknown to the person himself) they are meant to be. (Lake, 1978c, 118)

When the "success" of these defenses against these "basic wounds" begins to flag and the "murdered truth" begins to emerge into present reality, often in an altered form, then the second group of persons emerges: those who are considered psychologically deficient, neurotic or even psychotic. The "normal" person often hides a cryptic "wounded" person who emerges only due to some present life stressor. The manifestation of this emergence takes the form of presenting complaints, which are recapitulations of and reverberations from the earliest fetal experiences, perhaps, as Lake described, in "the uterus of a desperate, dissipated or dishonored woman whose hatred of life may take her own in suicide or that of the foetus in an attempted abortion which didn't quite come off" (Lake, 1981f, 65).

The various maternal-embryo/fetal dynamics of the blastocystic and implantation stages, of the rest of the first trimester, of prenatal, peri-natal and post-natal life, gives rise to "wounds" and the consequent reaction to these wounds which manifest themselves in particular patterns. The original formation of these particular coping pattern depends upon several components. The intensities and duration of stress, the "input" point in the "dynamic cycle" at which the stress comes, the active or passive reaction of the fetus to this stress, and the constitutional "diatheses" (Lake, 1986, 8) are all important predictive factors.

Diminution of resources at the "being" phase of input in the dynamic cycle gives rise to the most severe "personality disorders, the most disruptive of healthy self-hood and relationships" (Lake, 1986, 8): the schizoid, hysterical, and anxiety-depressive reactions. These "reactions" are all mediated by the severity and duration of the diminution and the response of the fetus. A reduction of maternal supplies at the "well-being" input phases results, depending again upon the severity and duration of the stress and the response of the fetus, in the maladaptive patterns of paranoia and anxiety-less depression.

Whatever the stress and whenever it strikes, the "womb-distressed" person, Lake writes, "complains *as if* it remembered the bad times it had been through. It reacts to the world around it *as if* it were still in the bad place, still having to 'feel its keenest woe.' It reacts defensively *as if* the attack were till going on" (Lake, 1981e, 4).

These reactive coping patterns, once used, are then utilized again and again, setting up particular paradigms of "wound management" that are recapitulated endlessly into adulthood. Lake wrote:

All the common diagnostic entities of psychiatric practice, hysterical, depressive, phobic, obsessional, schizoid, paranoid, have their clearly discernible roots in this first trimester. Each of them constitutes a particular view of the foetal-placental world and what goes on in it . . .it is important to recognize these 'world views,' since they are the same fixated patterns of perception which impose themselves, more mistakenly than accurately, on roughly similar events throughout life. (Lake, 1981g, 24)

When there is type of "block" from mother to fetus of "being itself", it is, as Lake described it, "an almost irremediable disaster. It is of all things the most destructive of the life of the organism" (Lake, 1986, 8). Three main psychopathologies or "wound management reaction patterns" result: anxiety depression, the hysterical personality reaction, and the schizoid personality disorder (in its most serious manifestation called schizophrenia).

Conclusion

Lake's theory was conceived in the context of his training, theoretical background, and experience with providing therapay and counseling to those who were psychologically wounded. Like any theory, the M-FDS was Lake's attempt to explain his observations. While his theory is groundbreaking and seminal, the research evidence for its veracity is still accumulating and only time will tell how useful it is in explaining the dynamics of prenatal life. A theory's value is most often seen in how well it explains the facts, but we can never confuse theory with the facts.

In the next chapter we turn to the "facts" of fertilization and conception. While the word "miracle" is probably overused in modern-day parlance, it rightly applies to the everyday processes of reproduction and procreation, especially the propitious moment of fertilization. That things can go wrong is taken for granted. But that so many things have to go right for any baby to be conceived is the real miracle, and this happens around the world thousands of times a day.

3

FERTILIZATION AND CONCEPTION

Life begins with conception . . . the soul also begins from conception.
For life takes its commencement at the same moment,
and in the same place, as the soul does.

Tertullian

INTRODUCTION

As long as human beings have existed, women have become pregnant and given birth. In the overwhelming majority of these instances, the "cause" of pregnancy was a particular act of sexual intercourse between a man and woman. In your case, it involved your particular mom and dad (assuming you weren't conceived in a test tube or Petri dish). While most of us would rather not think about it too much, your beginning probably took place in one of your mother's fallopian tubes when one of her ova "hooked up" with one of your father's sperm. While this is hardly news to you, the particular mechanical details of how this happens have only been known for a relatively short period of time. For instance, someone as recent as the eminent Charles Darwin never knew that "fertilization was accomplished by a single sperm" (Tannahill, 1980, p. 42). So if you keep reading, at least in this area, you will know more than Charles Darwin did, and presumably everyone else prior to 1882, the year Darwin died.

For fertilization to even have a chance of taking place, hundreds of other events must have already taken place. The sperm and ovum must be healthy and on time, the temperature must be just right, the environment of the fallopian tube has to be near perfect, and so on. The entire process has often been referred to as miraculous, and rightly so. Further, the "production" (called gametogenesis) of sperm and ova are subject to their own vagaries and difficulties. Your mother's ova were produced (called oogensis) and stored in her ovaries before she was even born and once she hits menarche, she "releases" just one every 28 days or so. Your father's sperm began their lives (called spermatogenesis) approximately 70 days earlier in the seminiferous tubules of one of his testicles and between 200 and 500 million were "released". If all goes right, just one of these sperm will penetrate the ovum, beginning the process of fertilization. Talk about competition!

Further, both sperm and ova are produced and stored and released within different "environments" and involving different organs, the structure and function of each requires understanding before we proceed. We will then examine the processes leading up to fertilization, and finally implantation

MALE STRUCTURES AND PROCESSES

External Genital Structures

Penis: The penis is the primary male sex organ, cylindrical in shape and composed primarily of sponge-like erectile tissue which engorges with blood during sexual arousal. This process allows for erection, which in turn makes sexual intercourse feasible. The shaft of the penis terminates in the acorn-shaped glans (which comes from the Latin word for acorn) and is packed with neural receptors which make it very sensitive. The ridge of the glans is called the corona and is even more responsive than the rest of the glans. During sexual intercourse, the friction on the glans and coronal ridge serve to stimulate ongoing arousal and lead to orgasm and ejaculation. Thus, the erect penis serves as the conduit to "deliver" sperm from the testicles, where they develop, to the vagina, allowing for the possibility of fertilization. During orgasm, the sperm join together with seminal fluid to constitute semen. In men who are uncircumcised, the foreskin covers the glans in an unaroused state. Arousal causes the foreskins to pull back and expose the glans to the stimulation of sexual intercourse. In males, the shaft and glans of the penis are homologous with the shaft and glans of the clitoris in females. The underside of the penis in males is homologous with the labia minora in females. There is a line running down the center of the underside of the penis where the tissue was fused together during prenatal development.

Scrotum and Testicles: The scrotum is the sac that loosely holds the testes in 2 separate chambers, allowing the testicles to hang down from the body. This allows the temperature of the scrotum to be a few degrees below body temperature necessary for healthy sperm production. But if the temperature in the scrotum falls too much below 95 degrees (for example, if someone was swimming in the ocean), the muscles in the scrotal sac contract and reflexively pull the testicles up toward the body, so they can be warmed and the developing sperm within protected. In males, the scrotum is homologous with the labia majora in females.

The main functions of the testicles are to produce and subsequently to store sperm, so that they are ready for possible fertilization. The word testis is derived from the Latin word for "witness" or "testify" because in ancient times men would cover their genitals with their hands when taking an oath (McAnulty & Burnette, 2001, p. 94).

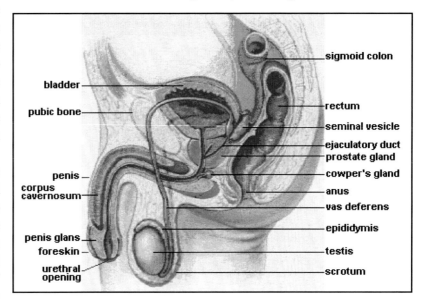

Contained within the scrotum, the testes are avocado-shaped (but not sized; the word avocado comes from the Spanish word *aguacate* which is derived from the Aztec word *ahuacati* which means testicle (Sex trivia, 2006) and measure approximately 1 X 1.5 inches. They are homologous with the female's ovaries. Each testis is subdivided into lobes, and within the lobes are the masses) of coiled snake-like seminiferous tubules (about 850 feet in each testis) where sperm are first produced. Interspersed among the tubules are interstitial cells (Leydig and Sertoli) which produce male hormones and protect and nurture the sperm. Like an assembly line, the sperm move from the seminiferous tubules to rete testes, another network of tubes and finally to the epididymous, where they continue their gradual development and attain motility. The epididymous, located on the top of the testes, is another bunched- up and coiled tube, which if stretched out, would be around 20 feet in length. It is here that the mature sperm are stored for up to 2 weeks until used. The testicles are connected to the man's body by means of a spermatic cord, which contains nerves and blood vessels which insure the survival and function of the testes.

Internal Genital Structures

Vas Deferens and Ejaculatory Duct: The testes are connected to the penis by means of the vas deferens, two long curving ducts which begins at the termination end of the epididymous and also store mature sperm. The vas deferens snakes up within the spermatic cords over the top of the bladder and continues on to the seminal vesicles and enters the prostate gland where it becomes a single ejaculatory duct. This duct connects in turn with the urethra, the tube which runs down the center of the penis and terminates in a small slit in the glans. The urethra is also connected with the bladder and allows for the expulsion of urine. Muscular sphincters control which of two processes (ejaculation or urination) occur at any given point, automatically prohibiting the other.

Seminal Vesicles *:* The seminal vesicles are small elongated pouches located directly behind the bladder which produce seminal fluid. During ejaculation, the sperm travel through the vas deferens to the seminal vesicles where seminal fluid is mixed in. This fluid, which constitutes about 70% of semen, is chemically alkaline and functions to neutralize the highly acidic environment of the vagina, insuring the survival of some (but not all) of the sperm. Seminal fluid is also rich in nutrients and includes fructose, and citric and amino acids, which all provide energy for the sperm and increase motility.

Sperm Production

Spermatogenesis begins in the seminiferous tubules of the testicles when germ cells, called spermatogenia, are generated. Each has the 46 chromosomes normal for human cells. In a process called mitosis, the 46 chromosomes replicate and each half of the resulting 92 chromosomes split into 2 separate cells called primary spermatocytes. Each cell retains half (46) of the chromosomes) and then, in a process called meiosis, divide again, resulting in secondary spermatocytes containing just 23 chromosomes. One last division occurs in which the secondary spermatocytes becomes spermatids, or immature sperm. The maturation process continues, eventually resulting in a mature sperm (about 0.05 milliliters in length) containing 23 chromosomes. Theses 23 join together with the 23 chromosomes of the ovum, allowing for a new person to eventually result, sharing half of her genetic material with her father and half with her mother. The testes are prodigiously productive,

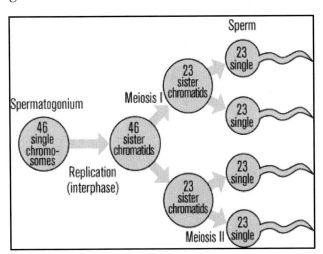

taking approximately 70 days to produce sperm from beginning to end and doing it at the astounding rate of 1000 sperm a second (Macdonald, 2005), or 300 million or so per day. That works out to about 12 trillion (12,000,000,000,000) sperm that a typical man will produce over his lifetime (Sex trivia, 2006).

Three elements comprise the mature sperm; the tail, the body (or connecting piece) and the all-important head containing the nucleus with the chromosomal material. The crown of the head is covered by an acrosome, containing enzymes to be released if and when the sperm comes in contact with an ovum.

These enzymes allow penetration of the membrane covering the ovum. On top of these enzymes are a layer of enzyme inhibitors (Nilsson, 1986), to prevent the enzymes from being used too early, or before the sperm reaches the ovum. The acrosome and rest of the sperm are also covered by a membrane.

Immediately below the head is the connecting piece, made up energy-supplying mitochondria. Finally, protein fibers make up the tail. These fibers contract on alternating sides, producing a wave-like action which propels the sperm forward at an approximate rate of about 3mm (0.12 inches) per minute. Sperm work hard, needing to whip their tales over 2000 times to swim an inch. It is still a mystery, but some sperm are better "swimmers" than others.

As noted earlier, ideal sperm production requires a temperature of 3-5 degrees below body temperature. The scrotum has a built-in "thermostat" which pulls the testis up toward the body if the temperature is too low to preserve heat and allow the sperm to develop. But if the scrotal temperature is too high, sperm development is also adversely affected. One of the queries that fertility specialists often have for men who are having difficulty conceiving is what type of underwear they typically wear. Briefs and other tight clothing effectively pull up the scrotal sac closer to the body, thereby elevating scrotal temperature and causing a greater proportion of the sperm to develop abnormally and have lower motility. The same result can be produced by taking too many hot baths (Macdonald, 2005) or having a job which a man to repeated exposure to high temperatures (for instance, close proximity to a pizza oven exposes).

Apart from temperature, there are numerous other potential causes of abnormal sperm production, often resulting in a reduced sperm count. Stress, various medications, drug and alcohol use, environmental exposure to chemicals and/or radiation, hormonal changes, cigarette smoking, infections and testicular injury have all been implicated as causal factors in reduced and abnormal sperm production, as well as a sperm's ability to "swim", called motility. Moderate amounts of coffee, on the other hand, apparently stimulate sperm to swim faster, further and harder (Macdonald, 2005). Coffee aside, there is significant research evidence to indicate that sperm count has decreased significantly in adult men over the past decades by as much as 50% (Auger et al, 1995; Carlson et al, 1992), no doubt due to the causal factors noted above.

Sperm may develop abnormally in many different ways. They may develop 2 tails or 2 heads, or be malformed in other ways. Needless to say, reduced motility, low sperm count and a greater proportion of abnormal sperm will all potentially influence not only whether a man can successfully produce children, but how genetically healthy any children he does produce will be.

FEMALE STRUCTURES AND PROCESSES

External Genital Structures

Vulva: Collectively known as the vulva or vulval area, the external female genital structures are richly supplied with neural connections, making them very sensitive to touch and thus potentially responsive to sexual arousal. The mons pubis is the mound of fatty tissue covering the female pubic bone, which after puberty, is covered with varying amounts of hair.

Labia Majora & Labia Minora: Two sets of skin folds, one inside the other, are found directly below the mons pubis and comprise the opening leading to the internal sex organ of the vagina. The outer lips are known as the labia majora and are homologous to the male scrotum. In an unaroused state, they loosely cover and thus protect the urethra and the vaginal canal. The process of delivery stretches the labia majora significantly, thus subsequent to giving birth the labia majora doesn't completely close (Slupik & Allison, 1996). The inner set of skin folds are smaller and are known as the labia minora. They fuse together at the top with the mons pubis to form the clitoral hood, a small flap of skin protecting the clitoris. In a state of arousal, both the labia majora and labia minora engorge with blood and pull back and out, effectively exposing the clitoris and the vaginal opening.

Clitoris: The clitoris is located just below the mons pubis where the lips of the labia minora join together to form the clitoral hood. It is homologous with the head of the penis, and as such is composed of the glans, the observable apex of the clitoris, and the shaft, the rest of the structure. Internally, it is composed of erectile tissue called corpora cavernosa, which engorge with blood and swell during arousal in a manner similar to a male erection. This engorgement is not as obvious because much of the clitoris is under the skin surface and thus not visible. Although it appears to be the size of a pea, the average clitoris is approximately 1 x ½ inches and like the male penis, varies in size from person to person. The clitoris is densely packing with neural receptors, making it highly sensitive.

Introitus: Also called the vaginal opening, the introitus connects the external genitalia with the internal genitalia and is the opening which allows for both sexual intercourse and, in some cases, for birth 9 months later. Two small bean-shaped structures called Bartholin's glands (homologous to Cowper's gland in males), are proximate to the vaginal opening and secrete lubricating fluid during arousal.

Perineum: Extending from the vaginal opening to the anal opening is an area of skin-covered muscle called the perineum. It is this area that may be cut during delivery to prevent tearing. Called an episiotomy, this procedure allows for the vaginal delivery of larger babies and has become somewhat common as the birth-weight of babies has gotten larger.

Internal Genital Structures

Vagina: Immediately within the vaginal opening is the vagina, a tubular organ that lengthens to the cervix and is approximately 4 inches in length (in an unaroused condition). Located internally between the rectum below and the bladder and urethra above, it is composed primarily of mucous membrane-lined smooth muscle. These muscles have the capacity for the extensive stretching to accommodate both sexual intercourse and birth. The outer third is enervated and thus sensitive to touch, unlike the inner two-thirds. The inside of the vagina remains moist due to ongoing secretions necessary to support "friendly" bacteria which contribute toward the maintenance of an acidic environment, which in turn protects a women from infection from "unfriendly" bacteria and other pathogens. Antibiotics can kill off the "friendly" bacteria, increasing the alkalinity of the vaginal environment, and resulting in a yeast infection. Sperm are considered to be "unfriendly" and pathenogenic by a woman's body and when present in the vagina, are attacked and dispatched by her immune system. Fortunately for all of us, some sperm do survive!

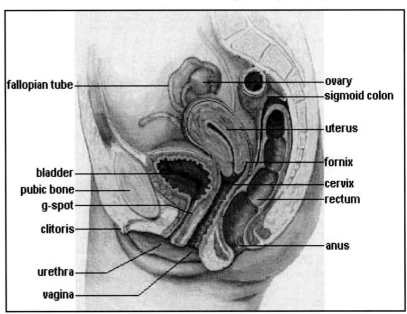

Cervix: At the inner-most end of the vagina is the *cervix*, which through the *cervical os*, connects the vagina to the lower end of the uterus. When sexual intercourse occurs and sperm are deposited into the vagina, they must swim through the cervical opening into the uterus and finally into the Fallopian tubes to have any chance of fertilization. Cervical glands produce a mucous which normally "plugs" the opening to protect the uterus from bacterial infection. During ovulation, hormonal changes occur in a woman's body which thin out the consistency of the cervical mucous, effectively allowing for the sperm to swim through. This is not the only "help" that sperm get from the cervix. It contains small sacs (called crypts), which help protect sperm from the acidic-like vaginal environment by secreting alkaline mucus.

Uterus: The uterus is an approximately 2 x 3 inch pear-shaped organ located directly above the vagina and cervix with the lowest part being the most narrow (called the uterus isthmus). It tapers out in the middle (the uterus corpus) with the roundish dome-like top (the uterus fundus) being the widest. Like the vagina, it is capable of remarkable stretching, which will be needed during the nine months of pregnancy when it becomes the womb. Subsequent to birth, it will shrink back to its original size.

The uterus fundus and corpus are comprised of three layers. The thin outermost layer is called the perimetrium, or serosal layer. It secretes the serous fluid that acts as a lubricant preventing friction between the uterus and surrounding organs as a woman goes about her day to day activities. The middle layer, called the myometrium, is what provides the powerful contractions so important during labor. During sexual maturity (from puberty to menopause), the innermost layer of the uterus (the endometrium) goes through a constant process of thickening and thinning. It becomes most substantial in the days immediately after ovulation, when a fertilization of a ovum by a sperm is most likely to have occurred. This thickening is caused by hormonal changes and is composed of blood and nutrient-rich tissue, maximizing the chances of survival of any blastocyst that implants in the uterine wall. If implantation does not occur, the enriched endometrial tissue sloughs off and produces the menstrual flow.

Fallopian Tubes: At the top and to either side of the uterus extend the two Fallopian tubes. Also called oviducts, they are approximately 4 inch long. The fallopian tubes connect the uterus with the ovaries and the channel which allow sperm to swim up, and ova and zygotes to float down. Narrow at the uterine end (called the isthmus), they gradually widen toward the ovarian end (called the ampulla). At the very end of the fallopian tubes are finger-like projections called fimbriae that "hover" over the ovaries. During ovulation, the ovum is released from the ovary and helped by the subtle waving movement of the fimbrae are gently propelled down the channel of the Fallopian tube. Also assisting the uterine-bound movement of the ovum are cilia, tiny hair-like projections within the inside wall of the fallopian tubes, as well as rhythmic contractions of the muscular walls of the tube. If sperm are present, fertilization takes place at some point in the Fallopian tube in the few days that the ovum is floating down toward the uterus.

Ovaries: At the filibriaeted end of the fallopian tubes are the 2 almond-shaped ovaries (one on either side of the uterus), homologous with the male testes. Approximately ¾ to 1.5 inches in length, they are not directly connected to the Fallopian tubes, but are held in place by ovarian ligaments which attach to the wall of the uterus. The ovaries have two main functions, the first as part of the endocrine system. They produce and release female sex hormones, including estrogen and progesterone. The second ovarian function is the storage and production of ova.

Following the changes that occur during puberty, the ovaries have a wrinkled, uneven surface and are covered with epithelial tissue. Beneath this tissue are numerous minute primary follicles, embedded in connective tissue called stroma. The follicles both store the ova (which have been present since the mother's own fetal development), and in sexually mature females, produce mature ova.

Breasts

While not technically part of the female reproductive system, they do contain alveolar glands which produce milk and thus ideal nourishment to the newborn after birth. The breasts, also called mammary glands, respond to the hormonal changes of the ovulatory cycle and pregnancy. The fatty tissue of the breast, called adipose tissue, rests on a muscular base called the pectoralis major. Normal variability in adipose tissue in various women is what accounts for the assorted shapes and sizes of women's' breasts. Functionally speaking (milk production), size does not matter. While most women (and men) are born with one set of breasts, there is a condition known as polythelia. In this condition, humans are born with more than 1 pair and as many as 8 pair (Jones, 1991).

At the peak of each breast is the pigmented round areola, with the nipple in the center. The nipple has an opening, connected to the lactiferous duct, which stores and releases milk. Connected to this duct are the 15-20 lobules of the alveolar glands, which actually produce the milk. The pituitary gland secretes the hormone prolactin, which initiates and maintains milk production in the period following birth.

Ova Production

Oogenesis occurs in the ovaries, and begins while still in the womb. As early as the 50th day after a woman's own conception, her ovaries produce primitive cells which begin to multiply at a great rate. By about the 5th month in utero, these cells number almost 7 million, but degenerate down to a still-impressive 700,000 to about 2 million at birth. This further decreases to around 400,000 by puberty. Most of these immature ova will never become mature, primarily due to the measured once-every-28-days-or-so release of one or maybe two ova. Thus, in a typical woman's lifetime, only 200-400 fully developed ova are released.

The process of ovum production begins with the primary oocyte, which has 46 chromosomes. In a process called mitosis, the 46 chromosomes replicate and each half of the resulting 92 chromosomes split into 2 separate cells with 46 chromosomes each. In a process called meiosis, these cells split again, replicate, and split again. Of the four "daughter" cells resulting from this process, three (called polar bodies) come out much smaller than the fourth and eventually disintegrate. The fourth is left as the final product of oogenesis, which we call the ovum.

The follicles of the ovaries store the ova. But the follicles themselves also develop through a process that takes over a year (375 days). A group of dormant and undeveloped primordial follicles grows and gradually becomes a mature or Graffian follicle containing one ovum. In the first half of the 28-day or so menstrual cycle, called the follicular phase, the Graffian follicle will begin to change. This process, called cumulus expansion, is stimulated by the secretion of hormone called (logically enough) follicle stimulating hormone (FSH). The follicle, and the ovum within, gradually mature, and in response to a spike in FSH and another hormone called LH (luteinizing hormone), will eventually burst. Both hormones are crucial for the process of ovulation (Siklósi et al, 2001). The hole produced, called the stigma, allows the ovum to escape the ovary and into the fallopian tube. This process occurs at the midpoint of the menstrual cycle, and is called ovulation.

Ovulation

The hypothalamus controls the processes of ovulation by directing the pituitary gland to release hormones in varying amounts and at varying intervals, particularly the LH and FSH noted earlier. Along with the estradiol and progesterone released by the ovaries, these four hormones rise and dip throughout the 28-day (or so) menstrual cycle, guiding processes in the ovaries and in the endometrium of the uterus.

During the second half of the menstrual cycle, called the luteal phase, the ovum travels down the fallopian tubes toward the uterus. If not fertilized, it will degrade in the fallopian tubes within 24 hours and be eventually expelled in the menstrual flow. However, if fertilized by sperm, it will implant in the wall of the uterus 5-12 days later. The hormones released in the first half of the menstrual cycle have signaled the endometrium of the uterus to begin thickening with oxygen and nutrient-rich blood. Thus, the uterus is ideally prepared 6-12 days after ovulation for any blastocyst that may implant in the wall of the uterus.

Ovulation is also accompanied by slight elevations in body temperature, and in some women, pain, and a heightened sense of smell (*Navarrete-Palacios et al, 2003*). This heightened sense of smell may help explain research findings that women's preferences for certain male smells and features changes over the menstrual cycle. Around ovulation, women tend to prefer masculine traits (and smells). This changes during the rest of the menstrual cycle when women tend to prefer traits (and smells) that signal stability over sheer masculinity. Men also report great preference for women's scent's around ovulation than at other times (Haselton, 2006; Roberts et al, 2003).

PRE-FERTILIZATION

Someone has estimated that at any given moment, there are about 2000 couples having sexual intercourse (right now), which comes out to about 200 million acts of sexual intercourse per day (Sex trivia, 2006). In the great majority of cases, the result will not be conception, pregnancy or birth. This is due to issues of fertility, timing, environmental factors, birth control and abortion. In fact, so many things can "go wrong" that it is a miracle that any of us were ever born.

Whether conception and pregnancy are intentional or not, female and male reproductive systems and the act of sexual intercourse are wonderfully designed to maximize the chances of conception. Both the form and function of the male and female sex organs serve to increase the likelihood that a sperm will "hook up" with an ovum.

As noted earlier, the sperm are sequentially blended with various fluids from the seminal vesicles, prostate and Cowper's glands during the several seconds of orgasm. These fluids provide energy (fructose) and other nutrients (enzymes, salts, nitrogen, creatine, cholesterol, & vitamin B12) for the sperm. They also are alkaline in chemical composition, protecting the sperm from the acidic vaginal setting.

During sexual intercourse, the forward-thrusting action of the penis within the vagina increases the likelihood the sperm will be "deposited" toward the cervical end of the vagina. The muscular contractions of orgasm and the spurting pressure of ejaculation have the same result. Sperm closer to the cervical opening have that much less area to swim and thus conserve energy and minimize their chances of demise in the hostile environment (at least for them) of the vagina. Women's muscular contractions during orgasm also "help" the sperm. Immediately after orgasm ends, the cervix drops into the vagina and, if semen is present, dips into the fluid several times. The net effect is like an elevator, assisting the sperm into and through the cervical opening to the uterus.

But the cervix also provides several other helpful actions. As we noted earlier, during ovulation the cervix releases an alkaline mucus, thus duplicating the "help" of the various glands in the male's body which contribute toward the blend of semen. The cervix also contains small sac-like crypts that function as temporary sperm reservoirs (rest areas?). Another adjustment that the cervix makes during ovulation is to "thin" out the cervical plug which protects the uterine environment from the vaginal one. This augments the chances of sperm to be able to traverse the cervix into the uterus. Finally, the cervical canal has small hair-like cilia, which gently sweep the sperm forward.

The uterus also functions to maximize the likelihood of fertilization. The smooth muscles of the uterus contract, effectively propelling the sperm toward the fallopian tubes. Similar to the cervix, uterine cilia also sweep forward the sperm. Finally, striations in the endometrial wall provide" canals" which direct the swimming sperm toward the fallopian tubes.

The net effect of male and female orgasm, along with the assistance of the cervix and uterus, is to greatly enhance the chances of pregnancy. Sperm are speedy swimmers and can cover about 1/10 of an inch per minute. (Macdonald, 2005). Given their small size, a comparative speed of an adult man would be 21/5 minute mile (Macdonald, 2005). But this speed requires about 2000 tail whips to swim an inch and uses up a lot of precious energy, so every bit of assistance helps. With cervical and uterine assistance, sperm can swim about 8 inches in an hour (vs. 6 inches without help).

What is the rush, you might ask? Unlike the Olympics, there is no silver or bronze medal in the up to 10-hour swimming "ultra-marathon" that sperm are competing in. Out of the 200 to 500 million sperm that start the race, there can potentially only be 1 winner. All the other sperm are losers and will die, some almost immediately and some lasting as long as 1 week (Macdonald, 2005). In this race, it is truly "do or die". The positive benefit to this process is the likelihood that the strongest and fittest sperm are most likely to win, increasing the chances of healthy fertilization.

Two different types of sperm are produced, those with an X chromosome and those with a Y. The Y-chromosome-carrying sperm are faster swimmers than X-chromosome-carrying sperm, and therefore are more often the "winners". Studies have typically shown that out of 1000 conceptions, 511 males and just 489 females are the result. Recent research in Italy has discovered that this rate fluctuates seasonally, higher (535 boys/465 girls) in the fall and lower (487boys/513girls) in the spring (Cagnacci, 2003). The result is that more baby boys are born than baby girls. This phenomenon was noted as early 1662 by John Graunt and statistically studied in 1710 by John Arbuthnot. In the last data available in the United States (2002) the ratio was 524/476 (CDC, 2005). Worldwide, the ratio is about 530/470.

But other factors, including age and ethnicity also influence the likelihood of whether a girl or a boy is conceived and eventually born. In the United States, older mothers (over 40) have the lowest total sex birth ratios (519/481) and younger mothers (15 to 19) have highest sex birth ratio (527/473). Chinese (537/463) and Filipino (536/464) mothers (1,072) had the highest differences between the number of boys born versus girls, while non-Hispanic African-American (515/485) and Native American (515/485) had the lowest. (CDC, 2005).

A trend that has been noted recently has found gradual declines in the proportion of male to female births in the US, Canada, Denmark, Russia, Taiwan and the Netherlands. The causes are multiple and are said to include industrial accidents, occupational exposure, and air pollution. (Davis et al, 1998; Mocarelli et al, 1998; Møller, 1996, 1998).

But how do the sperm find the ovum? At least part of the answer to this question is smell. Sperm contain olfactory receptor proteins, particularly one known as hOR17-4, which respond to various scents. One floral scent in particular, called bourgeonal, cause sperm to both change directions and to speed up, almost doubling its speed in high enough concentrations. At this point, researchers don't yet know if it is the ovum or some other structure which release the scents. (Spehr et al, 2003).

Once sperm reach the top end of the uterus, they come to a dead end and must either turn right or left into one of the fallopian tubes. About half swim each way, thus effectively reducing potential fertilizers by 50%. This number is reduced by 100% if no ovum is present in one (or in some cases, both) of the fallopian tubes. All the sperm will eventually expire and no possibility of fertilization or pregnancy exists.

But if an ovum is present in a fallopian tube, it has already been in transit for up to four days, having been "released" by one of the ovaries during ovulation. Usually just one ovum is released,

46

but in about 1 out of 80 times, 2 are released and three ova are released in about 1 out of 6500 times (Nathanielz, 1992, p. 14). This is one reason why twins and triplets are so rare. Like the sperm, ova are assisted in their progress by both the waving movement of the ovarian fimbrae and fallopian cilia, and the rhythmic contractions of the fallopian walls.

FERTILIZATION

Fertilization is the result of the smallest cell in the human body (the sperm) fusing together with a cell 85,000 times larger and the largest cell in the human body (the ovum) to produce not 2 cells, but one, a zygote (Foulk, 2001). Over time, this 1 cell will multiply into the trillions of cells which make up all the cells of a full-grown adult. While the numbers are quite amazing, it gets even more incredible (Macdonald, 205). This 1 cell will multiply itself into over 200 types of specialized cells, constituting the cells of the brain, bones, skin, liver, heart, eyes, kidneys, teeth and so on. The actual moment of fertilization almost always takes place somewhere in the 4-inch fallopian tubes, usually toward the uterine end and away from the ovarian end. In rare cases fertilization can also occur in the uterus or even rarer, in a test tube or Petri dish somewhere.

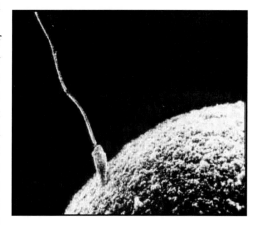

As the sperm have been swimming, the layer of enzyme inhibitors just above the acrosome have gradually been worn away, exposing the enzymes just at the time when they will be needed to chemically "drill" into the outer layer of the ovum. Several sperm usually arrive at the ovum at once and quickly attach themselves to special receptor sites located on the zona pellucida, the outermost layer of the ovum. This binding process capacitates the enzymes contained in the acrosome at the very tip of the sperm head. The sperm tail continues to wave while these enzymes work and both produce a burrowing process through the outside layer of the ovum. Once through, the sperm arrives at a space separating the outside membrane from the plasma membrane. In a split second of time, the sperm fuses with the plasma membrane and is literally pulled into the ovum by ovum-produced contractions. As soon as this happens, ovum-produced enzymes are released into the space separating the zona pellucida and the plasma membrane of the ovum. The instantaneous result is the deactivation of all of the sperm receptor sites and a hardening of the outside membrane, effectively blocking out all other sperm from entry.

CONCLUSION

Over the next several hours, the "winning" sperm and the ovum fuse together the genetic content that each has carried within their respective nuclei, producing the genetic blueprint so determinative to the person that will potentially result. Whether this person will be tall or short, have blue eyes or brown eyes, be happy or depressed, have a predisposition for musical, artistic, athletic or mathematical abilities, be a teacher or a psychologist, live to 100 or even survive the next few moments, are all determined to a degree by this process. It can be rightly argued that this is THE single most influential day of our lives and it is the topic of our next chapter.

4

GENETICS

Creator of the germ in woman,
Maker of the seed in man,
Giving life to the son in the body of his mother.

Akhnaton

INTRODUCTION

In the hours following fertilization, a unique genetic signature of DNA forms. Indeed, in all of human history past and all of the future to come, there will never be another combination of gene traits like the one that occurred when you were conceived. Every person (with the exception of identical twins or triplets) is absolutely genetically unique and always will be. In fact, a couple (one man and one woman) can produce 8 million different possible viable combinations of genetic material.

BASIC GENETICS

Chromosomes and Genes

The result of fertilization is that the 23 chromosomes of the sperm join together with the 23 chromosomes of the ovum to form 23 pairs (or 46 total). These chromosomes are made up of long strings (about 6 feet for each chromosome) of DNA (deoxyribo-nucleic acid). Often described as a double-helix, the DNA looks like a long twisting ladder with rungs. These rungs can separate in the middle, almost like a zipper and the two resulting half-ladders replicate them-selves into complete ladders again. This process, repeated over and over again, is what allows us to go from being a 1-celled zygote to a trillions-celled adult.

The DNA strands in the 23 chromosomes can be further reduced to the approximately 30,000 genes possessed by all human beings. The chromosomes differ in how many genes are contained in each. With the exception of the 23rd pair (the sex chromosomes), they are arranged from the largest (1 with 8000 genes) to the smallest (21 with fewer than 300 genes). Twenty-one is actually smaller than 22 due to a mistake in the original numbering system.

Chromosomes can actually be photographed and arranged into their pairs to get a person's karyotype, or "chromosome profile". Each gene controls (or shares control) one or more particular character traits. In some cases, an individual gene is determinative. In other cases, it is a combination of genes that determine the final outcome of a character trait. For instance, we used to believe that eye color was controlled by one pair of genes. But something as simple as the color of your iris is actually affected by at least 6 pairs of genes (and probably even more). It turns out that we don't inherit actual blue or green or brown pigment, but do inherit a predisposition for an amount of melanin, which is what actually determines eye color. People with no melanin (albinos) have pinkish colored eyes due to the blood vessels toward the back of the eyes. People with blue eyes have a little melanin, those with green eyes a bit more and those with brown eyes have the most.

The gene influencing a particular trait always appears in the same place in the DNA for all members of that species. For humans, Rh factor is always chromosome 1, blood type is always chromosome 9, and gender is always chromosome 23. Susceptibility to numerous genetically-based diseases is also controlled by the genes within chromosomes. For instance, chromosome 4 alone has genes associated with Huntington Disease, Williams-Beuren syndrome, Wolf-Hirschhorn syndrome, and PKU (Phenylketonuia).

Most genes have several variants known as alleles. Although each of us has particular alleles in common with numerous others, no one else (except an identical twin or triplet) has the same amalgamation you do. Different alleles influence how tall each person is likely to be, how resistant or sensitive each of us is to particular medications, how susceptible we will be to asthma, heart disease, diabetes, cancer, alcoholism or Alzheimer disease. The alleles also partially control what appear to be behavioral responses such as anxiety, depression and appetite. Alleles also direct the amount of melanin in skin and hair, determining pigmentation of both. Because brothers and sisters do not have exactly the same alleles, they can have varying shades of hair and skin, even though they have the same parents.

Patterns of Genetic Influence

As we have already noted, the way genes work can be relatively simple and straightforward or exceedingly complicated. But because each human being is a one-of-a-kind prototype, the way in which our particular set of 23 pairs of chromosomes will function is somewhat of a mystery. Even with all the progress of recent years by geneticists. There is still very much which remains unknown.

But what we do know is quite fascinating and instructive. The particular genes we inherit from each of our parents contain instructions which may or may not be the same at any given locus of each chromosome. When the gene instructions are the same, they are homozygous. If, for instance, both parents passed on genes for blond hair, the child is likely to have blond hair. When the gene directives from our parents are different from each other, they are said to be heterozygous. For instance, if the father passed on the gene for curly hair and the mother passed on the gene for straight hair. In the case of heterozygous gene instructions, what will the result be?

Dominant vs. Recessive: In the case of over 1000 different physical traits, only 1 gene governs the resulting outcome. In these cases, the gene instructions are relatively straightforward. Homozygous instructions will mean that a child will share the character trait with both parents. When there are heterozygous gene instructions, several outcomes are possible. In some cases, the child will follow both sets of instructions.

For instance, if the mother has type A blood and the father has type B blood, the result will be a child with type AB blood. In other cases, there will be an add-up-and-divide effect, where the child will express a trait somewhere in between the mom and the dad. Skin color would be a relatively typically example. Finally, there is the either/or effect, where 1 gene is recessive and thus is not expressed, and the other is dominant and is thus expressed. The recessive gene does not disappear, but remains dormant and can be "passed on" to the next generation.

| Dominant/Recessive Genetic Pattern ||
Dominant	Recessive
Clockwise Hair Whorl	Counter-clockwise Hair Whorl
Can Roll Tongue	Can't Roll Tongue
Facial Dimples	No Facial Dimples
Earlobe hangs	Earlobe attaches at base
Oval face	Square face
Broad eyebrow	Slender eyebrow
Separated eyebrows	Joined eyebrows
Long eyelashes	Short eyelashes
Almond eyes	Round eyes
Freckles	No freckles

Polygenetic Inheritance: We noted earlier the case of eye color, which is controlled by at least 6 different genes. As you look around at people, it appears that many of our physical and psychological traits are expressed along a continuum and are highly variable. This is called polygenic inheritance and probably governs numerous traits. Examples include skin color, intelligence, height, blood pressure, and head circumference (Turnpenny & Ellard, 2004). Congenital diseases and various childhood disorders also appear to be polygenetic (See table below) as well schizophrenia, autism, and bi-polar disorder.

GENETIC INFLUENCES

Sex Chromosomes

Gender: Although we have been referring without distinction to the 23 pairs of chromosomes, there are actually 2 distinct types. The first 22 pairs are called autosomes, with the pairs looking alike and having matching genetic loci. The second type of chromosome is found in the 23rd pair and since this pair governs maleness vs. femaleness is called the sex chromosome. Theses chromosomes come in 2 variations: X and Y. Females have two X chromosomes and males have one X and one Y.

Thus both males and females have at least 1 X chromosome, and this comes from the ovum, which ALWAYS genetically contributes an "X". Since a

Disorders Which Show Polygenic Inheritance	
Congenital malformations	Cleft lip and palate
	Congenital heart defects
	Neural tube defects
Acquired diseases	Asthma
	Autism
	Diabetes mellitus
	Epilepsy
	Glaucoma
	Hypertension
	Crohn disease
	Bi-polar disorder
	Multiple sclerosis
	Parkinson disease
	Rheumatoid arthritis
	Schizophrenia

female has 2 X chromosomes (and no Y chromosomes) in all the cells of her body, the process of meiosis (or splitting) always results in cells with an X chromosome. The cells that eventually become her mature ova thus always have an "X" on the 23rd pair.

Males, on the other hand, have 1 X and 1 Y in every cell of their body. The process of meiosis thus produces cells with X chromosomes and cells with Y chromosomes. Theses cells eventually develop into mature sperm, half carrying the Y chromosome and half the X chromosome. Thus, whether or not a particular person is a male or female is always determined by the "winning" sperm. If the sperm has an X at the 23rd chromosome, the result will be female; if the sperm has a Y, the result will be male. Your gender was thus determined by your father.

But your mother may also have influenced the likelihood of your gender. As we noted in chapter 3, relative birth rates of boys to girls is influenced by the age, ethnicity, pollution, and relative health of women. Further, the chemical balance within any woman's body can be fluctuates over time and as a function of environmental factors. Depending upon timing, it can be more or less weighted toward acidity or alkalinity, which further influences survival of X vs. Y carrying sperm.

Interesting, geneticists have determined that only a small part of the Y chromosome actually determines maleness. This part is called (logically enough) TDF (testis-determining factor) (Page et al, 1987). If it is missing, even an XY chromosomal make-up will develop into a girl. Thus, in order to develop into a male, the embryo must receive genetic instructions to masculinize. It is an oversimplification but many researchers believe that in the absence of these "become male" instructions, the default setting is to become a female.

Sex–linked transmission: The Y chromosome that all males inherit at the 23rd pair is considerably smaller than the X chromosome that all females have and is therefore missing many of the genetic loci that the X chromosome has. Because of this, males inherit genes from their mother that have no matching genes on the very-much smaller Y chromosome. The effect is that even a recessive gene on the X chromosome, because there is no possibly of a dominant countervailing gene on the Y, will be inherited and expressed.

There are over 400 human traits and diseases that seem to be encoded by genes on the X chromosome, and over 200 genes have been mapped. Below are a few of the most significant sex-linked gene factors.

Hemophilia: Because of significant intermarriage within the British, Spanish, German and Russian royal families of Europe in the 16th to 19th century, hemophilia was sometimes known as the "royal disease". There are several types of hemophilia, but all result in an impairment or inability to control bleeding, either external (caused by a cut) or internal (in muscles or hollow organs).

This is can present in continued external bleeding or in bruises visible in the skin. While it can be controlled by means of regular injections of the deficient clotting factor, it cannot be "cured".   Less than 1% of the population is affected by alls formed of this disorder.

Muscular Dystrophy: Muscular Dystrophy is a group of genetic disorder, of which Duchenne muscular dystrophy is the most common.   This disorder is manifested by progressive muscle weakness and finally, in the death of muscle cells. There is no cure or even any systematic treatment apart from physical therapy.

Red-green color blindness : Because it is sex-linked, genetic red-green color blindness affects males much more often than females. The genes for green and red color receptors are located on the X chromosome, so if there is a defective gene in a male, there will be a lack of a countervailing gene on the Y chromosome. Thus, the male will be red-green colorblind. Females can only inherit this colorblindness if BOTH X chromosomes have the genetic deficiency.

The gene for red-green color blindness is transmitted from a color blind male to all his daughters, but unless they also inherit this trait from their mothers, they will be unaffected. However, they will be carriers who can pass on the trait to their sons, and in much rarer cases, their daughters. The sons of an affected male will not inherit the trait, since they can only receive his Y chromosome and not his (defective) X chromosome.

In the United States, red-green color blindness affects about 7 percent of the male population but only 0.4 percent of the female population (2006, Howard Hughes Medical Institute). But there are cases where, due to isolated populations, and thus lesser genetic variability, the numbers are significantly higher. Examples include areas in rural Finland and on some isolated islands in Scotland.

Chromosomal Anomalies

Fragile X Syndrome: This syndrome is caused by genetic mutation or "breakage" is part of the X chromosome and is therefore found in both males (1 out of 1500) and females (1 out of 2500). Typical symptoms include intellectual impairment, protruding ears and in males with the syndrome, large testicles. Social impairment such as limited eye contact, shyness, and repetitive behavior partially account for the fact that some individuals with this disorder meet the diagnostic criteria for autism. The lower incidence in females is due to the likely presence of a second "non-fragile" X, which serves as a genetic counterweight to the mutation. Since males have the small Y chromosome with its missing genetic loci, they almost twice as likely to manifest the syndrome as females are. Males with this disorder are likely to exhibit greater symptomology, whereas females manifest symptoms along a continuum. The mildness of the symptoms in some females explains why the syndrome is likely to be underdiagnosed in them relative to males.

Turner Syndrome (XO): Names after Henry Turner, an endocrinologist from Oklahoma who first described the symptoms in the 1940's, Turner syndrome results when a girl is born either partially or completely missing significant genetic information on one of her X chromosomes. Thus, the chromosomal makeup for the 23rd pair is indicated as "XO". Turner's individuals are always girls, having female external genitalia. In the absence of treatment, they will undeveloped at puberty and cannot bear children. Common symptoms include intellectual impairment, shortness, a broad chest, low hairline and low set ears. But expressed symptoms are variable and differ from person to person.

In the United States, the incidence of Turner syndrome births is somewhere between 1 out of 2500 (NIH, 2004) and 1 out of 10,000 (OMIM, 2004) female births. This rate may be influenced by the availability of elective abortion. Research studies have reported that 72% (ranging from 27% to 88% depending upon the year and country) of fetuses are aborted following the prenatal diagnosis of Turner syndrome (Mansfield, Hopfer, & Marteau, 1999). Many more embryos start off with this condition, but in approximately 98% of all cases the result is a miscarriage (This syndrome accounts for about 10% of miscarriages in the United States (Turners Syndrome, 2006).

Incidentally, there is no equivalent syndrome ("OY") for boys. In any case where such a chromosomal anomaly might occur, viability is zero. No "cure" is available, but hormone treatments of various types are used to produce and maintain secondary sex characteristic development at puberty and into adulthood.

Klinefelter Syndrome (XXY or XXXY or XXXXY or XXYY): Named after Harry Klinefelter, a medical researcher from Massachusetts who first described the condition in 1942, Klinefelter syndrome occurs in about 1 out of 1000 male births (OMIM, 2004) and results from extra genetic information at the 23rd pair. Due to the presence of the Y chromosome, these individuals are male. Symptoms include small and underdeveloped genitalia, undescended testicles, large breasts, and in about 25% of the time, intellectual impairment. While no "cure" is available, hormone treatments (testosterone) are used to produce and maintain secondary sex characteristic development at puberty and into adulthood.

As with Turner and Down syndromes, the rates of Klinefelter syndrome may be skewed by the availability of elective abortion. Research studies have reported that 58% (between 22% and 97% depending on the year and country) of fetuses are aborted following prenatal diagnosis (Mansfield, Hopfer, & Marteau, 1999).

The XXY variant is the most common occurring variation of Klinefelters, with the added X chromosomes being rarer and rarer. The XXYY chromosomal makeup occurs only once in 17,000 births and has also traditionally been considered a variation of Klinefelters.

Superfemale syndrome (XXX or XXXX or XXXXX): First identified by Patricia Jacobs and her colleagues in Scotland in 1959, "superfemale" syndrome results from extra female ("X" chromosome) genetic material at the 23rd pair in females. This syndrome occurs in about 1 out of every 1000 female births (OMIM, 2004). Able to have children and developing normally at puberty, most individuals with this syndrome are never identified. Since this is not an inherited condition, but rather due to chromosomal abnormalities of the sperm or ovum, the syndrome will not be "passed on" to any future children. The risk of this occurring in a subsequent pregnancy is no more than in the population at large. Symptoms include slight increases in height and a slightly greater likelihood of intellectual impairment. The XXX variant is the most common occurring superfemale variation, with the added X chromosomes being rarer and rarer (tetra-X and penta-X).

Supermale syndrome (XYY or XYYY, or XYYYY): First described by Avery Sandberg and his colleagues in Buffalo, New York in 1961, the "supermale" syndrome results from extra male ("Y" chromosome) material at the 23rd pair in males. This syndrome occurs in about 1 out of every 1000 male births (OMIM, 2004). As with the superfemale syndrome, men with this syndrome are usually fertile and develop normally at puberty. Similarly, since it is not an inherited condition, but rather due to chromosomal abnormalities of the sperm, the syndrome cannot be "passed on" in subsequent generations. The risk of this syndrome occurring in any subsequent pregnancy is the same as the population at large.

As with the superfemale syndrome, in most cases symptoms are subtle. Thus, most individuals with this syndrome will never be identified. One study found that approximately 97% of males in the UK with this syndrome never even knew they had it (Allanson & Graham, 2002). Symptoms include above average height, some coordination difficulties that present as clumsiness or awkwardness during childhood and greater likelihood of moderate to severe acne during the adolescent years. Males with this syndrome are also likely to have IQs slightly lower (about 10-15 pints) than their siblings (Milunsky, 2004) and about 50% (Gardner, McKinlay & Sutherland, 2004) experience some type of learning disability in their school-age years, particularly with reading and language functions. Speech delays have also been noted in some XXY boys. But prognosis is very good with proper intervention.

Perhaps partially because of the above, boys and men with this syndrome are also at increased risk for behavior problems, typically impulse control. This behavioral trait has given the supermale syndrome some notoriety historically. On the basis of research involving almost 200 males at a prison facility in Scotland, a study in 1965 (Jacobs et al, 1965) found that 7 of the men evidenced the XYY genetic makeup. This occurrence (3.5%) was much higher than the population at large, and so the somewhat faulty connection was made with this syndrome and criminal behavior. Subsequent studies confirmed the likelihood of increased height and decreased intellectual functioning but did not conclusively establish increased aggression (Baker et al, 1970; Jacobs et al, 1971). In 1976, a further paper did conclude that XYY males were more likely to be imprisoned that XY males, but that this was more likely due to the decreased intellectual functioning. Lower IQ lead to decreased education outcomes and poorer socioeconomic status, which placed them at an increased risk of being apprehended and imprisoned (Witkins et al, 1976).

The inability to properly metabolize certain neurohormones may also be a factor explaining XYY outcomes. Supermales may lack the ability to properly metabolize neurohormones and neurotransmitters key to proper brain function. As Steen (1996) notes, a deficiency in the production of an enzyme called Monoamine Oxidase type A. may further influence the metabolization of serotonin, norepinephrine, and dopamine. This, in turn, may account for the behavioral responses which indirectly, but eventually, result in the increased rates of imprisonment.

Autosomes

Apart from the sex chromosomes at the 23rd pair, the other 22 pairs (1-22) are known as autosomes. These chromosomes give instructions about the color of our hair and eyes, how tall we will be, the shape of our faces and bodies, whether we are happy or tend to depression, whether we are likely to be alcoholics or schizophrenics, whether we have minimal or substantial artistic, musical or athletic abilities, and on and on it goes. Our genes have a say in the seemingly important factors of our lives, as well as the downright whimsical. For instance, the genes related to the following have been identified: right vs. left handedness, arm folding preferences, ability to move one's ears, ability to curl, fold, or roll one's tongue, perfect musical pitch, and novelty seeking personality trait, stuttering, tobacco addiction, and alcoholism.

As is perhaps self-evident, we have to be careful not to assume that our genes "control" and predict exactly what kind of person we will become. All genes are influenced to one degree or another by their environment and by our experiences in the real world.

Thus, a distinction must be made between or genotype, the specific sets of instructions our genes give us, and our phenotype, the set of observed characteristics in an actual person. Even identical twins or triplets, who share the same genotype, can exhibit quite different phenotypes.

Intelligence is just one example of how genotype and phenotype may differ. My parents may both have been geniuses. But if my mother used alcohol and drugs during key points in her pregnancy, and if I was dropped on my head during infancy, and if I was abused during childhood, all of these experiences would adversely affect my phenotype for intellectual ability, even though my genotype would have "predicted" that I too would be a genius. One's intellectual capabilities are influenced by early prenatal and postnatal experiences and environments, educational opportunities, and many other factors, in addition to one's genes.

The autosomes also give directions for predispositions to various disorders. There are hundreds of these, but we will take a look at some of the most important ones. They include chromosomal conditions such as Down syndrome and Williams syndrome, and genetic conditions such as PKU, Tay-Sachs Disease, and others.

Chromosomal Conditions

Down Syndrome: First identified in 1866 by J. Langdon Down, this syndrome, of which there are several types, is caused by extra genetic material at the 21st autosome (see karyotype on the right). Due to continued misunder-standing about the causes and to implicit racism, it was initially called mongolism or mongoloid idiocy, owing to the distinct facial features see in those with the syndrome.

Although identified by Down in 1866, it was not until 1959 that the cause of this syndrome was identified. Jerome Lejeune discovered the extra chromosome at the 21st pair and called the condition trisomy 21. The name was eventually changed to Down syndrome.

The distinct facial features of the disorder include a flattened out nasal bridge and small skin folds on the inner corner of the eyes. Other possible physical traits include a shorter neck, shorter height, a large and protruding tongue, hearing impairment, and muscle hypotonia. Mild to moderate mental retardation is also characteristic of the majority of those with Down syndrome. Even when intellectual capabilities are in the normal range, there is often some cognitive impairment or learning disabilities. Other problems associated with Down syndrome include higher rates of congenital heart disease, Alzheimer's disease, leukemia, and epilepsy.

The incidence of Down syndrome in the United States is approximately 1 out of 1000 births (OMIM, 2004). This rate may be influenced by the availability of elective abortion. Research studies have reported that 92% (between 62% and 100% depending on the year and the country) of fetuses are aborted following the prenatal diagnosis of Down syndrome (Britt et al, 1999; Mansfield, Hopfer, & Marteau, 1999).

The most clearly identified risk factor for Down syndrome is maternal age. The risk to women at age 20-24 is about 1 out of 1400. This steadily rises as women get older to reach 1 out of 25 for women over age 44 (Hook, 1981). But recently paternal age has been identified as a potential factor in Down syndrome etiology. In a large study done in New York state, researchers noted that up to 50% of Down syndrome births in women over age 40 may be a function of the father's age (Fisch et al, 2003).

Several different types of Down Syndrome have been identified.

Trisomy 21, discussed above, is by far the most common and accounts for up to 95% of all Down's cases. Every cell of the body has the extra chromosome at the 21st set.

Mosaicism is a variation in which some of the body cells have the extra chromosome and some do not. It is thought to be caused by the failure of chromosome pairs to separate properly during early cell division in the embryo. It accounts for 1-2% of Down syndrome cases and the expressed symptoms are often less severe that the trisomy-21 type.

Robertsonian translocation is a type of Down syndrome in which the part of chromosome 21 is attached to another chromosome, usually #14. Normal cell division is affected, causing some extra genetic material to be created at the 21st location. This type of Down's has no maternal age effect and accounts for 2-3% of the incidence of Down syndrome.

Williams Syndrome : Occurring in approximately 1 out of 20,000 (OMIM, 2004), Williams syndrome is due to missing genetic information (about 20 genes) at chromosome 7. This syndrome, also called "pixieism", is characterized by "elfin"-like facial features, along with deficits in intellectual functioning and typically good social skills. Perceptual difficulties and left-handedness are much more prevalent in Williams syndrome individuals than in the population at large.

Genetic Conditions: Unlike Down and Williams Syndromes, which are due to chromosomal abnormalities and cannot be inherited, genetic conditions are due to the inheritance of various DNA variants and can and are inherited. There are over 5000 different types, but we will examine the most common and significant of these.

Huntington's Disease: Name after George Huntington, a physician from Ohio who first described the disease in 1872, this disease is carried by a dominant gene on chromosome 4. It occurs in about 1 out of 10,000 births (OMIM, 2004) and the result is the production of a faulty protein which causes progressive and selective degeneration in the cells of the body, particularly neurons. Onset is usually between ages 30 and 50, although in 10% of cases, onset occurs before age 20.

Physical symptoms include chorea, which presents as jerky and somewhat uncontrollable motor movements, lack of coordination, loss of facial muscle control and therefore slurred speech, and difficulty in the coordination of the eating process, sometimes resulting in weight loss.

Cognitive deficits in abstract thinking, perceptual and special skills, and memory also occur at higher rates than in the population at large. Psychological deficits are more variable than physical and cognitive symptoms, but can include any of the following: anxiety, depression, aggressiveness, and compulsive behaviors such as alcohol and rug abuse, gambling, and hypersexuality.

There is no "cure" for Huntington, but symptom reduction and alleviation can be achieved through various medications and physical and speech therapy. Since this disease can be inherited, the children of Huntington sufferers are at risk.

Cystic Fibrosis (CF): First described in 1938 by Dorothy Andersen, cystic fibrosis is a recessive genetic disorder caused by a mutated gene in chromosome 7. It is found almost exclusively among persons of European ancestry and occurs in about 1 out of 2500 births of Caucasians in the United States (OMIM, 2004). It occurs in boys and girls equally and is the most common life-shortening recessive disorder (average age 36.8), although males seem to live a little longer than females (Rosenfeld et al, 1997).

The mutated CFTR (cystic fibrosis transmembrane conductance regulator) gene disrupts several pancreas-based metabolic functions. The disease gets its name from the cyst formation ("cystic") and scarring ("fibrosis") that occurs within the pancreas. The eventual result is the production of excess mucus throughout the body but particularly in the lungs and digestive tract. Thus, breathing difficulties are the most common symptom and result from frequent lung infections. Other symptoms include sinus infections, chronic gastrointestinal problems, liver and pancreatic diseases. Due to poor absorption of nutrients in the gastrointestinal tract, those with this disorder of have poor growth rates, or abnormal growth such as clubbing, an enlargement of the fingers as seen in the photograph to the left.

Most of those with cystic fibrosis are infertile. Males with the disease are born without the vas deferens. Although their testes can produce sperm normally, the "delivery" system is missing and so 97% are infertile (Augarten et al, 1994; Dodge, 1999). Twenty percent of CF women are infertile, mostly as a function of too-thick cervical mucus which adversely affects the passage of sperm thought the cervical canal (Gilljam et al, 2000).

Because it is a genetic disease, no "cure" for CF is available. Symptom reduction and alleviation can be achieved through various antibiotics, enzyme replacements, and the use of nebulizers (see photo at left). Since this disease can be inherited, the children of CF (mostly women due to high rate of male infertility) sufferers and are at risk. But because CF is a recessive trait, many individuals who do not have CF are nevertheless "carriers" and can pass on the gene to any children should they procreate with another person with the recessive gene. In fact, approximately 1 out of 25 people of European descent are carriers. Although less common in other ethnic backgrounds, it is common enough to warrant attention: 1 out 29 of Ashkenazi Jewish descent; 1 out 46 of Hispanic descent; 1 out of 65 of African descent; 1 out of 90 of Asian descent (Hamosh et al, 1998; Kerem, Chiba-Falek, & Kerem, 1997; Rosenstein & Cutting, 1998).

Sickle-cell Anemia: First described in 1910 by Chicago physician James Herrick, and named "sickle-cell anemia" in 1922 (but sometimes also called Herrick Syndrome), sickle cell disease is the name of a group of disorders of which sickle-cell anemia is the most common. It occurs most commonly in those of African heritage or those who came from a part of the world where malaria is or once was prevalent (the Middle East and parts of Asia). One out of 500 African-Americans have sickle-cell anemia (OMIM, 2004), being the most common genetic disorder among African-Americans.

Interestingly, there are descriptions of what appears to be the disease in medical literature from the 1870s in Africa. It was called *ogbanjes* ("children who come and go"), probably because it caused many children to die young. A history of a sickle-like condition has been traced by to 1670 in one family from Ghana (Konotey-Ahulu, 1973).

The disease is caused by a partly recessive gene. Thus, both mother and father have to be carriers of the recessive gene in order for it to be expressed in their child. In this case, there is a 25% (1 out of 4) chance that their child will have sickle-cell anemia (see figure at right). But there is a 50% chance they will be on the recessive trait to their children. Thus 1 out of 12 African-Americans have the sickle-cell trait and are carriers.

The sickle-cell trait was actually adaptive, in that those with the sickle-cell trait (the carriers of the recessive gene) are relatively resistant to malaria. Malaria is caused by a parasite that has a complicated life-cycle, with a portion spent in red-blood cells. The presence of sickle cell anemia and sickle cell trait adversely affects the malaria-causing parasite's survival. Hence, the beneficial effects of this trait in parts of the world where malaria once ran rampant. But in places where malaria is not a problem, the sickle cell trait and anemia are not adaptive. Thus, rates among African-Americans are lower than West Africans.

Since the gene is not completely (and "cleanly") recessive, carriers also have some sickle cells, enough to make them resistant to malaria, but not enough to adversely affect them with expressed symptoms.

Sickle cell anemia is caused by a defective gene on chromosome 11 which causes the production of mutated beta globin, a component of hemoglobin which is the oxygen-transport protein found in red blood cells. The result is weak blood cells which easily break and form pieces, some of which resemble sickles. The pieces eventually clog up the blood vessels and do not effectively and efficiently transport oxygen.

No permanent 'cure' is available and the anemia (lack or oxygen) may result in damage to internal organs (especially the spleen and liver) and bones in the body. Lifespan is shortened and averages around 40-45 years. Treatment includes blood transfusions or bone-marrow transplants.

Phenylketonuria (PKU): First described in 1934 by Norwegian physician Ivar Folling (and still called "Folling's Disease" in Norway), PKU is a recessive disorder that occurs in the United States in approximately 1 out of 10,000 births (OMIM, 2004). But rates around the world vary considerably, occurring in Ireland in 1 in 4,500 births (DiLella et al, 1986) but in Finland fewer than 1 out of 100,000 births (Guldberg et al, 1995).

A defective gene on chromosome 12 prevents the synthesis of the enzyme phenylalanine hydroxylase, which in turn is needed in order to convert phenylalanine (from protein foods) into tyrosine, both essential amino acids. This result is that the phenylalanine accumulates, eventually causing neurological damage by blocking other essential amino acids from reaching cells in the body (particularly the neurons). This occurs after a child is born, because during pregnancy, the mother's body is performing the phenylalanine to tyrosine conversion.

Undetected and untreated, PKU will result in intellectual impairment, including severe to moderate mental retardation, spasmodic muscle twitches and uncontrolled movements, seizures, and hyperactivity. PKU is readily identifiable through a blood test called the Guthrie heel prick test which is routinely done in the United States. If identified early enough and treated, the negative outcomes associated with PKU can be prevented and those with PKU live a perfectly normal life. Treatment includes a low-phenyl lime diet, including avoidance of breast milk and other high phenylalanine foods (nuts, cheese, meat, and starchy foods). Amino-acid providing supplements are also used. This diet must be life-long.

For a pregnant woman with PKU, phenylalanine level regulation is crucial for the health of developing fetus. Even if her baby is only a carrier of the PKU gene, her PKU may cause high levels of PKU in the intrauterine environment, since it does cross the placental barrier. Elevated levels of phenylalanine may cause mental retardation, microencephaly (literally "small head"), and heart and general growth problems (Lee et al, 2005; Souse et al, 1997). Thus a child who doe not have PKU may suffer the adverse consequences from her mother's PKU. But when pregnant mothers do maintain low phenylalanine levels throughout pregnancy, there is no increased risk of problems or complications.

Tay-Sachs Disease (TSD): Named of British ophthalmologist Warren Tay and American neurologist Bernard Sachs, this disease was first identified in the 1880s. It occurs primarily in those of Jewish Ashkenazi (from Germany, Poland, Russia, Hungary and Eastern Europe) descent and is very rare in other ethnic groups. In this population is occurs in approximately 1 out of 5000 births (OMIM, 2004). Like sickle-cell anemia, it is a genetic disorder which serves to make its carriers resistant to another disease, in this case tuberculosis (Craig & Dunn, 2007).

It is a recessive trait in which a gene on chromosome 15 fails to produce the enzyme hexosaminidaseA which eventually results in high levels of a fatty acid called ganglioside accumulating in the neurons. The result is eventual blindness, deafness, muscle atrophy and paralysis, with death usually occurring before age 3. No cure or treatment is available and even with the very best of care, those with TSD almost never live past age 5.

Babies with the disorder appear to develop normally, but as the ganglioside fats accumulate, they begin to cause damage. Among the earliest signs is a red spot that appears in the retina where the optic nerve enters the back of the eye, indicating neural damage in the brain.

Genetic screening is available and has been very effective in greatly reducing the incidence of the disease, either by way of prenatal diagnosis and selective abortion (which raises considerable ethical considerations) or by means of registries of Jewish men and women who arc carriers of the recessive trait. These registries anonymously flag potential marriage partners that they as a couple would have increased chances of having TSD children. The couple then may chose to avoid marriage.

GENETIC COUNSELING

The difference between genotype and phenotype means that most people's recessive traits will remain hidden. It is estimated that each of us are "carriers" of at least 5 potentially deadly recessive traits and many others that are less problematic (Craig & Dunn, 2007). Our unawareness of these genetic traits doesn't mean we don't potentially pass them on; we do. Sadly, these recessive traits tend to enter our awareness when they are expressed in a person's phenotype or there are fertility problems with a particular couple.

Because of the amazing recent advances in research and technology, a field called genetic counseling has emerged over the past 30 years. It includes the analysis of medical records, family histories, and various genetic tests to create a comprehensive picture of genetic risks.

For most people, it is not needed. But there are family factors that suggest some potential parents are at risk for conceiving a child with a recessively expressed disease or syndrome. Some of the family factors that would be important to identify include the following:

- Family history of any genetic condition such as hemophilia, sickle cell anemia, or phenylketonuria, Tay-Sachs disease or Huntington's disease.
- Prior conception or birth of a child with a birth defect, learning disability, or medical disorder.
- Prior history of two or more stillbirths or miscarriages.
- Prior history of infertility.
- Mother is over age 35 and/or father is over age 55.
- Mother has any a chronic health condition (such as diabetes), or has a family history including heart disease, high blood pressure, mental illness, cancer, or diabetes. (Stuart & Solis, 2001).

CONCLUSION

Once the process of combining the chromosomes of the mother and father has been completed, the resulting zygote quickly begins to change and grow as it makes its way down the fallopian tube and into the uterus. Eventually, if all goes well, it will land on the wall of the uterus and begin to implant. The events from the end of fertilization to the end of implantation are called the germinal period and last less than 2 weeks. This is the topic of our next chapter.

5

GERMINAL DEVELOPMENT AND IMPLANTATION

Before I shaped you in the womb,
I knew all about you.
Before you saw the light of day,
I had holy plans for you.

Jeremiah 1:5a
The Message

INTRODUCTION

Although we are most familiar with the division of the prenatal period into trimesters, we do this only as a convenient way of dividing up the approximately 9 months (actually 266 days) of pregnancy into 3 equal segments. But biologically speaking, the term "trimester" has no real meaning. The three "stages" that do have biological meaning are not at all equal in length. The first, which is the subject of this chapter, is the germinal stage. It lasts only 2 weeks, from fertilization until the end of implantation. The second is the 6-week long embryonic stage, and it lasts from the end of implantation to the end of the second month. The last phase is the fetal stage, and it takes up the last 7 months of pregnancy and ends at birth.

In order to standardize the structural development of the germinal and embryological stages, a system of 23 stages was developed. Called the Carnegie Stages (after the Carnegie Institute), each is based on developmental structural changes and roughly corresponds to time since fertilization.

GERMINAL DEVELOPMENT

The Zygotic Phase

Within 24 to 48 hours after fertilization, the single fertilized cell resulting from the fused union of the sperm and the ovum begins to divide. A series of mitotic divisions results, with a doubling of cells with each division. The nucleus splits in half, and the cell divides. This process, called cleavage, starts slowly and then begins to pick up speed. The first division results in 2 cells (called blastomeres), then these 2 cells produce 4 and so on. Every cell produced has the exact genetic information that the original cell has. The zygote, however, doesn't get any larger, because with each cleavage, the blastomeres are half the size of the previous cells (Gilbert, 1989).

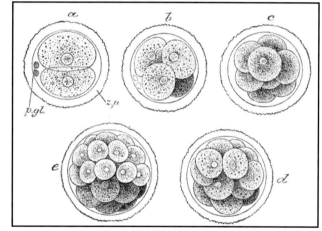

The Morula Phase

As this process continues, the zygote becomes a morula, a spherical mass with between 16 and 32 blastomeres. Even at this early stage, these cells begin to organize into the group of cells that will become the baby and another group that will become the placenta and umbilical cord (Nathanielz, 1992).

The Blastocyst Phase

By day 4 or 5, a small fluid-filled bubble emerges in the morula, and it will continue to grow, eventually becoming the amniotic sac. At this point the morula becomes a blastocyst, and by the 6th day after fertilization has over 100 cells.

All of this takes place in one of the fallopian tubes, which connect the ovary to the uterus, the destination point of the blastocyst. As we noted earlier, the movement of the zygote/blastocyst is assisted by the fallopian cilia and the rhythmic contractions of the muscular walls of the tube. At this point it is encased in a non-adhesive protective shell known as the zona pellucida to prevent it from attaching to the wall of the fallopian tube (Norwitz, Schust & Fisher, 2001).

As it moves toward the uterus, the cells in the blastocyst continue differentiating. The outer ring of cells, called the trophoblast, will become the placenta, umbilical cord and amniotic sac. The inner mass of cells, called the embryoblast, will become the embryo itself. This inner cell mass, consists of stem cells, and at this point in development, they have the amazing ability to become any one of over 200 types of cells (Macdonald, 2005).

After approximately 6-7 days, the blastocyst enters the uterus and within 72 hours "hatches" from the zona pellucida, thereby exposing the trophoblast cells and allowing for adhesion to the wall of the uterus. This typically (but not always) takes place in the upper posterior (fundal) section of the uterus. The blastocyst will eventually "land" and begin the process of implantation, officially beginning the long months of pregnancy.

IMPLANTATION

The Three Stages of Implantation

The process of implantation includes three different stages (Staun-Ram & Shalev, 2005), the first 2 relatively short in duration and the third taking longer to happen.

Apposition: The first stage, called apposition, includes the initial, somewhat unstable, adhesion of the blastocyst to the wall of the uterus. Small protrusions from the blastocyst (called microvilli) latch onto small protrusions (called pinopodes) in the wall of epithelium.

Stable Adhesion: The second stage is a continuation of the first and is called stable adhesion, because the "latching-on" process involves more contact between the blastocyst and the uterine wall is thus more "secure".

Invasion : The final stage is the invasion process, in which the blastocyst literally buries itself in not only the outer wall of the uterus (the endometrium), but also penetrates in second layer of the uterus, called the myometrium. This process results in the infiltration of the maternal blood supply, establishing the beginning of utero-placental circulation (Norwitz, Schust, & Fisher, 2001). By day 10 after fertilization, the blastocyst is completely buried in the wall of the uterus and the uterine epithelium has grown a layer of cells over the implantation site (Pijnenborg, Robertson, Brosens & Dixon, 1981).

Once this invasion occurs, the cells of the trophoblast begin interacting with cells in the uterus, giving and taking "orders" and influencing and being influenced by the mother's cells (Klimek, 2001; Vigano, Mangioni, Pompei, & Chiodo, 2003). This back-and-forth communication network establishes a chemical dialogue referred to as "cross talk" (Hill, 2001). It is the foundation on which successful pregnancy relies. Where there are problems and a failure to synchronize occurs, implantation will fail and a miscarriage will take place (Barnea, 2001; Jaffe, 2001).

Testing for Pregnancy

The chemical dialogue of the "cross talk" means that pregnancy can be detected using "pregnancy tests". The cells of the trophoblast secrete a hormone called human chorionic gonadotropin (hCG), which prompts a woman's ovaries to continuing releasing progesterone. The result of this progesterone is the continued swelling and capillary growth of the endometrial wall near the blastocyst. This greatly increases the chances of the embryo's survival. The release of hCG also "tells" a woman's ovaries to temporarily (during pregnancy) stop ovulation and consequently menstruation (Nilsson & Hamberger, 2003 in Craig & Dunn page 78).

The presence of hCG can be detected in both urine and blood tests from implantation onward (about 12-15 days after fertilization). Urine tests are generally less accurate than blood tests, and can indicate a false result from a number of causes other than pregnancy.

PROBLEMS IN IMPLANTATION

Genetic Causes

It has been estimated that between 50 and 70% of all zygotes do not survive the first two weeks of the germinal period. Some of these are lost because of genetic issues. Missing (for example, Turner's syndrome) or extra genetic material (for example, Down Syndrome), damaged chromosomes (see photographs at right), or recessive inheritance (for example, Huntington's disease) can all be causes of lack of viability and miscarriage.

Timing Issues

The timing of implantation has also been identified as potentially problematic. Research has found that the ideal time for implantation is 8-9 days after ovulation. The risk of pregnancy loss increases with each day following. Wilcox, Baird and Weinberg (1999) found that at day 9 implantation, 13% of pregnancies ended in loss, with each subsequent day resulting in a greater percentage of miscarriages; day 10 (26%), day 11 (52%), day 12 and following (82%).

Maternal Causes

The uterine and fallopian environment can also be the source of implantation problems. It is estimated that 75% of pregnancy losses are due to failures of implantation (Wilcox et al, 1988). The causes of many of these miscarriages are never known, but evidence does indicate that the presence of certain maternal conditions and/or factors potentially increases the likelihood of failure to implant.

Regardless of the cause, failure to implant may result in a heavy menstrual period that arrives a little late and contains the unimplanted blastocyst. Women may never even know that they were temporarily pregnant (Craig & Dunn, 2007, 78).

Endometriosis: A common source of implantation difficulties is endometriosis, a condition where the endometrial tissue from the uterus "migrates" to other parts of the body. It has been referred to as "reverse menstruation", because instead of flowing out of the body, the tissue flows into and attaches to the fallopian tubes, the ovaries, the pelvic cavity, the bladder, the rectum and in extreme cases even the lungs, arms, legs and brain. This tissue, wherever it migrates, continues to respond to hormonal changes in a woman's body over the menstrual cycle, building up and then sloughing off in 28-day cycles. Since there is often nowhere for this "flow" to leave the body, it builds up, causing inflammation, scarring, blood-filled cysts, and adhesion (the connection of 2 normally separated organs or bodily structures).

Endometriosis does tend to run in families affecting somewhere between 2-7% of all women and being a factor in 25-50% of women reporting infertility. But the presence of endometriosis does not always result in infertility, since only 30-40% of women with the condition are infertile.

Endometriosis can causes fertility problems in a variety of ways. The build-up of the endometrial tissues can simply get in the way and block access of the ova and sperm to each other, preventing fertilization. Even if fertilization occurs, the tissue can block access of the zygote to the uterus. The scarring in the uterus can cause the endometrium to be inhospitable and impenetrable to a blastocyst should it "land", thus preventing implantation. Adhesion of the various organs can prevent them from functioning and can be so extensive that are literally immobilized (Endometriosis, 2005).

Uterine Fibroids: Another cause of implantation failure is the presence of non-cancerous tumors in the uterus. Called fibroids, they can be as small as a peanut or as large as a grapefruit and are relatively common, affecting up to 25% of all women. They tend to develop between the ages of 30 and 50 and are more commonly found in overweight and African-American women, and in women who have not had children (Uterine Fibroids, 2006). Women who have taken birth control pills causing increased production of estrogen are also more likely to have fibroids, due to the stimulative effect that estrogen has on fibroid growth (Slupik & Allison, 1996).

Most women with uterine fibroids will not experience any symptoms. Symptoms, when they are present, include heavier-than-normal menstrual flow, pain in sexual intercourse, and bowel or urinary symptoms due to pressure from the fibroids. The presence of these symptoms depends on where the fibroids are growing and how large and numerous they are.

While fibroids do not necessarily cause infertility or miscarriage, they can at times impede movement and access of sperm, ova, and zygotes. For instance, they may block the cervix or a fallopian tube or may prevent a blastocyst from implanting in the uterine lining.

If a woman with fibroids does get pregnant, they may grow in size during the 9 months of pregnancy due to increased estrogen levels and blood flow. While most women are able to give birth, the baby may be born premature because there is simply not enough room in the uterus for both the baby and the enlarged fibroids.

Previous Abortions: According to Lurie and Shoham (1995), legal first or second trimester abortions do not significantly raise the risk factors for implantation problems later on. But late-term abortions do raise risks for a variety of reasons. The abortion procedure known as dilation and curettage (D&C) is associated with increased risk of cervical or uterine scarring. Implantation problems may be the result, due to the inability of the blastocyst to adequately adhere and survive the implantation process..

Further, any abortion (or other procedure) that requires the dilation of the cervix (to allow for the insertion of a suction tube) can weaken the cervical structures, causing what is known as an incompetent cervix. The result may be a premature dilation during pregnancy. While rare, any abortion that utilizes a suction tube (the majority of abortions), can result in perforation of the uterus or large blood vessel or the intestine. If this occurs, surgery is needed, which may cause complications of fertility. Finally, any foreign object entering the uterus introduces the possibility of uterine infection, which may also influence future fertility.

Previous Sexually Transmitted Infections : Women who have experienced previous sexually transmitted infections, especially the bacterial infections Chlamydia and gonorrhea, are also at greater risk for fertility and implantation complications (Westrom, 1994). Both infections are associated with the incidence of ectopic pregnancy (discussed below) and pelvic inflammatory disease (PID) (Low et al, 2006). PID is caused by a migration of the bacterial infection from the vagina to the uterus, fallopian tubes and ovaries, resulting in inflammation and eventual scarring. Sexually transmitted infections are not the only cause of PID. Other potential causes may include a staph or strep infection, or any procedure which introduces the potential for infection (for example, a gynecological exam, IUD insertion, childbirth, miscarriage, abortion, or an endometrial biopsy).

The symptoms of PID may range from nonexistent to severe. Particularly when caused by chlamydial infection, symptoms are typically absent and thus the infection is often ignored and PID may go untreated. When symptoms are present, they may include abdominal pain, irregular menstrual discharge, and painful sexual intercourse. Without treatment, PID causes normal tissue to scar, blocking access of sperm, ovum and zygotes to each other and the uterus. The scarring in the uterus can cause the endometrium to be inhospitable and impenetrable to a blastocyst, thus preventing implantation. If the zygote is blocked in the fallopian tube and cannot reach the uterus, the risk of ectopic pregnancy greatly increases.

PID results in infertility in approximately 1 out of 8 women who have the infection. Multiple episodes of PID increase rates of infertility. Approximately 1 million American women experience an episode of PID each year. Risk factors are increased for younger women, particularly teenagers, because their cervixes are not fully developed, increasing susceptibility. The more sex partners, and the more sex partners a woman's partner(s) has/have had, increase risk due to greater exposure to bacterial infections (CDC, 2006).

Ectopic Pregnancy

As we have read above, a consequence of several maternal risk factors is the occurrence of implantation in a place other than the uterus, most often in one of the fallopian tubes (and thus sometimes called a "tubal pregnancy"). But implantation can also occur on the ovary, cervix, or even in the pelvic cavity. Ectopic pregnancies are most often caused by some blockage (for instance, a fibroid or endometriosis) or condition (for instance, scar tissue caused by a bacterial infection) which delays or prevents the zygote from reaching the uterus. Other potential causes may includes fallopian tube defects, previous surgery, or the increased levels of estrogen and progesterone caused by birth control pills (which slow zygotic movement through the fallopian tubes). The "morning after pill" (emergency contraception) has also been linked with greater increases in risk for ectopic pregnancy. But for many ectopic pregnancies, there is no known cause. These types of pregnancies are relatively common, occurring from 1-2½ % of all pregnancies.

No matter what the cause, the implanted embryo cannot survive and if allowed to grow, can eventually produce in a rupture of the fallopian tube, resulting in severe abdominal pain and heavy internal bleeding. Untreated, an ectopic pregnancy can cause death. A procedure called a laparoscopy is performed to remove the implanted embryo.

PROBLEMS IN FERTILITY

Numerous factors influence fertility, including genetics (Rutter, 2003), nutrition, ethnicity, culture, sexual behavior, timing, and many other variables. Among the most profound changes affecting fertility over the past several decades has been the introduction and common use of various birth control mechanisms as well as the selective use of abortion. When coupled with the delay of both first marriage and child-bearing typical of modern western societies (Hobcraft, 2003), it is clear that the patterns of procreation have changed significantly (Rutter, 2003). One example of these changing patterns is the rise in the industrial west of the proportion of multiple births relative to single births. Due to the relative increase in the number of factors affecting infertility, particularly maternal and paternal age, and coupled with significant technological advances in ameliorating infertility, it is not surprising that the result is an increase in the number of multiple births due to assisted conception (Derom & Bryan, 2000).

Fertility Drugs

Two common types of fertility drugs are available for women having difficulty conceiving. Taking these drugs would normally be advised only after looking at other lifestyle factors that may influence fertility. These may include diet, smoking, alcohol and drug use, stress, and environmental exposure to toxins (Younglai, Holloway & Foster, 2004).

Other factors may affect male fertility problems, resulting in low sperm motility and sperm count. In addition, tight clothing may be a contributing factor in increasing scrotal temperature and thereby influencing sperm production adversely. Hormonal factors may also influence male infertility, particularly testosterone, LH (luteinizing hormone) and FSH (follicle-stimulating hormone). Thus, the fertility drugs discussed below may be prescribed for men as well. All of these facts should be considered by women seeking to get pregnant prior to the ingestion or injection of fertility medications.

Clomiphene : Clomiphene (sold under the brand names Clomid and Serophene) is taken orally and works by stimulating hormone production and release of FSH and LH, triggering ovulation and the subsequent release one or more ova. Since FSH and LH have multiple effects on a woman's body, side effects can include ovarian swelling, breast tenderness, insomnia, nausea, depression, weight gain, fatigue, and general irritability. There is also a 1 in 10 chance of having a multiple conception (twins, triplets or more).

Clomiphene causes ovulation within 3 months in 80 percent of women. Forty percent of these women will eventually get pregnant. If clomiphene is not successful in producing pregnancy, then a second type of fertility drug called gonadotropins is often prescribed.

Gonadotropins : Human menopausal gonadotropins (hMG) come in various forms and are sold under a variety of brand names (Pergonal, Repronex, Menogon, Fertinex, Follistim, Puregon, Pregnyl, Novarel, Profasi, Ovidrel). All variations of this class of fertility drugs include FSH or a mixture of LH and FSH and are administered by injection. The result is similar to clomiphene, except multiple ova are almost always produced and released at ovulation. This means that both the chances of getting pregnant are higher (up to 60% success rate) and the chances of conceiving multiples higher (up to 40%). Side effects include bloating, weight gain and fluid retention.

Artificial Insemination (AI)

When endometriosis or some other factor is present that makes sexual intercourse difficult or when male factor infertility has been identified as the contributing factor in an inability to conceive, a technique called artificial insemination is used to increase the chances of conception. The woman tracks her menstrual cycles for several months, determining when her fertility may be at its peak. A sample of sperm is collected from the donating male and processed or "washed". This effectively reduces any debris or abnormal sperm, producing a highly concentrated dose of healthy, motile sperm. The sperm are then injected directly into the woman's uterus through a catheter. The process may be combined with fertility drugs to maximize success.

Advantages of the procedure include its relative quickness and the fact that it is generally less invasive than some of the processes discussed below. It only takes an hour or so and fertilization takes place normally in the fallopian tubes. The main disadvantage of artificial insemination is the "hassle factor". Couples must track the woman's menstrual cycle, and be available at the time of her maximal fertility to provide a sperm sample and then wait until it is washed and then have it inserted.

Success rates range from 40 to 50% and can be significantly increased with the concomitant utilization of fertility drugs (Comhaire & Thiery, 1986). Success rates decrease in older couples and when endometriosis and/or PID are present.

Assisted Reproductive Technologies (ART)

When fertility drugs or artificial insemination are unsuccessful in producing pregnancy, more technologically complicated and invasive techniques are available. All are relatively expensive, have complications (Grudzinskas, 2000), and have no guarantee that they will work. All types of ART can also use donor (15% of the time) or non-donor (85% of the time) sperm and ova (CDC, 2004). Success rates vary considerably by type of contributing problem, age, and numerous other issues. According to the CDC (2004), success rates of all ART procedures resulted in no pregnancy 65% of the time, single-fetus pregnancy about 20% of the time, multiple-fetus pregnancy over 12% of the time, and ectopic pregnancy almost 1% of the time (CDC, 2004). But these pregnancies were not all successful, with over 15% resulting in miscarriages, about 54% in singleton births, and 29% in multiple births (CDC, 2004). Of live births, 64.6% were singletons, 31.6% were twins, and 3.8% were triplets or greater (CDC, 2004).

In Vitro Fertilization (IVF): In vitro fertilization is by far the most common ART process, accounting for over 99% (with and without ICSI which is discussed below) of ART procedures (CDC, 2004). It is a process in which ova are taken from the women's (or donor's) ovaries, often after she has taken several doses of fertility drugs to stimulate ova production. These ova are fertilized by the man's (or donor's) sperm outside the body (in a Petri dish or test-tube). Two or 3 days later, one or more zygotes are inserted into the uterus, usually by means of a catheter, with implantation naturally occurring. The process is often combined with drug treatments to insure the maximal receptivity of the endometrial wall of the uterus.

Due to the invasiveness of the procedure, potential side effects are numerous and include general discomfort, ectopic pregnancy, miscarriage, prematurity (Corabian & Hailey, 1999), and Ovarian Hyperstimulation Syndrome, resulting is thrombosis, enlarged ovaries, liver, kidney, and cardiorespiratory problems (Myrianthefs et al, 2000). There is also a relatively higher risk of multiple conceptions.

Success rates vary considerably depending on various factors, including hCG levels (Hauzman et al, 2001) and the age, with younger women having better outcomes than older women. The CDC reports success rates (live births) of between 31 and 34% of all women for the year 2002 (the last year the data are available).

Gamete Intrafallopian Transfer (GIFT): Accounting for only .2% of all ART procedures (CDC, 2004) and very similar to IVF, gamete intrafallopian transfer involves the harvesting of ova and the combination with sperm into a mixture that is injected directly into the fallopian tubes through a small incision in a woman's abdomen. Fertilization and implantation thus take place naturally. Success rates (live births) for GIFT are around 25% (CDC, 2004).

Zygote Intrafallopian Transfer (ZIFT): Accounting for only .5% of all ART procedures (CDC, 2004) and also very similar to IVF, zygote intrafallopian transfer involves the harvesting of ova and the fertilization by sperm outside the woman's body. The zygotes are then inserted into the fallopian tube (instead of the uterus as with IVF) with the expectation of natural implantation taking place. Success rates (live births) for ZIFT are around 26% (CDC, 2004).

Intracytoplasmic Sperm Injection (ICSI): Intracytoplasmic Sperm Injection (ICSI) is a procedure that is used when male factor fertility is an issue and is used in tandem with IVF (about half of IVF procedures also use ICSI). Ova and sperm are collected and the fertilization process is achieved artificially by injecting a sperm directly into an ovum. After 2 days, the resulting zygote(s) are then placed into the uterus, with the expectation of normal implantation. ICSI has several potential disadvantages, the most prominent being it short-circuits the natural process of conception which insures that only the strongest and hardiest sperm are able to fertilize an ovum. It also shares all of the IVF risk factors since it is a part of the IVF process.

Assisted Hatching: With the IVF, ZIFT, and ICSI, procedures, fertilization takes place outside the women's body, so the natural processes may be subtly affected. One such process involves the protective shell of the ovum known as the zona pellucida. It encases the zygote and allows for smooth transition down the fallopian tube. But for implantation to occur, this shell must dissolve allowing for "hatching" of the blastocyst. This exposes the "sticky" cells of the trophoblast and increases the chances of adhesion to the endometrial wall. When fertilization takes place outside of the body, the zona pellucida does not naturally decompose and allow for "hatching" to take place. Thus, a procedure called "assisted hatching" is sometimes used to "help" the implantation process.

MULTIPLE BIRTHS

While it is clear that the various assisted reproductive technologies do contribute to the greater likelihood of multiple births, such births also occur normally and naturally and have been a source of great interest and attention throughout history. The data show that the incidence of multiple births is increasing in industrialized countries. For instance, the proportion of twins in the United States has steadily increased since 1996.

The reasons for this steady increase include the above-cited influence of ARTs, but other factors may also play a role. For instance, folic acid supplements are thought to be a contributing factor. Women have been advised to take such supplements prior to conception to prevent neural tube defects such as anencephaly and spina bifida. A side effect of pre-conceptual folic acid intake is the increase in multiple conceptions. The increased use of oral contraceptives is also associated with increased risk of multiples. Women who have taken oral contraceptives for longer than 6 months and then conceive shortly after discontinuing their use double their chances of conceiving multiples.

The delay of childbirth generally and the resulting older age of first-time mothers contributes to the increased likelihood of multiples. Women over 40 are more than 4 times more likely to give birth to multiples than women under age 20. Further, the more babies a woman has had, the greater the chances with each subsequent pregnancy of being a multiple.

Finally, ethnicity also seems to affect multiple conceptions. As can be seen from the table at the right, women of African heritage have a significantly higher rate of multiple deliveries than white, Asian and Native American women. This is particularly true for those of Yoruba heritage, a large ethno-linguistic group in West Africa, primarily in Nigeria. The Yoruba have among the highest rates of twin births in the world, a ratio between 45 and 55 per 1000 live births. The all time winner for multiples is a small village in Brazil where the rate is over 100 per 1000 live births (Matte et al, 1996).

Multiple Types

Non-identical Multiples: Also known as fraternal, or dizygotic (or trizygtoic), these types of multiples develop from separate ova and separate sperm. As such, they are no more genetically similar than sibling brothers or sisters. After implantation, each multiple develops separate placentas and each has his or her own amniotic sac.

With parents of differing ethnic backgrounds, fraternal twins can be very distinct in the shade of their skin. Although rare, there have been documented cases where a woman has given birth to fraternal twins with 2 different fathers. If sexual intercourse with 2 different men happens relatively close together in time and during the window of fertility following ovulation, 2 separate ova may be fertilized by sperm from different fathers. It is thus possible to be a half-sibling and twin simultaneously.

Apart from some of the factors we noted earlier, non-identical twinning and other multiple conceptions do tend to run in families, but only on the mother's side, not the father's. But as we noted earlier, they are more likely to occur when ART procedures are utilized.

As you would expect statistically, for non-identical twins, about 25% are boy/boy combinations, about 25% are girl/girl and about 50% are boy/girl. Fraternal twins constitute about 2/3 of all twins, the identical type consisting of the other 1/3. As far as triplets go, non-identical triplets account for almost 95% of triplets, the rest being of the relatively rare identical type. It is also possible to have triplets where 2 are identical and the other is non-identical. So presumably, someone could be a twin and a triplet at the same time. About 500 sets of quadruplets are born in the United States each year and they are almost always of the non-identical type.

Identical Multiples: Multiples that develop from a single ovum and a single sperm are called monozygotic. As such, each twin or triplet shares the exact same gene pairs with his or her fellow multiples, and therefore must be the same gender. But quite amazingly, they do not share the same finger-prints.

Identical multiples do not tend to run in families and thus they seem to develop as a "quirk" of nature rather than caused by any predisposing factors. As such, rates of identical multiples are very similar are the world. Identical triplets are only about 5% of triplets overall and identical quadruplets are exceedingly rare. The latest case where this occurred was in April of 2006, when a 26 year-old woman from Madras, India gave birth to four identical girls. The chances of this occurring have been estimated as about 1 in 11 million. Indeed, since 1930, there have been fewer than 50 documented cases of identical quadruplets, with the majority of them being female.

Although we do not know why it happens, identical multiples result from a single zygote that splits into 2 (or 3) separate zygotes at some point early in its development, almost always before the 8th day and before implantation. This usually occurs with the first several zygotic divisions. There is no explanation for why this happens, it just does!

Some identical twins are "mirrored" and share traits exactly, but on opposite sides of their bodies. For example, one twin might be right-handed and the other left-handed. One twin may have a birth mark on the right thigh and the other at the same exact place on the left thigh. One twin's hair may part on the left and the other at the same place on the right. Mirroring can also produce a condition known as situs inversus, where the organs are on the opposite side of where they normally are (for instance, the heart is on the right instead of the left, called dextrocardia). Mirroring is associated with a relatively late "split" (over 9 days).

Identical twins and triplets come in three different types, depending on exactly when the "split" occurred which separated them into two or three persons. Each type differs in terms of amniotic sacs (amniotic) and placentas (chorionic).

Diamniotic and Dichorionic (Triamniotic and Trichorionic) : These multiples, although identical, develop separate amniotic sacs and separate placentas. This type of identical is most likely to have "split" before day 3 after fertilization.

Diamniotic and Monochorionic (Triamniotic and Monochorionic): The most common type of identical twin (about 75%) involves separate amniotic sacs, but a shared placenta. Splitting most likely occurred between the 3rd and 8th day after fertilization. With triplets or even quadruplets, there can be a shared placenta with separate amniotic sacs, or any combination possible. For instance, 2 may share a placenta of even an amniotic sac, with the third (or fourth) having separate ones.

Monoamniotic and Monochorionic : The rarest of all identical twin types results from a "split" between the 8th and 14th day after fertilization. These twins share the same amniotic sac and placenta. This type of twin is also most likely to have complications and most likely to miscarry.

One of these complications is called twin/twin transfusion syndrome (TTTS). Because these twins are sharing a placenta, there may be an imbalance in how much blood flow is reaching each. The result may be that one twin does not get enough blood and thus the oxygen and nutrients that it delivers and consequently develops slowly. The other twin may get too much blood, causing high blood pressure and stress on his or her heart. But this twin grows faster and may be much larger than her sibling (see photo above). Approximately 3 out of 4 fetuses suffering from TTTS will die without surgical intervention.

Conjoined Twins: Previously referred to as "Siamese twins", conjoined twins are monozygotic, monochorionic and mono-amniotic. Because they share the same amniotic sac and thus significant physical contact, the fusing together of skin at some point of the body during development can occur. Once delivered via a C-section, these conjoined twins are relatively easy to separate. With sharing organs, however, or when the fusing is substantial as in the photograph to the right, complications and difficulties are much more significant.

CONCLUSION

The germinal period ends at the conclusion of implantation. Less than 2 weeks have passed since fertilization, but the accomplishments of any new embryo are considerable. She or he has survived considerable odds just to make it this far. The next chapter takes up the growth and tasks of the 6 week-long embryonic stage, when even more amazing events occur.

6

EMBRYONIC DEVELOPMENT

An ancient said that the embryo is a living thing; for that the soul entering into the womb after it has been by cleansing prepared for conception, and introduced by one of the angels who preside over generation, and who knows the time for conception, moves the woman to intercourse; and that, on the seed being deposited, the spirit, which is in the seed, is, so to speak, appropriated, and is thus assumed into conjunction in the process of formation.

Theodotus of Byzantium

INTRODUCTION

The embryonic period begins immediately after implantation is completed and will last until the end of the second month, when the fetal phase will commence and last until birth approximately 7 months later. The word "embryo" comes from a Greek word meaning "to swell" (Craig & Dunn, 2007), and quite a lot of swelling goes on in the embryonic period. According to Cherry (1973), during the first month of pregnancy, the embryo's weight will increase by 10,000 times and by another 74 times during the second month.

Embryonic development requires 2 complimentary processes. First, the cells forming the embryo itself (called the embyroblast) begin very quickly to develop and specialize into the hundreds of different cells a human being needs to survive and function. Second, the cells forming the trophoblast also begin to shape themselves into the placenta, the umbilical cord and the amniotic sac to allow for the survival of the embryo. We begin this chapter with a consideration of this amazing process.

EMBRYO SUPPORT STRUCTURES

The Placenta

The placenta has often been called the only throw away organ that human beings will ever have. It is truly an amazing organ and a combination lung-kidney-digestive system-hormone producer. Not bad for a disposable organ!

It is disc-like in shape and grows steadily larger through the early weeks of pregnancy, significantly outpacing the growth of the embryo/fetus early on (Genbacev, 2001). It is fully formed by about 18 weeks. At delivery it will weight a little more than a pound on average. It is a little over an inch thick and almost 8 inches in diameter.

The placenta is actually composed of two complementary parts, one which is part of the embryo/fetus and the other part of his mother. This means that the placenta is a "joint" organ and contains cells from 2 distinct persons. This happens nowhere else in natural biology (Nathanielz, 1996). What makes this amazing is that in just about every other situation, cells from another organism are considered by the body to be pathogens to be killed. Our immune systems protect us constantly from anything "foreign" (like a bacterial infection) to our bodies by marshalling our T and B lymphcytes to get rid of these cells. This is one reason why transplanted organs are so often rejected by the body.

But the placenta does not operate according to these rules (Blaschitz, Hutter, & Dohr, 2001). When things are going "normally", it allows the cells from 2 separate organisms to cooperate and not "kill" each other. But this necessary cooperation does not always occur. It has been theorized that some miscarriages are caused by a mother's immune system "rejecting" the embryo/fetus and attacking the placental fetal cells as pathogens (Nathanielz, 1996; Urban et al, 2001).

The placenta is the mediator between the maternal and fetal systems. It extends itself into the uterine walls on the maternal side by means of the villi, thereby gaining access to oxygen, nutrients, and everything else a baby needs to grow and thrive (water, electrolytes, protein, lipid carbohydrates, vitamins and antibodies). The embryonic blood (in the villi) and the mother's blood (in the intervillous space) are separated by a thin membrane, called the placental barrier. This membrane is several layers of cells thick and is porous enough to allow oxygen and nutrients to be exchanged between the blood of the mother and that of the embryo. The blood vessels in the villi then deliver the oxygen and nutrients from the mother to the baby through the umbilical cord.

But whatever is in the mother's blood stream in addition to oxygen and nutrients is also potentially transferable to the baby, including alcohol, drugs, stress hormones, and some viruses and other infectious diseases. We will discuss some of these teratogens in later chapters.

The extension of the placenta into the mother also allows for the disposal of embryonic "trash", analogous to the post-natal urine and fecal matter. This waste is "picked up" and delivered via the umbilical cord to the villi, and finally passed on to the mother's body to be discarded via her normal excretory processes.

So the placenta is truly an intermediary organ, making deliveries of food and oxygen to the embryo/fetus, and also picking up the "garbage". It is also an organ which multi-tasks constantly, carrying out many different crucial functions.

Placental Functions

The Lung Function: Without oxygen, the embryo/fetus cannot survive. Since the fetus does not have access to the outside world where its lungs (even if they were developed enough) could get oxygen, he must rely on his mother's lungs, and then get it "second-hand" from her blood. Further, unlike glucose and fat, oxygen cannot be stored for later use. Thus, the most crucial task of the placenta is to constantly procure, absorb and deliver oxygen to the growing baby. As the fetus grows, its oxygen needs increase and so does the importance of the placenta's lung function.

Oxygen is delivered in both maternal and fetal system by means of hemoglobin, or red blood cells. Each hemoglobin cell can carry up to 4 molecules of oxygen, but fetal blood has a special type of hemoglobin that is more efficient than maternal blood. But the placenta is still completely dependent on how much oxygen is available in the mother's blood. This oxygen availability is influenced by how much hemoglobin she has in her blood; less hemoglobin will result in lower oxygen availability.

Further, the actual "oxygen load" of maternal hemoglobin is also influenced by the amount of carbon dioxide in her blood, and by the oxygen content in the air she is breathing. A woman that is smoking or breathing in polluted air, or stuck inside a poorly ventilated area will deliver much less oxygen to her baby. If prolonged, this oxygen deficiency can lead to retarded fetal growth and is associated with both pre-maturity and miscarriage.

Hemoglobin cells contain iron. If a pregnant woman does not have adequate amounts of iron, she will be anemic and her ability to transport oxygen to her organs and to her baby will be greatly reduced.

The Kidney Function: After we are born, our kidneys help regulate the concentrations of various ions and water within our bodies so that we can perform all the various functions and activities of our daily lives. Acting like a thermostat, the kidneys release various minerals and remove various toxic byproducts and compounds, insuring the correct chemical composition throughout our bodies and the constancy of the internal environment (Nathanielz, 1996). Due to the immaturity of the fetal kidneys, and their inability to adequately perform these regulatory tasks, the placenta serves as the mineral, compound and fluid regulator for the embryo and fetus throughout the pregnancy.

The Digestive System Function: The basic elements required by the growing embryo/fetus include glucose, various fats, water, amino acids, vitamins and mineral ions. The placenta delivers these elements from the mother to the baby in 2 general ways; an active process and a more passive one. The active process is generally a quicker delivery mode, but requires the placenta to use energy (in the form of glucose). The passive process is slower, but does not tax energy stores nearly as much.

The Passive Process: The passive process of transportation requires that the concentration of whatever substance be higher in the maternal blood than in the fetal blood. When there is a concentration differential, natural diffusion takes place from the area of high concentration to the area of low concentration. This process almost works like gravity. Water on a hill will run down, not up. So passive transportation will occur from high to low concentration areas.

In the case of both glucose and oxygen, maternal blood usually has higher concentrations than fetal blood. This state is maintained because the fetus is removing the glucose and oxygen from his blood constantly to utilize it for growth. In the case of glucose, the fetus may store it for later use.

The Active Process: The passive process does not work for every element that the embryo/fetus needs to grow. Therefore, the placenta also employs an active delivery mechanism. For instance, most of the mineral ions are actively transported because passive diffusion does not work. Glucose can also be conveyed by means of glucose transporters which act as mini-shuttle buses quickly delivering glucose when there is the need. The down-side of the active process is that it increases the placenta's need for fuel, sometimes in direct competition with the baby. When there is a glucose shortage due to a mother's diet, the fetus gets less due to the placenta's needs and must either use whatever reserves it has, or do without (Nathanielz, 1996). As we will see in a later chapter, this may be a significant factor in the long-term health of the baby and a negative fetal programming process begins.

The Endocrine Function: The placenta also functions as a hormone producer and even is powerful enough to alter the various hormones produced by the mother's body. Almost from the very beginning, the placenta and mother's body begin a chemical "conversation" in which hormones serve as the "words" of communication. This chemical "cross-talk" is coordinated and, when all goes well, functions to maximize the embryo/fetal environment, and therefore, the embryo/fetus.

Among the hormones released by the placenta is estrogen, which along with progesterone, is involved in numerous processes necessary to maintain healthy pregnancy. For example, one crucial result of the increased levels of estrogen is the redirection of blood flow in the mother's body to the uterus. As pregnancy proceeds, there is a 50-fold increase in blood volume to the uterine area (Nathanielz, 1996).

Another hormone produced and released by the placenta is somatomammotropin, also called placental lactogen. It functions in several ways, promoting fetal growth by increasing the amount of glucose and fat in the maternal blood. It also "tells" the mother's breasts to start getting larger in readiness for breast-feeding.

An adequate amount of progesterone in the mother's system is crucial to the maintenance of pregnancy. Early on in pregnancy, before the placenta is able produce enough progesterone itself, it gets "help" from the mother by releasing a hormone called human chorionic gonadotropin (hCG). This hormone passes into the mother's body and "instructs" her ovaries to continue producing progesterone for a longer period than usual (Rao, 2001). Every 28 days, one of the ovaries produce an ovum by means of a follicle, which bursts at ovulation and releases the ovum. Following ovulation, this follicle morphs into a structure called the corpus luteum, which routinely produces progesterone for about 2 weeks and then dissolves and dies away during menstruation. But the presence of hCG early in pregnancy causes the corpus luteum to delay its demise and keep working until the placenta can take over its progesterone production duties (Nathanielz, 1996).

Finally, the placenta also plays an endocrine role in the process of labor at the end of the pregnancy. In response to oxytocin, a hormone jointly produced and released by the baby and the mother's pituitary glands, the uterus contracts and the placenta releases prostaglandin hormones. These prostaglandins stimulate the uterus to contract even more and they also incite the greater release of oxytocin in a feedback loop process. This is what makes labor begin with relatively mild and widely-spaced contractions and proceed inexorably to relatively intense and closely-spaced contractions.

Placental Previa: Affecting about 1 out of 200 women, placenta previa is a condition where the placenta is attached and grows in the lower part of the uterus, near or even over the cervix. When the cervix begins to dilate in labor, it may separate from the uterine wall and bleed. It is more common in pregnancies with multiples and in women who have had multiple pregnancies. Interventions may include bed rest, avoidance of travel and sexual intercourse, and in more serious cases, performance of a C-section.

Placental Abruption: Premature separation of the placenta from the wall of the uterus is called placental abruption and occurs in approximately 1 out of 80 deliveries. It is potentially problematic, depending on when it occurs. If it occurs close to delivery, it is not nearly as much of a problem as an earlier abruption may be.

In most cases, the cause of placental abruption is unknown, although certain factors seem to increase its chance of occurring. These factors include maternal hypertension, dietary deficiencies such as a lack of adequate folic acid, smoking, alcohol consumption, uterine scarring, an overly short umbilical cord, and a physical injury to the mother, such as a fall or a car accident. Women who have experienced placental abruption with one pregnancy are at greater risk in subsequent pregnancies, with a rate of reoccurrence estimated as high as 10%.

Separation of the placenta may be partial or complete. A total separation of the placenta from the uterine wall is very serious and will result in premature delivery 20% of the time it occurs, with miscarriage and fetal death occurring in 15% of the cases. Total abruption cuts off the fetus from her mother's blood supply, and thus oxygen and nutrients. Symptoms of placental abruption vary a significantly and may include lower-back pain, uterine sensitivity and tenderness (60% of the time), contractions (35% of the time) and/or bleeding (approximately 75% of the time). A diagnostic ultrasound may be useful in identifying the problem, although the results are often imprecise.

Placental Correlates with Birth Weight: Because the placenta is so important, it should come as no surprise that its weight has been found to be positively correlated with the weight of children at birth (Sanin et al, 2001). Birth weight is an important indicator of health. While the average baby's weight is a little over 6 times as heavy as his or her placenta, research has found that for every ounce heavier the placenta is, the corresponding baby increases her weight by almost 2 ounces. But ethnic differences also affect the placental to birth weight ratio. For unknown reasons, Asian and Hispanic women have the lowest placental weight to birth rate ratio and Caucasian and African American women the highest (Cohn, 2002).

The Umbilical Cord

While the placenta is quite an amazing organ, the umbilical cord is also a marvel of nature. It connects the baby to the placenta and develops from the remnants of the yolk sac and the allantois present early on in embryonic development.

The Yolk Sac and Allantois: The primitive yolk sac comes from cells that have split off from the inner cell mass of the blastocyst. The yolk sac is thus outside the embryo and is filled with vitalline fluid, which help nourish the embryo in the early weeks of life (Hesseldahl & Larsen, 2005). As the embryo grow, so does the volume of the vitalline and thus the yolk sac. This continues until about 10 weeks (Kupesic & Kurjak, 2001). By this time, the placenta and umbilical cord have grown and matured. The yolk sac is no longer needed and gradually "shrivels away" (Macdonald, 2005).

The allantois also emerges from the blastocystic cells and serves as a primitive excretion and waste collection structure. Both the yolk sac and allantois contribute to the structural form of the umbilical cord as it slowly develops.

This rudimentary form of the umbilical cord begins in the 4 to 6 week stage and is initially stalk-like, very short in length and relatively speaking, thick in diameter. It does not have the flexibility it will later have. This umbilical stalk develops from the center of the placenta. By around 10 weeks, it begins to elongate and take on the distinctive flexible cord-like formation. This is facilitated by the emergence of Wharton's jelly.

Wharton's Jelly: Named after the English physician Thomas Wharton who first described it in 1656, Wharton's jelly is a type of specialized tissue which has elastic effects and thus can be stretched, bent, and twisted without harm. Because it is made up of flexible fibers encased in gelatin-like mucus, the umbilical cord can function effectively while allowing for considerable fetal movement and eventually, the process of labor and delivery.

Good maternal nutrition tends to be associated with greater amounts of Wharton's jelly. Low levels of Wharton's jelly are associated with fetal complications and miscarriage. When there are umbilical problems such as twisting, kinking or knotting, these tend to occur at points in the umbilicus where Wharton's jelly is minimal or absent. Finally, for whatever reason, males tend to have more Wharton's jelly than females (Collins, Collins, & Collins, 1990).

Cord Function: The umbilical cord primarily serves as the transit system of oxygen and nutrients from the mother/placenta to the fetus and of waste products from the fetus back to the placenta/mother. By 31 weeks, it has been estimated that the umbilical cord must carry 70 quarts of blood per day, moving at 4 miles an hour (Collins, Collins, & Collins, 1990). In a normal pregnancy, the umbilical cord has 1 vein delivering oxygen and nutrients and 2 arteries returning waste products. Any exception to this pattern (4-vessel or 2-vessel cord) is potentially problematic and associated with fetal malformations and miscarriage. Stressful conditions such as maternal smoking and anoxia (decrease in oxygen availability) are associated with over-branching of the cord vessels, and thus fetal complication, miscarriage and stillbirth (Collins, Collins, & Collins, 1990).

Cord Differences: Apart from the number of vessels (a little less than 99% have 3, 1% have two, with 4 and 5 being very rare), umbilical cords differ from fetus to fetus. Some (about 5%) are straighter (associated with increased complications) and others more twisting and spiraling (about 95%) in formation (Strong, Elliot, & Radin, 1993; Petrikovsky & Gross, 1996; Dado, Dobrin, & Mrkvicka, 1997). Further, because active fetuses have longer cords than inactive ones, the cord is thought to elongate in response to fetal activity. The elongation occurs up to 36 weeks, but the most rapid changes occur before 28 weeks and then seem to slow (Naeye, 1992). It is not surprising that twins and triplets tend to have shorter umbilical cords than singletons, probably due to the sheer lack of space in the uterus for activity. On average males also seem to have longer cords than females do.

Overly short (less than 13 inches) or overly long (more than 26 inches) cord length has been associated with various complications and neurological abnormalities (Naeye, 1985; 1992; Sornes, 1989), including deficits in IQ (Collins, Collins, & Collins, 1990). The average birth length of the umbilical cord is about 24 inches and first pregnancies tends to result in shorter cords than subsequent one.

A predisposition to rupture and the prevention of fetal descent during labor are associated risks of short umbilical cords. Umbilical cords of less than 10 inches are further associated with cerebral palsy and IQs lower than 80. Long cords are not harmful in and of themselves, but seem to present a greater risk of fetal entanglement at various points in the pregnancy, especially birth (Collins, Collins, & Collins, 1990).

Navel Formation: At birth, the cord is clamped and subsequently cut. Since there are no nerve endings in the cord, this cutting is not painful. There is also ordinarily no significant loss of either maternal or infant blood and the clamp (see below) stops the flow of any blood that is present in the cord at birth. This blood has been discovered to be rich in stem cells and some parents now opt to have it saved and stored in a cord blood bank for potential future use.

The umbilical cord eventually falls off and leaves a scar, which forms the navel or belly button. Because there is only a fewer layers of skin covering the abdominal muscles, this scar does not "heal over", but instead leaves a permanent mark. Like any scar that is semi-randomly caused (the following off of the umbilical cord), they can vary quite significantly in shape, size, depth, and overall look. Generally speaking, they can present as a depression ("innies"; 90% of people) or as a protrusion ("outies"; 10% of people). For those unhappy with their particular belly button, plastic surgeons now offer a procedure called umbilicoplasty.

The Amniotic Sac

The embryo (and later the fetus) is surrounded by fluid and contained within a resilient and very flexible thin 2-layered pouch. The inner layer is called the amnion, and gives its name to both the sac itself and the fluid within the sac. The outer membrane is called the chorion and connects with and is technically part of the placenta. Both membranes are transparent (allowing light to pass through) and very tough, necessary to prevent harm to the baby (Yeh & Rabinowitz, 1988).

Amniotic Fluid: Around 2 weeks after fertilization and just a few days of implantation, the amnion begins to grow. As it grows (and the embryo and fetus within), it fills up with a watery fluid containing various electrolytes (ions), carbohydrates, proteins, and fats. At the 10th week, there is just a little over 2 tablespoons present but by week 34 there is over 68 tablespoons (a little more than a quart).

This fluid has several beneficial functions to the growing baby. It serves primarily to protect the fetus by cushioning any pressure or blow from outside the womb. It also acts as a lubricant and facilitates free movement within the amniotic sac, providing buoyancy, and allowing for activity and "exercise" by the growing baby. The fetus also breathes in the amniotic fluid into her lungs, allowing a kind of "practice breathing" to better prepare her lungs for the immediate task of breathing in air as soon as she is born. The fluid also keeps the baby warm. It is slightly higher in temperature (99.7 degrees F) than the mother's body (98.6 degrees F).

Later on in pregnancy, the fetus will drink the amniotic fluid, getting up to 100 calories per day and allowing her gastrointestinal tract to "practice" digestion. The "taste" of amniotic fluid is affected by a mother's diet and seems to influence the development of post-natal food preferences as well as odor learning (Mennella, Johnson, & Beauchamp, 1995; Schaal, Marlier, & Soussignan, 2000). By 15 weeks, a fetus will increase his consumption of sweet-tasting amniotic fluid, and will decrease his drinking of bitter-tasting amniotic fluid (Mennella, Jagnow, & Beauchamp, 2001).

In a normal pregnancy, the amniotic sac will rupture as by-product of the contractions of labor and delivery. The "spontaneous rupture of membranes" (SRM) is commonly referred to as the "water breaking". In some births, this does not happen, and an amniotomy, or "artificial rupture of membranes" (ARM) is performed by the attending nurse, midwife or obstetrician.

Amniotic Sac Problems: Similar to the placenta and the umbilical cord, at times the amniotic sac can malfunction in a variety of ways.

Premature Rupture: When the amniotic sac leaks prior to 38 weeks or the "water breaks" prematurely, labor and delivery often have to be either induced or a C-section performed. Preterm premature rupture of membranes (PPROM) is a condition associated with either structural defects in the cervix or uterus or a bacterial infection.

Oligohydramnios: Approximately 8 percent of pregnancies are affected by a condition called oligohydramnios, or too little amniotic fluid in the amniotic sac. It is most commonly seen in pregnancies that are more than 2 weeks overdue or if there is leaking in the amniotic sac. Beyond these 2 situations, oligohydramnios is usually associated with the presence of birth defects (early pregnancy) or poor fetal growth (later pregnancy). This condition is associated with complications, miscarriage and prematurity (Oligohydramnios, 2006).

Polyhydramnios: Too much amniotic fluid, a condition called polyhydramnios, affects about 2 percent of pregnant women. In most cases, complications are minimal or mild and often spontaneously resolve. However, if too much amniotic fluid builds up, polyhydramnios is associated with premature rupture of the amniotic sac, premature delivery and miscarriage. It is also associated with, and perhaps caused by, potential birth defects (Polyhydramnios, 2006).

EMBRYONIC GROWTH

Calculating embryonic and fetal age is done in a variety of ways, and is sometimes confusing. Gestational age is used to calculate a woman's due date and is calculated from the end of the a woman's last menstrual cycle. Fertilization age is calculated from fertilization. Thus, gestational age is always 2 weeks over fertilization age. For purposes of clarity, we will use fertilization as the beginning point and so age is calculated as the number of weeks or months since fertilization. A full-term baby is thus 38-40 weeks. Since every baby is a bit different, and development is dynamic, somewhat dependent and influenced by the fetal and maternal environment, each week or month should be understood as being within a range of a couple of days on each side.

The Gastrula

Very soon after implantation, a process called gastrulation (Hamilton, Boyd & Mossman, 1962) begins, whereby the stem cells of the embryoblast differentiate into three "layers" called the endoderm, the mesoderm and the ectoderm. These three eventually differentiate further into the various components of the body.

The innermost layer is called the endoderm and will eventually produce most of the internal organs of the body, including the lungs, liver, tongue, pancreas, thyroid, larynx, trachea, digestive tract, and bladder. The middle layer is called the mesoderm and will eventually differentiate into the heart, spleen, skeletal and smooth muscles, kidneys, spleen, blood cells and vessels, connective tissue including bone and cartilage, bone marrow, lymphoid tissue, and gonads. The outermost layer, called the ectoderm, will eventually become the epidermis (including skin, nails, and hair), lenses of the eyes, tooth enamel, pituitary and mammary glands, sense organs, sinuses, mouth, anal canal, and most importantly, the brain and entire nervous system.

Patterns of Development

Once gastrulation has occurred, the embryo quickly begins to develop in 2 overall patterns. Development tends to begin with the head and proceed down the body. This principle, called cephalocaudal development, explains why the top of the embryo (cephalic) containing the brain and the head is so much bigger than the bottom (caudal) of the embryo containing the rest of the body.

A second principle influencing development is proximodistal development, whereby organs closest to the center of the body (proximo) such as the spinal cord develop prior to organs further away from the center (distal). This process means that the nervous system and heart develop first, and are thus functional and can support the outer structures when they emerge.

Organogenesis
On about day 9, the embryonic cells begin to arrange themselves in a shield-like form, with a broader top and narrower bottom (Flanagan, 1996). A central streak runs through the center (see the line on neural plate stage to the right).

Neurulation: The very first stage of organogenesis is called neurulation, which occurs between the 18th and 26th days. Ectodermal cells first cluster along the central streak into a flat neural "plate", and when enough are present, then folds in on itself to form a "groove". This neural groove begins to elongate and close in the middle, eventually forming the neural tube with open bulges on either end.

The top bulge will become the brain and the tube itself is a proto-spinal cord. This neural tube substantially defines the embryonic structure in early pregnancy.

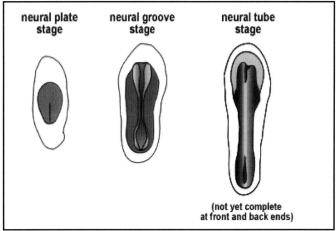

Nervous System Development: During the third week, the nervous system develops rapidly so that by the 18th day after fertilization, primitive nerve cells are present and by the 20th day the brain, spinal cord, and the basic components of the entire nervous system exist.

By 25 days, the embryonic brain has three main vesicles separated along two main grooves, foreshadowing the eventual division of hindbrain, midbrain and forebrain (Lambert, Bramwell, & Lawther, 1982).

By the 5th week right and left hemispheres of the brain are already apparent (Tanner & Taylor, 1965). At around the 32nd day, the spinal nerves begin to sprout from the brain stem (England, 1996) and the final 5 divisions of the brain emerge from the earlier 3.

The prosencephalon divides into 2 parts, the telencephalon (cerebral cortex, amygdale, & hippocampus) and the diencephalon (hypothalamus, thalamus & pituitary gland) .The mesencephalon becomes the midbrain, while the rhombencephalon divides into 2 parts, the metencephalon (pons and cerebellum) and the myelencephalon (medulla)

At 5 weeks, cranial nerves commence sprouting from the brainstem and by the end of the 6th week, the "nervous control system" begins to control the muscles of the developing child. Detectable brain waves emerge at 48 days or so. As development continues into the fetal stage, two large bursts in neural cell proliferation occur at approximately 15-20 weeks and 25 weeks. By 24 weeks, the grooves and ridges called sulci begin to appear in the expanding cerebral cortex.

As the brain develops, the other organs of the body are simultaneously forming and coordinating their functional capacities with the parts of the brain devoted to those areas. While development continues according to the cephalocaudal and proximodistal principles, the speed and process of development differs with each particular organ.

Heart Development: Beginning at day 13, a clump of mesodermic cells move into position where the heart will form. Around days 18-19, these cells begin to form into 2 "tubes" connected at the top into a U-shape (Flanagan, 1996) and by the 22nd day have fused into 1 "cardiac tube" (England, 1996) no bigger than a poppy seed. By day 21, small capillaries begin to appear, and the arrival of the first heart beat, although just an initial twitch and then irregular and weak, occurs at 22 days. Within days, all of the other heart cells are beating in unison, establishing a circulation through the minute blood vessels. These first beats of the heart will be repeated 4 billion more times if the fetus lives to be 100 years old. By the 4th week, the 1-chambered heart is beating a regular 80 beats per minute and gets incrementally faster every day (Macdonald, 2005).

The heart is among the first organs to develop and become functional, because without it, there would be no way to deliver the nutrients and oxygen to the other developing organs. The heart cells continue to grow and differentiate so that by the 49th day, a 4-cavity heart is functional.

Simultaneous to the development of the heart, the cardiovascular system is gradually developing out of the mesoderm. During intra-uterine life, the circulatory system passes through two stages, the first called the vitelline, in which the embryo is living essentially on its own resources, lasts until the beginning of 5th week. The second stage, called the placental, lasts from the 5th week until birth. With the development of the placenta and umbilical cord, the embryo/fetus depends upon his mother for nutrients (Tuchmann-Duplessis & Haegel, 1971).

Other Internal Organ Development: A recognizable liver is clearly apparent by 28 days, with distinct "liver cells" evident one week earlier. Between weeks 6 and 10, the abdominal space in the embryo/fetus is mostly occupied by the liver as it grows. Large carbohydrates reserves are stored in the liver before birth to provide a source of nourishment for the newborn until breast-feeding is well-established. (England, 1996).

The lung buds are evident by the 27th day and the various bronchi slowly emerge and make several divisions, forming the substantial part of the lungs. By the end of the first month the embryo has a windpipe and oral cavity, a primitive kidney, and the beginnings of a stomach (Meredith, 1978). There is a discernible pancreas and intestines, but it will be well into the second month before an anal opening develops.

Sensory Organ Development: Parallel to and interconnected with the development of the central nervous system is the development of the various specialized sense receptors and their neural pathways to the brain. Initially, the sense receptors develop from placodes, where clumps of cells gather and thicken and then form in the organ (Tuchmann-Duplessis & Haegel, 1971).

The Visual System: The visual system begins to develop very early, by the 18th day, and actually originates from two of the three germ layers; the optic nerve and lens emerge from the ectoderm, while the mesoderm contributes the accessory structures of the eye (Tuchmann-Duplessis & Haegel, 1971). The optic primordium develops for approximately 10 days before the lens primordium emerges at 29 days. The complexity of the eye and the various visual structures accompanying it account for the long and gradual development of the visual system. The optic vesicle, the external layer of which forms the retina, begins to differentiate at approximately 40 days and continues until the 7th month. The optic nerve gradually develops out of the axons of differentiated ganglionic cells in each eye, which progress toward the emerging brain, and cross over each other forming the optic chiasma. As with the olfactory sense, these axons correspond to the specialized area of the central nervous system, and particularly the occipital lobe of the brain (Tuchmann-Duplessis & Haegel, 1971). This process starts at about 5 weeks, when eye buds also begin growing from the forebrain (Lambert, Bramwell, Lawther, 1982). The various other visual components, including the cornea, the iris, and the sclera, all gradually emerge and are all present by the 3rd month (Gilbert, 1989). The final event of the visual system is the separation of the eyelids during the 7th month.

The Olfactory System: The olfactory system originates as two placodes which are already apparent at 30 days. These placodal cells gradually differentiate, forming the olfactory epithelium, or nasal cavity. At about 6 weeks, these differentiated cells make contact with the olfactory zones in the emerging brain, which in turn induces the development of olfactory bulbs. The axons of the specialized receptors gradually become more and more interconnected to the cortical area corresponding to the olfactory system. This process occurs from the 46th through the 84th day (Tuchmann-Duplessis & Haegel, 1971).

The Auditory System: The auditory system originates early in the fourth week with the emergence of the otic placode (Gilbert, 1989). The development of the ear, including both the sense of hearing and the sense of balance, is complex and involves all three embryonic germ layers. The endoderm is the source of the inner and outer ear, the ectoderm is the origin of the middle ear, and the mesoderm participates in the formation of all three. Very early on the ganglionic cells from the otic placode form two different clusters, the ganglion of Scarpa and the ganglion of Corti. The axons of these neurons progress towards the metencephalon and eventually bunch together to form the acoustic nerve.

During the fifth and sixth weeks the primordia of the semicircular ducts appear and the cochlear and vestibular ganglion are clearly discernable along with the utricle and sacula (Tuchmann-Duplessis & Haegel, 1971). The development of the semicircular canals, the cochlea, the organ of Corti all gradually differentiate, as do the bones in the middle ear so that the sense of hearing is at least structurally functional from 20 weeks (Chamberlain, 1983).

The Gustatory System: Of the various sense organs, the sense of taste is the last to develop. It is not until the 7th week that the tongue is finished developing and not until the very end of the embryonic period that the taste buds begin to form on the tongue's surface.

Physical and Structural Growth

For most of the first month of development, the neural tube and the developing nervous system essentially define the shape and structure of the embryo. But starting in the second month, the shape of the embryo begins to be defined by other structural and physical components.

Fourth Week: By day 26, the embryo begins to change shape, curving into a c-shape and the arm buds begin to appear (Carnegie Stage 12, 2006). The arches that give form to the face and neck are slowly becoming apparent and the eye buds and ear buds are just beginning to emerge (Carnegie Stage 13, 2006).

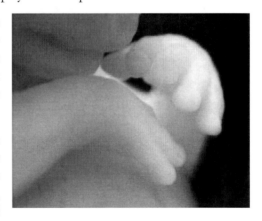

Fifth Week: By day 30, the head goes through a growth spurt to accommodate the huge growth in the brain. The nasal plate (the nose) is discernable and the esophagus forms. The process of ossification begins and the trachea, as well as the Eustachian tubes, thyroid, parathyroid and thymus glands all develop (Meredith, 1978). The leg buds are apparent and the arm buds grow longer and more cylindrical, tapering at the ends into hand plates. Innervation has started in the arms (Carnegie Stage 14, 2006).

During the fifth week, the trunk of the body gets substantially thicker. While the head is still very large relative to the overall body, the enlarging body gives the embryo a more human –like appearance. (Carnegie Stage 15, 2006). Toward the end of the 5th week, the hands become clearly distinct from the arms and shoulder. The leg buds begin the process of elongating and tapering into feet buds and innervation begins in the lower limbs. By the end of the 5th week, the foot is distinguishable from the thigh and leg (Carnegie Stage 16, 2006).

Sixth Week: In the 6th seventh week, the trunk becomes a bit straighter and both the wrist and finger buds are clearly observable, as are the cell buds that have started to specialize into the genitalia. The intestines begin development in the umbilical cord and in the 9th week will migrate into the embryonic abdomen (Grand et al., 1976; Pringle, 1988; Sadler, 2005; Spencer, 1960). The jaws continue to progress and the various plates of tissue growing in from 4 sides over the prior several weeks have formed the embryo's face, which along with the eye buds and eye lids, give the face a more characteristic human-like shape.

By the 6th week, the muscles and now ossifying skeletal structure are both developed enough to allow for the first minute but discernable moves, albeit involuntary (Moss, 1990). The kidneys also produce a very small amount of urine for the first time (Carnegie Stage 18, 2006).

Seventh Week: The 7th week is very eventful, producing the ear buds on the sides of the head and the gonads (testicles and ovaries). The trunk of the body straightens and elongates. Cartilage, muscle and bone continue to grow, solidify and strengthen. The fingers get longer and more distinct and the arms are long enough for the hands to approach each other across the abdomen. (Carnegie Stage 19, 2006). The knees and ankles are distinguishable and proportional and the toes buds are notched (but still webbed) and have the beginnings of toe-nails. Like the hands, the legs are long enough for the

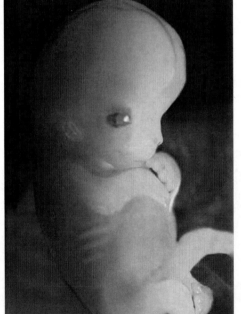

fan-shaped feet to approach each other (Carnegie Stage 20, 2006). The nipples and hair follicles begin their formation and by the end of the seventh week all major and essential organ systems have begun to form.

The eyes, though well-developed, are still on the sides of the embryonic head. As development continues into the 8th week and early fetal period, the eyes migrate forward onto the face. The ears are also set low on the head and will migrate up over the next few weeks (Carnegie Stage 21, 2006).

Eighth Week: Brain waves begin in the 8th week and are measurable using an electroencephalogram (EEG) (Hamlin, 1964; Goldering, 1982). Voluntary movement (controlled by the brain) is possible now and the penis and clitoris are also developing. The fingers are clearly and fully separated and both fingers and the feet continue to lengthen, with the toes become more defined. While a stubby tail is still present, it is much smaller than it previously was. While the eyes are closed, the retinas are fully developed (Carnegie Stage 22, 2006). Eye lids begin to come together from the top and bottom about half way. During the last part of the embryonic period, a precursor layer of skin cells replaces the thin ectoderm of the embryo and the tail finally disappears completely (Carnegie Stage 23, 2006).

CONCLUSION

The embryonic period typically concludes at the end of the eighth week and the fetal period begins. This division is somewhat arbitrary because there is no clearly distinct delineation in the activity or development of the emerging child to allow for the division. The signal marker for the end of the embryonic period is perhaps the brain. All the basic brain structures are present prior to the beginning of the fetal stage, as are all of the major organ systems. The final 7 months of pregnancy will be used to expand and grow and this is the topic of our next chapter.

7

FETAL DEVELOPMENT

You made all the delicate, inner parts of my body
and knit me together in my mother's womb.
Thank you for making me so wonderfully complex!
Your workmanship is marvelous—how well I know it.
You watched me as I was being formed in utter seclusion,
as I was woven together in the dark of the womb.
You saw me before I was born.
Every day of my life was recorded in your book.
Every moment was laid out
before a single day had passed.

Psalm 139:13-16
New Living Bible

INTRODUCTION

The fetal stage takes up the last part of the first and all of the second and third trimesters. While the embryonic stage was one of initial development, the fetal stage is more one of consolidation, growth and developing functionality. It is in the fetal stage that the term "psychological" can begin to be tentatively, but legitimately, employed to describe behaviors, emotional states, and cognitive processes not unlike that of the neonate. We will consider this topic in depth in a later chapter, but here we will focus on the physical development of the fetus.

THE THIRD MONTH (Weeks 9-12)

At the beginning of the third month, the fetus is around 2 inches in length and weighs a very slight .3 (8 grams) of an ounce. But by the end of this month, she will be 3 to 4 inches long and weigh almost an ounce (25 grams). Thus, growth is very rapid, with a doubling of length and a tripling of weight. Her head is very big relative to her body (almost ½ of her overall length). Her face, including the nose and lips (Timor-Tritsch et al., 1990), is well-formed and now has a distinctly human look.

Sexual Differentiation

External Genitalia: We noted in the last chapter than the gonads had begun to differentiate and the external organs also have made their "budding" appearance. What causes the genitals to develop into male or female ones is the presence or absence of the Y chromosome, which causes the production and secretion of male hormones collectively called androgens. Female development is the default pathway of development, so the absence of androgens results in female genitalia. The presence of androgens will produce male genitalia.

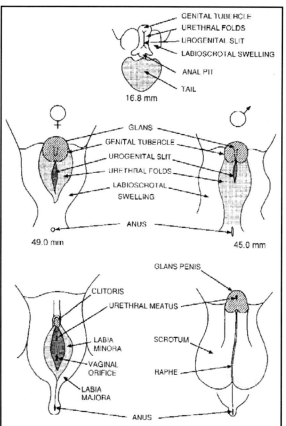

At 6 weeks, the genitals are undifferentiated (see image at the top to the right) and both males and females appear the same. In males, Leydig cells begin producing testosterone and Sertoli cells begin producing Mullerian inhibiting hormones (MIH), resulting in subtle changes by the beginning of the third month (8 weeks).

As the third and fourth months proceed, the genitals begin to differentiate considerably. In the male, the genital tubule becomes the penis; in females it becomes the clitoris. The urethral folds in males become the urethra and in females become the labia minora. The labioscrotal swelling becomes the labia majora in females and the scrotum in males. The urogenital slit becomes the vaginal opening in females and the seam running the length of the underside of the penis in males. The glans, packed with neural receptors and thus very sensitive, becomes the head of the penis. The undifferentiated gonads become the ovaries in females and the testis in males. By 10 or 11 weeks, the external genitalia are clearly identifiable as male or female (O'Rahilly and Müller, 2001).

Internal Genitalia: Both males and females also initially have 2 sets of internal ducts, Mullerian and Wolffian. Boys produce Mullerian inhibiting hormone (MIH), causing the Mullerian ducts to gradually recede and the Wolffian ducts to remain and differentiate into the vas deferens and seminal vesicles. In the absence of MIH, girls retain the Mullerian ducts which differentiate into the uterus and fallopian tubes.

During the third month, the uterus is identifiable in females (O'Rahilly, 1977). The ovaries have developed enough to begin the process (oogonia) of producing all of the immature ova cells (oocytes) that she will release from her ovaries as a mature adult woman in each menstrual cycle (O'Rahilly & Müller, 2001).

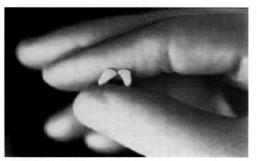

Physical Development

The skeletal structure is fully present and will continue to strengthen and develop (Cunningham et al., 2001). These bones, along with the muscles of the fetus continue to strengthen, allowing for slightly more vigorous movement such as flexing of the arms and kicking of the legs, stretching, squinting, and opening her mouth, sighing and yawning (de Vries et al., 1982). The mother cannot feel her baby yet because he is so small. The fetus can turn his head and frown.

The trunk of the body, legs and arms continue to elongate into a shape more similar to what she will look like at birth. But because the fat a baby puts on does not start until the end of the second trimester, the appearance is of very thin child.

The hands and feet continue to develop. By the end of the third month, the fetus can make a fist with his hand, suck his thumb (Liley, 1972), usually the right one (Hepper et al., 1991) and even grasp an object (Robinson & Tizard, 1966; Valman & Pearson, 1980). Individual fingers and toes can be moved and are sensitive to touch (Humphrey, 1964; Humphrey & Hooker, 1959; Robinson & Tizard, 1966; Valman & Pearson, 1980), and fingernails and toenails are starting their development and can clearly be seen (O'Rahilly and Müller, 2001). The unique fingerprints that identify each and every person appear at about 10 weeks (Babler, 1991; Penrose & Ohara, 1973).

The eyelids are fully developed and fuse together to protect the sensitive and complicated development of the eyes (Andersen et al., 1965; O'Rahilly & Müller, 2001; Pearson, 1980). He will not open them up again for a couple of months, in the 28th week of pregnancy.

The tooth buds that will produce his 20 baby teeth appear (Pringle, 1988). When these teeth begin to emerge from his gums in the months after birth he will vigorously use his vocal cords, which develop in this month (O'Rahilly & Müller, 1984).

All the organ systems are present and functioning, however minimally, and will continue to grow, develop and increase their functionality. The heartbeat, however faint, can be heard using a Doppler stethoscope, a device which magnifies the sound. Blood circulation increases as the heart pumps and capillaries continue to develop.

The digestive system begins to show activity, now able to absorb small amounts of glucose and water (Koldovský et al., 1965). At 9 weeks the fetus begins to swallow amniotic fluid (de Vries, 1982; Petrikovsky et al., 1995) and the stomach begins to produce its own "juices". The fetus can hiccup and does. Likewise, the kidneys begin limited function, producing very small amounts of urine that seep into the amniotic fluid. Red blood cells begin to be produced by the liver and the pituitary gland begins its production of hormones (Blumenfeld, 2001).

Chorionic Villus Sampling

Chorionic villus sampling (CVS) is a test available since 1983 (Simoni et al, 1983; Smidt-Jensen et al, 1984; Ward et al, 1983) and is given to women between the 10th and 12th weeks of pregnancy (Simpson, 2000). It is designed to obtain genetic and chromosomal information about the growing fetus. Since the cells of the fetus, the placenta, the chorion, the umbilical sac and umbilical fluid all develop from the original zygote, cells from all can be analyzed to produce the same chromosomal and genetic information. A few weeks later in pregnancy, a procedure called amniocentesis can be used to ascertain virtually the same information that CVS will produce. The exception is neural tube defects, which CVS cannot be used to diagnose (CVS, 2006).

CVS is not a test routinely given to pregnant women, nor should it be because it does have some risk of producing complications and even a miscarriage (about ½ to 1% occurrence rate) (Olney et al, 1995). Rather, it is used in situations where there is a moderate to high increased risk of chromosomal or genetic defects or other anomalies. Some of these risk factors include maternal (and in some cases paternal) age, the presence in a previous pregnancy or child of a birth defect, and/or a family history of genetic disorders or defects (Jenkins & Wapner, 1999).

The chorion is the outermost layer which emerges from trophoblast and contributes to the development of the placenta. On the chorionic surface are wispy finger-like projections called villi that attach to the uterine wall and function to help supply the placenta and thus the fetus with nutrients and oxygen from the mother's blood. CVS is thus a procedure to get a small sample of these villi and remove it from the mother and analyze it's genetic and chromosomal content.

Types of CVS: There are two types of CVS.

Transcervical CVS: The first type of CVS is called transcervical CVS and it is the most commonly utilized. In this type of CVS, the villi sample is obtained by inserting a thin tube through the vagina and the cervix into the uterus and using suction to remove a small sample of villi. The process is aided by the simultaneous use of ultrasound to guide the positioning of the tube. Generally, no anesthetic is required, the process is painless, and the procedure takes less than 10 minutes to perform.

Transabdominal CVS: The second type of CVS is much less commonly used. Called transabdominal CVS, it is most often used in cases where a woman has a tipped (or retroverted) uterus, which makes the transcervical CVS problematic and increases the likelihood of complications and miscarriage (about 5%). The process is similar except the tube is inserted directly through the woman's abdominal wall and as such, a local anesthetic is often used. Risk factors for complications and miscarriage are about the same as for transcervical CVS (1/2 to 1%) (Olney et al, 1995).

Following the procedure, it is routine to monitor the fetus' heartbeat using ultrasound to insure a positive fetal response. A few hours of rest are recommended. About 20% of women report cramping following the procedure and about one-third of women have a few days of limited bleeding or spotting (CVS, 2006).

Depending on what genetic or chromosomal risk factors are suspected, results are may be available within a few days or may require as long as 2 weeks to be fully analyzed. CVS can produce information on all chromosomal disorders, but not all genetic ones. Further, using CVS to diagnose metabolic disorders is very difficult and usually must be confirmed later by an amniocentesis (Zaret, Jatlow, & Katz, 1997).

In slightly more than 19 out of 20 cases, CVS results confirm that the baby is healthy, while in 3 or 4 cases out of 100, the results confirm the existence of a genetic or chromosomal problem. Most of these cannot be treated and so parents are presented with often wrenching ethical choices regarding what to do with the information. In some cases, selective abortion is chosen. Other parents will use the information to prepare psychologically for a baby with the challenges characteristic of the specific diagnosed chromosomal or genetic syndrome.

In some cases, however, the CVS results can allow for treatment in utero, and thus can help mitigate and even prevent problems from developing. A good example of this is a disorder called CAH (congenital adrenal hyperplasia), a birth defect that is inherited and causes female fetuses to develop male-like external genitalia. CAH girls are lacking an enzyme, which can be treating prenatally (in the 10th to 16th weeks) by hormone treatments, effectively preventing the necessity for surgery after birth (CVS, 2006).

CVS vs. Amniocentesis: While the overall risk of complications and miscarriage for CVS is slightly higher than for amniocentesis (which is about ¼ to ½ %), CVS seems to be safer earlier in pregnancy (Philip et al, 2004) and amniocentesis much safer after 14 weeks (ACOG, 2001). But CVS done prior to 10 weeks also carries higher risks of causing birth defects such as abnormal development of the tongue and lower jaw and missing or shortened fingers or toes (Zaret, Jatlow, & Katz, 1997). But research has found that this risk essentially disappears after 10 weeks. Thus, CVS is only rarely done prior to 10 weeks (Olney et al, 1995).

While CVS test results are more than 99% accurate, they are slightly less accurate than amniocentesis results, and are a bit more likely to give inconclusive results due to the presence of some of the mother's cells in the sample (in about 1-3% of the time) and, in rare cases, discrepancies between chorionic villi cells and fetal cells (Zaret, Jatlow, & Katz, 1997). If this happens, an amniocentesis procedure is often recommended after waiting for a few weeks.

THE FOURTH MONTH (Weeks 13-16)

At the beginning of the fourth month, the fetus is between 3 and 4 inches long and weighs a little more than an ounce (about 30 grams). By the end of the fourth month, she will be about 4/1/2 inches long and will weigh 3.5 ounces (about 100 grams). Thus, she will have tripled her weight during this crucial month.

Fetal Breathing

Toward the end of the third month, indeed as early as 10 weeks (Connors et al, 1989) and in the early fourth month, the fetal lungs begin a process of breathing amniotic fluid in and out of the lungs. This process allows for "practice" (using amniotic fluid instead of air) for the necessary task done immediately after birth. The fetus will not "drown" because getting oxygen is not the point. He gets that from his mother's blood stream by way of the placenta and umbilical cord. Initially, this breathing is rather irregular and erratic, but as he goes into the fourth month and beyond, the breathing patterns regularize and gradually become quicker and more vigorous (Dawes, 1976).

Even after these breathing patterns are regularized, distinct patterns of breathing continue. One occurs only when the fetus is in REM sleep and occurs most often (about 90% of fetal breathing activity). It is rapid and somewhat irregular and episodic, interspersed with periods of apnea. Periodic "sighs" accompany this type of breathing. The second type of breathing is much slower (about 1 to 4 breathes per minute) and deeper and seems to be accompanied by gasps that resemble coughing or grunting. The first pattern (but not the second) is accompanied by increased blood pressure and fetal heart rate (Cosmi, La Torre, & Cosmi, 2001).

There are normal variations in fetal breathing, but various outside factors can also influence breathing (Kaplan, 1983). Any drug that is a central nervous system depressant (alcohol, general anesthetics, & barbiturates) slows down fetal breathing while the opposite occurs with nervous system stimulants such as caffeine (Devoe, Murray, Youssif, & Arnaud, 1993), nicotine, cocaine. Smoking tobacco tends to cause a decrease (by up to 20%) in fetal breathing because of the hypoxia (lack of oxygen), even though it contains nicotine (Manning, 1976). Maternal exercise also tends to result in a decrease in fetal breathing (Jakobovits, 1983).

Lanugo

Babies in the fourth month are still relatively thin and very slowly begin to put on fat, starting with the cheeks first and only later and gradually in the shoulders, back, and abdominal area (15 weeks), and arms and legs (16 weeks) (Poissonnet et al., 1983; Poissonnet et al., 1984). But adding fat is a slow and very gradual process and the big additions do not occur until the third trimester.

Perhaps because of this relative slenderness, babies grow a type of fine hair called lanugo that functions as a type of insulation to keep the baby warm. Adolescent and adult anorexics will also grow lunugo hair to keep them warm in the absence of the normal presence of fat in the human body. The lanugo, along with the amniotic fluid, also reduces friction within the womb similar to the way adult underarm hair minimizes chafing as we move and use our arms.

Lanugo hair will last until around the 7th or 8th month, when it will gradually all drop out and be replaced by the normal vellus hair, a kind of fine "peach fuzz". The lanugo covers most of the body, with the exception of the palms of the hands and sides of the fingers, the soles of the feet and the sides of the toes, the lips, and in boys, the penis. It tends to be thickest in the trunk, limbs, and face. The photo to the left is of a premature baby's back.

Mecomium

The late 3rd and early fourth months also bring the first appearance of mecomium, a kind of fetal feces (Abramovich & Gray, 1982; O'Rahilly & Müller, 2001; Ramón y Cajal & Martinez, 2003). It is not surprising that the appearance of mecomium and lanugo happen simultaneously, because the mecomium is actually partially composed of lanugo hair that has been shed and swallowed by the fetus. Other dead cells, along with digestive enzymes and proteins, constitute the remainder of the mecomium content (Grand et al., 1976).

"Quickening"

Although movement begins as early as 6 weeks, most women cannot feel it. The first sensation of fetal movement usually occurs some time in the fourth month and usually between 14 and 18 weeks (Sorokin & Dierker, 1982). But some women report feeling a fluttering movement as early as 12 weeks (Leader, 1995) and generally speaking, women tend to identify movement earlier in their subsequent pregnancies and later in their first. This perception of movement, traditionally called quickening (Spraycar, 1995; Timor-Tritsch et al., 1976) is often a psychologically significant moment for pregnant women.

Physical Development

The existence of the mecomium implies that the baby has something to digest, process and excrete. Amniotic fluid is part of this "food", and its taste is discernibly different depending upon the mother's diet. In the fourth month, the fetus has taste buds covering the inside of the mouth, but by the 9th month they will only remain on the roof of the mouth and tongue (Lecanuet & Schaal, 1996; Miller, 1982; Mistretta & Bradley, 1975).

During the fourth month, the internal and external genitalia continue to develop. But gender-specific behavioral differences seem to appear for the first time. For instance, research has found that as early as the fourth month, female fetuses seem to move their jaws more frequently than males do (Hepper, Shannon, & Dornan, 1997).

Due to cephalocaudal development, the upper limbs of the body first reach their final proportions at the beginning of the 4th month. The lower body is a bit delayed and takes a few weeks longer to reach its appropriate proportions (Moore & Persaud, 2003). Due to the increases in body growth, the proportion of the head to the overall body is a little more than 1/3.

During this month, the heart goes from pumping several quarts of blood through the body every day to about 25 quarts per day. Bone marrow also begins to form and the liver and pancreas produce their appropriate fluid secretions.

The baby's skin appears a dark red, owing to blood flow beneath his near transparent skin. This is due partially to the relative absence of fat we noted earlier. The eyebrow and scalp hair may make their appearance and for babies that will eventually have darker hair, the hair follicles will commence the production of melanin, which gives hair (and skin) its pigmentation.

The fourth month sees the baby's eyes and ears in an almost neonatal-like appearance, due to the fact that both have almost reached their final position on the head. The muscles in the face have developed, allowing for a much greater range of facial expressions, including frowning and squinting.

Prior to the fourth month, a withdrawal response to stimulation occurs. But in this month, the fetus will respond to gentle stimulation positively (Lecanuet & Schaal, 1996; Reinis & Goldman, 1980) and even exhibits an early version of the rooting reflex (Bates, 1987) whereby light stimulation on his cheeks will cause him to turn toward what he expects to be the nipple, a source of food (Mancia, 1981).

Amniocentesis

Amniocentesis is a relatively common test first used in 1882 (Woo, 2006) to remove excessive amniotic fluid and used for diagnostic purposes beginning in the 1930s (Fuchs & Riis, 1956; Menees, Millar, & Holly, 1930). It is given to women between the 15th and 20th weeks of pregnancy and is used to obtain a sample of amniotic fluid for the purposes of either diagnosing (or ruling out) various genetic and chromosomal factors that may be present in the growing fetus. Because the amniotic fluid contains actual cells from the skin and digestive tract of the fetus (along with proteins and fetal urine), amniocentesis provides more accurate information than CVS because there is almost no risk of maternal cells interfering with the results (Amniocentesis, 2005).

As we noted earlier, amniocentesis provides much of the same information that CVS does, but is used at a later point in the pregnancy when CVS (usually the 10th to the 12th weeks) becomes a bit more risky. Amniocentesis is also more accurate than CVS and provides a more complete and comprehensive genetic and chromosomal profile of the fetus. But it cannot identify some possible problems such as cleft palate or congenital heart disease.

Similar to CVS, amniocentesis is not routinely performed on pregnant women, partially due to the slightly elevated risk of miscarriage in approximately ¼ to ½ % of the time (Olney et al, 1995). Thus, amniocentesis is recommended only in particular situations: when the mother is over age 35 (ACOG, 2005a); when there is a family history of genetic disorders or defects (Jenkins & Wapner, 1999); when there has been a previous pregnancy or birth of a child with some genetic or chromosomal disorder; when there has been a previous pregnancy or birth of a child with a neurological problem (such as a neural tube defect); and when a previous blood test, ultrasound or CVS has indicated the need for further information and clarification.

Amniocentesis is also occasionally employed in the third trimester to determine if a baby's lungs are developed enough for delivery (in situations where an early delivery may be advisable or even necessary). It may also be employed to diagnose any uterine infections or to determine how severe fetal anemia may be in situations of Rh disease (when the baby and mother have different blood types that are incompatible) (Amniocentesis, 2005).

Using an ultrasound to guide the process and prevent harm to the fetus, a thin needle is inserted through the abdominal wall, uterus and amniotic sac and a small sample (1-2 tablespoons) of the clear amber-colored amniotic fluid (resembling urine in color) is removed. The procedure takes less than an hour and while some women report no discomfort, others relate feelings of cramping when the needle is inserted and/or pressure when the sample is withdrawn. Sometimes a local anesthetic is used, but it is often not necessary.

Following the procedure, it is routine to monitor the fetus' heartbeat using ultrasound to insure a positive fetal response. A day or so of rest is recommended, as is the avoidance of any strenuous activity (Amniocentesis, 2005). About 1-2% of women report cramping, leakage of amniotic fluid, and/or spotting following the procedure (ACOG, 2001).

The fetal cells in the amniotic fluid are separated, removed and grown in a laboratory for 10-12 days. This cell culture is then tested and analyzed for genetic and chromosomal anomalies (ACAG, 2005b). Results are available within 3 weeks (ACOG, 2005a). Levels of AFP (alpha-fetoprotein) are also contained in the amniotic fluid and can be measured in just a few days. Elevated levels are associated with neural tube defects (Amniocentesis, 2005).

As with CVS, amniocentesis provides positive news to most women. In cases where the results indicate some genetic or chromosomal defect, prospective parents have difficult choices to make regarding future actions (Kocun et al, 2000). This may or may not include selective abortion or it may result in a preparation process to meet the challenges of a differently-abled child. While most birth defects diagnosed by amniocentesis cannot be treated, some can. Inherited metabolic disorders such as biotin deficiency and methylmalonic acidemia can be successfully treated and result in perfectly healthy children (Harrison, Golbus & Fillylife, 1981). Amniocentesis can also be a very effective diagnostic tool in identifying disorders and congenital problems which are amenable to fetal surgery (Adzick et al. 1993; Flake & Harrison, 1995; Harrison et al. 1982; Meuli et al, 1997; Sydorak & Harrison, 2003).

While the risk of miscarriage from an amniocentesis in the second trimester is very small, it may be three times higher if done in the first trimester (CEMAT, 1998) and thus CVS is recommended and safer in this period (Philip at al, 2004). Several other complications, also very rare, must be noted, including infection, injury to the fetus from the needle (Olney et al, 1995), and an increase in clubfoot, a fetal deformity (Farrell et al, 1999). Maternal factors have also been found to increase complications from an amniocentesis procedure. These include maternal hypertension and being significantly overweight (Johnson et al, 1999).

THE FIFTH MONTH (Weeks 17-20)

At the beginning of the fifth month, the fetus is about 4 ½ inches long and weighs less than 4 ounces (about 125 grams). By the end of the fifth month, she will be a little over 7 inches long and will weigh 10.5 ounces (about 300 grams). She is about the size of a large banana. Thus, in this month, she will almost double in length and almost triple in weight.

Vernix

During the fifth month, the fetus's sebaceous glands begin to produce a waxy white substance called vernix caseosa. It is composed of a combination of sebum (oil produced by sebaceous glans) and sloughed-off dead skin cells. Along with the lanugo discussed earlier, the vernix works as a lubricant, protecting the skin of the fetus as it moves around in the now-somewhat crowded uterus (Campbell, 2004; Moore & Persaud, 2003).

REM Sleep

During the fifth month, rapid eye movement sleep (REM) can be measured. This is the type of sleep that in children and adults we are most likely to dream and there is no reason to believe that dreams are not also part of fetal sleep. The question of what the fetus is dreaming about is one that will probably never be answered. Apart from the dreaming aspect of REM sleep, it seems crucial for brain development and function. In fact, the fetus spends about 80% of their time in REM sleep, with the remaining 20% devoted to non-REM sleep and wakefulness.

Why so much REM sleep? Much is still unknown about REM sleep and so definitive answers to this question are not answerable at this point. But researchers believe that the brain activity occurring in REM sleep contributes directly to the maturation of the brain structures by providing stimulation to the brain (Mirmiran, 1986). Similar to what we have seen with fetal breathing as a type of practice preparing the fetus for later life, so REM sleep provides active "practice" for the brain as it grows. One example of this seems to involve the eye and parts of the brain governing vision. Activity in these neural cells in necessary to prepare for later vision and REM sleeps appears to do this. It is speculated that REM sleep does this for multiple other brain functions as well.

Underlying this speculation are studies that show negative outcomes when REM sleep is disturbed. Much of this research has been done on animals. For instance, when rats are deprived of REM sleep early in life, numerous negative consequences occur in adulthood. It is thought that such REM disturbances may be associated with later apnea, cardiovascular and respiratory problems and result in increased vulnerability to various diseases later in life (NIH, 2006).

Physical Development

With the brain and nervous system development that REM sleep promotes and pain awareness allows for, neural function is at a relatively high level. From the 19th week on breathing activity, movement, and heart rate begin to follow daily cycles called circadian rhythms (de Vries et al., 1987; Goodlin & Lowe, 1974; Okai et al., 1992; Romanini & Rizzo, 1995). The heartbeat can now be heard with a just a stethoscope and the lungs continue to develop significantly (DiFiore & Wilson, 1994; Pringle, 1988).

Fetoscopy

Fetoscopy is a general term used to refer to various procedures that evaluate and treat a fetus. Two different types of fetoscopy are used, one being non-invasive and external, while the other is invasive and is known as endoscopic fetoscopy. This second type of fetoscopy was first pioneered in 1954 (Westin, 1954).

Types of Fetoscopy

External Fetoscopy: External fetoscopy employs a device very similar to a stethoscope (but with a headpiece) in order to listen to the fetal heartbeat. It is used after about 18 weeks, because prior to this time, the fetal heartbeat is too faint to hear without the use of a Doppler stethoscope, a device which amplifies the sound of the heartbeat. The fetoscope is placed on the mother's abdomen and moved around until the heartbeat is discernable. Ideal fetal heart rate is 120 to 160 beats per minute. Anything significantly higher or lower than this may require further interventions.

Endoscopic Fetoscopy: The second type of fetoscopy is invasive and uses a device called an endoscope, which is tipped with a fiber-optic camera. Similar to the process used with CVS, it is inserted either through the vagina or through the abdominal wall (Deprest & Gratacos, 1999). It is used to "see" the fetus for either diagnostic or surgical purposes.

As with external fetoscopy, endoscopic fetoscopy is usually done during or after the 18th week of a pregnancy. By this time, the placental, amniotic and fetal structures are developed enough to provide useful diagnostic data. Because endoscopic fetoscopy does have risks to both mother and baby, it is not routinely given. Rather, it is used when there are significant indications of a possible problem and/or if there is a strong family history of birth defects. Risks include infection, bleeding, excessive leakage of amniotic fluid, premature rupture of the amniotic sac requiring early delivery, and miscarriage rates of 3-5% (Fetoscopy, 2006) or as high as 12% when fetoscopy is done in conjunction with surgery (Youngerman-Cole, 2006).

The procedure itself takes between 1 to 2 hours and usually includes administration of a sedative (both to relax the mother and to prevent the baby from moving excessively) and a local anesthetic. Often used in conjunction with ultrasound, the endoscope is inserted and the procedure is done. If surgery is being done, the procedure takes longer and is more complicated. An ultrasound is often repeated the next day to ensure a positive fetal response (Gratacos & Deprest, 2000).

Women report that they often feel some discomfort in the form of pain or pressure as the procedure is occurring, with feelings of nausea and/or mild cramping following the fetoscopy. Women are encouraged to avoid strenuous activity for several weeks (Yang & Adzick, 1999).

When used in conjunction with ultrasound and other devices, endoscopic fetoscopy can be used to ascertain a wide variety of types of information. These include samples of fetal or umbilical cord blood which can be used to diagnose hemophilia (Firscheim, 1979), sickle-cell disease (Alter et al, 1976; Fairweather, Ward & Modell, 1980; Hobbins & Mahoney, 1977), CGD (chronic granulomatous disease), an type of immune disorder disease (Newberger et al, 1979), galactosaemia (Fensom et al, 1979), and Tay-Sachs disease (Perry, 1979).

A fetoscopy can also be used to procure a sample of fetal skin tissue, which can be used to diagnose Duchenne muscular dystrophy (Golbus et al, 1979a; 1979b) and Weber-Cockayne Syndrome (Rodeck, Eadi & Godsden, 1980) Fetal liver tissue samples are used to diagnose OTC (ornithine transcarbamylase) deficiency (Rodeck, Patrick, & Pembrey, 1982). Finally, the clear images of a fetoscope can identify physical malformations which can be sued to diagnose spina bifida and neural tube defects (Rodeck & Campbell, 1978a; 1978b; 1979).

Results involving images are immediately available. Those involving tissue or blood samples may take a few days or up to a week. An overly active fetus, hydramnios (excessive amniotic fluid), very cloudy amniotic fluid or a mother who is excessively overweight may all be factors limiting the usefulness of endoscopic fetoscopy.

THE SIXTH MONTH (Weeks 21-24)

At the beginning of the sixth month, the fetus is about 7 – 7 ½ inches long and weighs around 11-12 ounces (325-350 grams or so). By the end of the sixth month, she will be almost 8 ½ inches long and will weigh 1.2 pounds (about 550 grams).

Sensory Capabilities

While all of the sense organs are functioning somewhat prior to the sixth month, their development reaches a level where their sensory capabilities are approximating their post-natal level. Here we discuss the physical development of each (we will discuss the various psychological aspects in a later chapter).

Vision: As noted earlier, the eyelids have been closed since the 9th week in order to protect the developing eyes. But by the end of the 6th month (about 24 weeks), they re-open (Campbell 2002; O'Rahilly & Müller, 2001). While there would appear to be very little to see in utero, light can pass through the mother's abdominal wall and the fetus will respond behaviorally to bright flashing lights (Fulford et al, 2003; Robinson & Tizard, 1966). Fetal exposure and response to light may influence long-term vision (Noback et al., 1996).

Hearing: As early as 20 weeks, the cochlea, necessary for hearing, has reached full maturity (Lecanuet & Schaal, 1996) and thus allows the fetus to hear and respond to many different sounds (Hepper & Shahidullah, 1994; Querleu et al., 1989). Just like newborns or even adults, fetuses will exhibit a blink-startle reflex in response to loud noises (Birnholz and Benacerraf, 1983; Campbell, 2002). Apparently, this reaction can be seen in females earlier than in males (Lecanuet & Schaal, 1996). And just like newborns or adults, a fetus will respond somewhat negatively to loud sudden noises with a prolonged increase in heart rate and abrupt behavioral changes such as excessive swallowing of amniotic fluid (Visser et al., 1989). Prolonged loud noises may negatively affect hearing long-term (Gerhardt, 1990; Petrikovsky et al., 1993; Pierson, 1996).

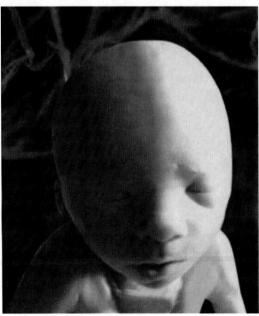

Taste: As we noted earlier, amniotic fluid subtly changes in flavor depending upon the mother's diet. Functioning fetal taste buds have been present for over a month and a fetus will alter his intake of amniotic fluid, increasing it in response to a pleasant taste and decreasing it in response to a bitter taste. Sometimes, the fetus will change his facial expression in response to the taste (Lecanuet & Schaal, 1996; Liley, 1972; Mennella, Jagnow, & Beauchamp, 2001; Moore & Persaud, 2003; Reinis & Goldman, 1980). These early gustatory experiences seem to predict some post-natal food preferences (Beauchamp, 1995**).**

Smell: The sense of smell is operational by 26 weeks (Bradley & Misretta) and has been documented in premature babies (Lecanuet and Schaal, 1996). As with the sense of taste, variations in amniotic fluid as a function of a mother's diet seem to predispose the fetus for postnatal preferences in smell (Mennella, Johnson, & Beauchamp, 1995; Schaal, Marlier, & Soussignan, 2000).

Touch: Fetal sensitivity to touch is seen as early as the third month. In the fourth month, a fetus that is gently stroked will respond positively (Lecanuet & Schaal, 1996; Reinis & Goldman, 1980). There is a large body of research showing the positive benefits of therapeutic massage on premature and mature babies (Agarwal et al, 2000; Barnard & Bee, 1983; Hasselmeyer, 1964; Mathai et al, 2001; Rose et al, 1980; Scafidi, Field, & Schanberg, 1993; White-Traut et al, 1993). Much more controversial has been the debate regarding fetal pain, especially in the light of some abortion techniques such as D&X (also known as partial-birth abortion) which arc done in the second and third trimesters without fetal anesthetics. A recent review of the evidence (Lee et al, 2005), stated that there was no way to prove that fetuses can feel pain prior to the third trimester, and therefore the question remains somewhat open. But the exact same argument has been used in previous years to argue that infants do not feel pain when circumcised or operated on. Subsequent research has indicated that this was (and is) untrue.

Numerous other studies indicate evidence to the contrary. Since one cannot ask a fetus (or a newborn) whether they are experiencing pain, one infers its existence by neural capability and behavioral responses. Thus, as Anand (2006) and others (Anand & Hickey, 1987; Glover & Fisk, 1999; Smith, Gitau, Glove, & Fisk, 2000; Valman & Pearson, 1980) have argued, the evidence is strong that pain can be experienced very early on in pregnancy. The structural and hormonal mechanisms are present which would allow for pain sensation. Fetal behavioral responses to painful stimuli are also plentiful. For instance, at 16 weeks, the insertion of a needle into the fetus will trigger a hormonal stress responses (norepinephrin and cortisol) as well as avoidance behavior such as pulling away from needle (Giannakoulopoulos et al., 1994; Giannakoulopoulos et al., 1999; Glover & Fisk, 1999; Smith et al., 2000).

Fetal Viability

The sixth month is also considered the absolute cut-off for survival outside the mother's womb. While most infants born in the 6th month will still not survive, there are a few that will if intensive medical care is available.

Even though the lungs have started to develop at 4 weeks after fertilization, and the fetus as been practicing fetal breathing for months, the lungs continue to develop even in the third trimester.

Gestation (weeks)	Survival to discharge (%)
21	0
22	1
23	11
24	26
25	44

Thus, for premature babies, their lungs are often too immature to function adequately outside the womb. What makes survival even theoretically possible at this point is the baby's lungs begin to produce surfactant, a slick substance that allows the alveoli, (the air sacs) in the lungs to inflate and also keeps them from collapsing and sticking to each other when they deflate.

But fetuses at this stage only have about 5% of the total surfactant they actually need and will eventually produce. While replacement surfactant can help, along with corticosteroid treatments and respirators (Draper, Manktelow, Field, & James, 1999), survival is still unlikely. Even if the fetus does survive, they are at serious risk for developing respiratory distress syndrome (RDS), brain damage, cerebral palsy, learning disabilities, developmental disabilities, blindness, and various lung diseases (Marlow et al, 2005; Wood et al, 2000).

A large on-going study being done in the UK (called EPICure) has followed over 2000 babies born very early and has found that the survivor rate of 22 week-old fetuses is about 1% (see table above). By just three weeks later (at 25 weeks), this number has jumped to 44% (Costeloe, Gibson, Marlow, & Wilkinson, 2000). Two follow-up studies were done at 2 ½ years (Wood et al, 2000) and at 6 years of age (Marlow et al, 2005). As you can see from the table to the above, outcomes were serious, even for survivors.

One factor that several studies have found is that the weight of the fetus is a more important factor than the actual gestational age as far as survival and outcome goes (Williams et al, 1982; Costeloe, Gibson, Marlow, & Wilkinson, 2000).

Summary of outcomes among extremely preterm children				
Outcome	22 wk	23 wk	24 wk	25 Wk
At 6 years of age survived with:	Per cent			
Severe disability	0.7	2	5	6
Moderate disability	0	4	4	8
Mild disability	0.7	2	7	12
No impairment	0	1	3	8

Ultrasound

Initially developed and used in World War II as a means of locating submarines and other objects underwater, ultrasound is now primarily used as a medical test. Also called a sonogram, because it uses sound waves, it is most prominently associated with obstetrical testing. It can be used at any point in pregnancy, but is most often utilized in the second and third trimesters when the fetus is large enough and developed enough to be able to provide an "image" to evaluate.

Because it is noninvasive, it cannot give genetic or hormonal information, but is instead used to indicate the size, age (often by the size of the head; see image at right of baby at 14 weeks), gender, level of development, and the position of the baby. Sonograms are also utilized to determine the presence of observable physical birth defects such as hydroencephaly, microencephaly or the distinct physical characteristics associated with Down syndrome. It can likewise indicate abnormalities in bone structure, kidneys, bladder or heart.

Ultrasound is additionally used to reveal the existence of multiple babies (twins, triplets or quadruplets), and to observe fetal heartbeat (as early as the 5th week), breathing and movement (as early as the 7th week). It can provide information on the amount of amniotic fluid, the location and size of the placenta, and the presence of any uterine abnormalities or tumors. Finally, as we have previously indicated, ultrasound is often used in conjunction with CVS, fetoscopy and amniocentesis to minimize the risks of these procedures.

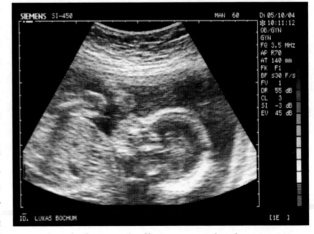

Ultrasound imaging uses high-frequency sound waves to produce images of the baby or placenta. A device called a transducer sends the sound waves through body tissues, which are reflected back by the various internal body structures. These "echoes" are then picked up by the transducer, and transmitted electronically onto a viewing screen (see image of a 23-week old baby above). These images can be videotaped or printed out as a "photograph".

Since the transducer is placed directly onto the skin of the abdomen, and moved around and positioned to get the best image, a lubricant gel is applied to the skin to decrease the friction caused by the transducer. This gel is merely wiped off after the procedure.

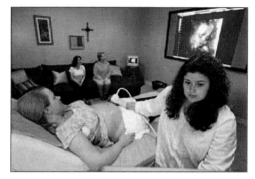

Women are asked to drink a lot of water (4 to 6 full glasses of water) prior to an ultrasound because a full bladder tends to enhance the resulting images. The bladder is in front of the uterus and when empty tends to cause the uterus to be positioned in between the pelvic bones. Since bones obscure the sound waves from the transducer, this interferes with the clear imaging of the baby. A full bladder, however, pushes the uterus up from the pelvis, maximizing the chances of a clearer image. The full bladder almost serves as a "window" into the uterus and thus the baby.

Ultrasound does not utilize the radiation found in other procedures (x-ray and CT scans), but rather uses sound waves. It is generally considered to be completely safe and because of this, its use has become more and more routine. There are, however, several studies that have connected exposure to ultrasound and left-handedness, especially in boys (Kieler et al, 2001; Kieler et al, 2002). A recent study found that mice exposed to ultrasound experienced some cerebral cortex damage (Ang et al, 2006). But so far, human studies have not found such effects (Kieler et al, 2005; Stark et al, 1984).

There is some debate about the potential negative effects of multiple ultrasounds. One study found that repeated ultrasound exposure produced slightly smaller birth weights (Newnham et al, 1993) but other studies have not found this result (Bellieni et al, 2005).

Recent developments in sonography have made the images much more sophisticated and thus much more useful. The addition of 3-D (still images like the one on the right) and 4-D (video images) scans have also produced a market for prenatal pictures as keepsakes. When produced in

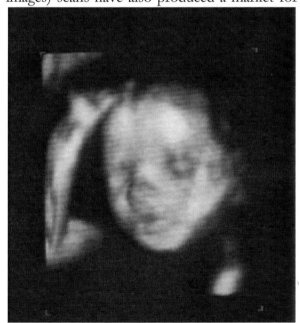

non-medical facilities with names such as Fetal Fotos, Peek-a-Boo, Womb with a View, and Baby Insight, the FDA has warned against such keepsakes, primarily due to the still unknown long-term effects of exposure and repeated exposure to sonography. These facilities may use sound levels that are stressful and potentially harmful to the baby (Rados, 2004).

Ultrasound has also been somewhat controversial when used to determine sex for the purposes of gender selection. In cultures such as China and India where male children are highly prized, ultrasound has been used to identify female fetuses, who are then subsequently aborted. While this is illegal in both countries, a recent study estimated that over the past 20 years, up to 10 million female fetuses have been aborted in India alone (Sheth, 2006).

THE SEVENTH MONTH (Weeks 25-28)

Fetal Development

At the beginning of the seventh month, the fetus is about 8 ¾ inches long (crown to rump) and weighs around 1.5 pounds. By the end of the seventh month, she will weight around 2.5 pounds and will have an overall length of 15 ½ inches (about 10 inches or so from crown to rump).

The seventh month begins the third and final trimester. During the final three months or so of pregnancy, there is vigorous brain development, particularly myelination of the 100 billion neurons that are already present. Thus, brain weight increases dramatically (Mancuso & Palla, 1996). The thin appearance of the fetus begins to change and fat deposits begin to appear beneath the skin all over the body (England, 1983). As the lanugo hairs begin to fall out, these fat deposits serve to insulate the child and serve as energy storage deposits to be drawn on immediately after birth. The combination of brain growth and fetal fat storage results in increasing calorie needs.

The fetus also continues to develop physically and movement is more common and vigorous. Although room in the uterus is limited, babies will perform "somersaults", "walking" up the side of the uterus and flipping over (Liley, 1972).

Fetal Surgery

Advances in technology combined with greater levels of knowledge over the past 50 years have created a new subfield in surgery. The earliest attempts at therapeutic operations on fetuses came in the 1960s (Nihoul-Fekete, 1990). The problem at hand during this time was Rh incompatibility, and the first successful intrauterine fetal blood transfusion occurred in 1965 (Menon & Rao, 2005). Since that time, many more fetal problems have been addressed and numerous other partially successful procedures devised (Brunner, 2003; Cortes & Farmer, 2004; Pringle, 1986).

Types of Fetal Surgery

Obstructive Uropathy: Progress was initially slow, but in 1981 the first successful surgery was performed to correct a urinary blockage in an unborn baby (Lanzetta, 1992). Since this time, surgery to treat various urinary tract obstructions has become more common because these abnormalities are among the most common birth defects. If the urethra becomes obstructed or does not develop properly, urine has no way to leave the body and backs up, causing an enlarged bladder and contributing to kidney damage. The level of amniotic fluid may consequently decrease relative to fetal urine. This in turn hampers fetal lung development. If the condition is serious enough, it can even result in fetal death. A prenatal surgical intervention, in which a shunt is inserted to open up the urethra (Clark et al, 2003), is often life-saving and the long-term prognosis for such interventions is good (Baird et al, 2005; Freedman et al, 1999; Holmes, Harrison & Baskin, 2001; Shimada, 1998).

Congenital Diaphragmatic Hernia (CDH): The first successful prenatal surgery to repair a diaphragmatic hernia occurred in 1989. CDH is a condition in which the diaphragm forms incompletely. The result is inadequate and hampered lung development, because the inadequate diaphragm allows the lower organs (stomach, spleen, liver, and intestines) to enter into the chest cavity. This can occur on both sides, or on either the right or the left. If left untreated, numerous long-term problems can result, including asthma, scoliosis, hearing problems, brain damage and even fetal death (Conforti & Losty, 2006). Because CDH occurs in 1 out of 2500 babies, this type of fetal surgical intervention has been among the most common.

The surgical intervention techniques involve repairing the herniated diaphragm (Grethel & Nobuhara, 2006; Harrison et al, 1997; Wilson, DiFiore & Peters,1993) or using a procedure called fetal tracheal occlusion (FETO). The trachea is temporarily blocked (occluded) by means of a small balloon. This traps fluid in the lungs and stimulates lung growth, displacing and pushing the abdominal organs back into their normal cavities. The balloon is removed immediately after birth of the baby (Chiba, 2000). But outcomes for this type of surgery are still being evaluated with some studies finding little or no benefit to the prenatal intervention (Harrison et al, 2003; Smith et al, 2005) and others reporting better results (Deprest, Gratacos, & Nicolaides, 2004; Deprest et al 2005; Deprest et al, 2006).

Regardless of the type of intervention for CDH, it may or may not be the best option due to less than ideal outcomes. The decision to surgically intervene depends upon numerous factors, the most important being how severe lung development is being hampered by the CDH (Cass, 2005; Colvin et al, 2005; Cortez et al, 2005).

Congenital Cystic Adenomatoid Malformation (CCAM): Surgery for another congenital disorder was first successfully achieved in 1990. CCAM (congenital cystic adenomatoid malformation) is an abnormal growth of a cystic mass in the lungs. Most of the time these masses either disappear over time or are too small to cause problems. But they may grow large enough to interfere with lung normal development and cause pulmonary hyperplasia. They may also grow large enough to put enough pressure on the heart to cause heart failure. Occasionally, they may become infected or cancerous or cause pneumonia. Surgery to remove these masses has been somewhat successful (Davenport et al, 2004), depending on how localized and contiguous the mass is (Adzick et al, 1998; Adzick & Kitano, 2003; Choi, 2001; Kitano & Adzick, 1999; Kitano et al, 1999).

Sacrococcygeal Teratoma (SCT): The first successful surgery to remove a tumor called sacrococcygeal teratoma (SCT) occurred in 1992. Occurring in 1 out of 30,000 babies (Makin et al, 2006), this tumor is usually benign (90% of the time) and develops and grows at the base of the spine in the coccyx area. They can grow quite large (at time as large as the fetus) and have extensive blood vessel development, effectively robbing the growing fetus of oxygen and nutrients. This can result in significant stress on the fetal heart and delayed fetal development. If the tumor is large enough, surgery may be done to remove the tumor. Results have been somewhat mixed due to the presence of other complicating factors (Chan et al, 2002; Hedrick et al, 2004; Hirose & Farmer, 2003), but one study found overall survival rates of over 75% (Makin et al, 2006).

Spina Bifida (Myelomeningocele): Spina bifida, also called myelomeningocele, was successfully treated in utero by surgery for the first time in 1998 (Menom & Rao). Spina bifida is a disorder in which the spinal vertebrae do not close and form properly around some point on the spinal cord. Affecting 1 out of 1000 babies, spina bifida has numerous consequences as the baby grows prenatally. Left untreated, the spinal cord is exposed and the result may be neurological problems, partial or full paralysis, bowel and bladder problems, and fluid buildup in the brain (hydrocephalus).

Surgery for spina bifida includes repair to the spinal column (Brunner & Tilipan, 2005; Kohl et al, 2006) or the insertion of a shunt (Moise, 2003). While the treatment of spina bifida prenatally is thought to improve long-term outcomes (Brunner et al, 2004), it is not yet clear how beneficial this treatment is will be (Walsh & Adzick, 2003).

Risks of Fetal Surgery: What makes fetal surgery possible are the various other techniques which are used to diagnose any problem in the first place. Ultrasound, amniocentesis, fetoscopy, CVS, and other tests both identify the problem, and in some cases, assist in the surgical intervention.

Once an abnormality has been identified, all possible non-surgical interventions are usually considered before surgery. Due to the relative novelty of this field, many risks and complications continue to remain for both babies and mothers. All surgical procedures noted above are associated with much higher risk of premature delivery, often before 30 weeks. Thus, babies who survive the procedure often must also struggle with the consequences of prematurity and low birthweight. This prematurity is a direct consequence of breeching the uterus, whether by means of incision or puncture (Menon & Rao, 2005). Blood loss, amniotic fluid loss, placental difficulties, premature rupture of the amniotic sac, and other complications (Longaker et al, 1991; Sydorak et al, 2004) are all associated with fetal surgical procedures. Long-term studies have also shown a 21% incidence of neurological damage (Menon & Rao, 2005). It is important to note, however, that all of the risks above must be balanced with the risks of outcome in the absence of fetal surgical interventions. In some cases this would be close to a 0% survival rate.

THE EIGHTH MONTH (Weeks 29-32)

At the beginning of the eighth month, the fetus is about 10 inches long from the crown of the head to the rump and almost 16 inches overall. She weighs around 2.5 pounds or so. By the end of the eighth month, she will weigh around 4.5 pounds and will have an overall length of about 19 inches.

In many ways the eighth month is functionally a continuation of the seventh month. The baby continues her physical activities in preparation for her life outside the womb. She alternates between time periods of activity and rest (DiPietro et al., 2002). These patterns function to coordinate the various parts of the body with the brain, and represent the process of integration so important to post-birth functioning.

She continues to add body fat to her body and also accelerates the storage of iron, calcium and phosphorus, all important for the burst of growth that she will experience in the weeks after she is born. The fetus continues to practice breathing, spending up to third of her time breathing the amniotic fluid in and out of her lungs, even while sleeping (Connors et al., 1989: de Vries et al., 1985; Patrick et al., 1980; Visser et al., 1992). The alveoli in the lungs continue development in preparation for life after birth and will do so until about 8 years of age (Lauria et al., 1995).

THE NINTH MONTH (Weeks 33 to Birth)

The final month in utero includes the addition of a couple of inches in length and an almost doubling of weight. The heart is now pumping approximately 300 gallons of blood per day. The baby continues to store fat, exercise, practice and build up antibodies.

Most babies spend the bulk of pregnancy in the head up position. But approximately 6 or 7 days prior to birth, the baby usually drops her head down into the pelvic cavity. At some point in time, the fetus initiates the process of labor (Liley, 1972) by releasing large amounts of estrogen (Moore & Persaud, 2003) into the mother's blood stream. This has a cascading effect, causing the increased release of several other hormones, resulting in the muscular contractions in the abdomen (Cunningham et al., 2001), and finally concluding with birth.

CONCLUSION

The end of the fetal stage marks a huge milestone in development. In seven months, the fetus has gone from approximately 8 grams to 3400 grams and has grown from 2 inches to an average at birth of 21.5 inches. This is quite an amazing transformation! But if the physical growth is impressive, how much more impressive are the functional capabilities. At the end of this relatively short period of time, the fetus officially becomes a baby. But the only real difference is whether she is still inside her mother or has made the profound transition into the world at large. The fact that we spend our first 9 months of life inside another person means that we are utterly dependent, in a way we will never be again, on our mothers. What she eats, drinks, smokes, and feels, is essentially we her baby eats, drinks, smokes and feels. Our next chapter examines the mother's perspective in the developmental process of pregnancy.

8

MATERNAL DEVELOPMENT

I begin to love this creature,
and to anticipate her birth
as a fresh twist to a knot,
which I do not wish to untie.

Mary Wollstonecraft

INTRODUCTION

It is a truism of developmental psychology that all development is driven by some irreducible combination of nature and nurture, of genetics and environment. This is as true for the embryo and fetus as it is for the infant or adolescent. In the last several chapters, we have concentrated primarily on the physical development of embryo and fetus. But this development takes place in a very unique and well-defined environment, the "nurture" of the mother's womb. Never again in our lives will our development be so utterly dependant upon another person. We inherited half our "nature" (in the form of 23 chromosomes) from our mothers, but for the first 9 months of our lives, we will receive all of our direct "nurture" from her. Any other "nurture" influence, including our fathers, is mediated by our maternal environment. When all is essentially well, this mediation serves as a cocoon of protection which allows the embryo and fetus to grow and thrive and prepare for life outside the womb. But when, for whatever reason, the maternal environment is less than ideal, the womb can be a place not of nurture, but of potential harm.

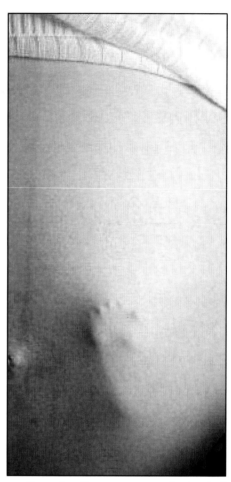

In this chapter we will examine the nine months of pregnancy from the mother's (and father's) point of view. Although she IS the environment for her baby, she exists and functions in a larger milieu which includes family, work, home, school, church, and culture. Within these larger contexts, she influences and is influenced by all she has experienced and continues to experience. She thus becomes a funnel of sorts, a psychological placenta, for her baby. Consequently, her attitudes and behaviors, her stressors and relationships, her joys and sorrows, her expectations and anxieties WILL influence her child for better (in most cases) or for worse.

PRE-CONCEPTION

Even before any child is conceived, the maternal and paternal environments have the potential to profoundly influence a future child. As we discussed in chapter 4, a man's production of sperm begins over 2 months prior to being ejaculated into the vagina in an act of sexual intercourse. The production of healthy sperm may be adversely affected by age, diet, licit and illicit drug use, alcohol use, stress, lead exposure, temperature, and other variables. Ova production begins many years earlier, while a woman is still in her mother's womb. Like sperm, healthy production of ova may also be negatively affected by many of the same factors.

If a mother-to-be and a father-to-be are making choices pre-conceptually which are essentially healthy (physically, emotionally, psychologically and spiritually), they maximize the chances of BOTH an ideal "nature" (the chromosomes contained in the sperm and ovum) and a beneficial "nurture". This is true whether a couple is intentionally trying to conceive or conception comes as a surprise.

A healthy diet is among the most obvious and straightforward factors that contribute to a healthy conception and early pregnancy. Fruit, vegetables, whole grains, calcium-rich foods such as milk and yogurt, and adequate protein are all important. Pregnant women (and women who are attempting to get pregnant) need to avoid or significantly reduce the intake of "junk" and overly-processed food, caffeine, alcohol, and certain fish (tuna and salmon) that may have elevated levels of toxins such as mercury. Quitting smoking and the use of "recreational" drugs such as marijuana are also strongly advised. While taking a multi-vitamin is recommended, mega-doses of certain vitamins can be harmful. Especially important for the woman, both prior to conception and in early pregnancy, is getting enough folic acid (at least 400 micrograms per day), which prevents neural-tube defects.

All of these are important because by the time many women find out that they are pregnant, a significant amount of development in the brain of the embryo has already occurred. Waiting to change one's eating, drinking, or smoking habits until after pregnancy begins may be too late.

THE FIRST MONTH

Maternal and Embryo Size

During the first month the embryo is very small, beginning the month at about 0.006 inch long and ending the month somewhere between 0.16 inch and .2 of an inch long. Until the legs grow significantly, the length is measured from the top of the head to the rump. Weight is still almost negligible.

While changes are occurring in the mother's body, they are not apparent in any weight gain or "showing" early on. By the end of the first month, some women have gained a few pounds, most noticeable in the legs, abdomen, and breasts. But women who have morning sickness and nausea may have lost weight in the first month. Many women will not even know they are pregnant for much of the first month, but by the end, "signs" of pregnancy are often present.

Early Signs of Pregnancy

The first indicators of pregnancy may a missed menstrual period, fatigue, nausea, frequent urination or breast tenderness or enlargement. But every woman is different and every pregnancy unique, so the particular changes may be more or less present in different women.

Pregnancy Tests: As we noted in an earlier chapter, once the blastocyst implants in the uterine wall, production of human chorionic gonadotropin (hCG) commences at high enough levels to be measured by both urine and blood pregnancy tests. This occurs approximately 10-15 days after fertilization and so often a pregnancy test can tell a woman she is pregnant much sooner than a missed period would indicate. The urine pregnancy tests are generally less accurate than blood tests, and are more likely to indicate a false result caused by a number of factors other than pregnancy.

Nausea and Vomiting in Pregnancy (NVP): Nausea, with or without vomiting, and occurring at any time of the day is an early symptom of pregnancy for 80-90% of women (Tierson, Olsen, & Hook, 1986). Studies have found that a little more than half of women report vomiting along with the nausea (Klebanoff et al., 1985) It may begin as early as the 6th week and usually ends by the end of the first trimester (about 13 weeks). But for some it may extend into the second trimester and some women experience it on and off throughout the entire pregnancy. It has historically been called "morning sickness" because for some women it is present when they awake and seems to gradually improve as the day goes on.

There is no confirmed treatment of NVP, although some women report that eating dried crackers (like Saltines) in the morning seems to help. A recent study suggested that medical marijuana may help (Westfall et al, 2006), although this may do more harm than good considering potential side effects. Treatment of morning sickness by the use of Thalidomide represents one of the great tragedies in the history of modern medicine. In the late 1950s and early 1960s it was sold as a treatment for morning sickness until it was discovered it caused severe birth defects. Almost 10,000 children were born with various deformities before it was removed from the market. In response, laws were passed to insure adequate testing of all drugs prior to their use on humans.

Benefits of NVP: The causes of morning sickness have traditionally been seen as an inconvenient by-product of the significant hormonal changes (hCG and estradiol) that occur during early pregnancy (Masson, Anthony, & Chau, 1985; Lagiou et al, 2003; O'Brien & Zhou 1995) and a potential threat to the embryo and fetus (Godfrey et al, 1996; Fall et al 2003). But others have cited the adaptive function of NVP (Profet, 1992). Flaxman & Sherman (2000) examined dozens of studies and concluded that NVP serves a prophylactic function because it produces an aversion to foods that are likely to have toxins particularly harmful in the embryonic and early fetal periods (Little & Hook, 1979; Profet, 1992). Various meats, fish, poultry, eggs, strong-tasting vegetables, and alcoholic and caffeinated beverages are the most commonly cited aversions, and are also the most likely to have pathogens and toxins.

It may seem counter-intuitive that some vegetables are potentially problematic. But plants produce toxins, called teratogenic phytochemicals, to defend themselves against insects and disease. Adults normally tolerate them without becoming sick because their relative amount is small (Freeland & Janzen, 1974). But the growing embryo is vulnerable to these phytochemicals, and morning sickness tends to occur right at the moment of greatest vulnerability, effectively preventing harm during organogenesis and brain development.

Further, because the embryo is extremely small at this point, the loss of nutritive substances caused by vomiting and eating less are not as important as they would be later on in pregnancy when greater growth is occurring (and morning sickness has usually stopped). This may explain the fact that women who have morning sickness with vomiting are less likely to miscarry than those that do not have morning sickness or have it without vomiting (Klebanoff et al., 1985; Petitti, 1986; Tierson, Olsen, & Hook, 1986; Weigel & Weigel 1989a; 1989b).

NVP may also stimulate greater placental growth by reducing maternal energy rates, effectively funneling nutrients to the placenta and away from the mother (Lumey, 1998; Huxley, 2000: Pepper & Roberts, 2006). Because a mother's immune system is naturally suppressed early in pregnancy to prevent rejection of her child, NVP is also protective of the mother at a time of her greater vulnerability to toxins and pathogens (Flaxman & Sherman, 2000).

Hyperemesis Gravidarum: Even if somehow beneficial, morning sickness is not enjoyable. For most women NVP is relatively harmless, but a severe form of nausea and vomiting called hyperemesis gravidarum may be problematic due to dehydration and loss of nutrients. It is thought that the very rapid increase of hCG and estrogen may be causal factors. Women who are overweight, pregnant for the first time and pregnant with multiples are more likely to experience the condition (Hyperemesis Gravidarum, 2006).

Vomiting more than 3 or more times per day, losing 10 or more pounds, feeling lightheaded and dizzy, and dehydration are all indicators of the condition. In these cases, treatment is advised and often centers on intravenous hydration (Hyperemesis Gravidarum, 2006). Studies have found that tactile massage (Agren & Berg, 2006) and/or ingesting ginger (Borelli et al, 2005; Fischer-Rasmussen et al, 1991) have been helpful in alleviating symptoms

Estimated Date of Delivery

Naegele's Rule: Although pregnancy officially begins with implantation, calculating a woman's estimated date of delivery (EDD) is an inexact science. The standard way of calculating the due date is called Naegele's Rule (named after a German obstetrician from the 19th century). The calculation assumed that a due date would be 280 days after a woman's last menstrual period (or 266 days after fertilization). Naegele's Rule seems more complicated than it actually is (subtract 3 months from the first day of a woman's last menstrual period and then add 7 days). So if the first day of the last menstrual period was January 1st, this would give us a due date October 8th (January 1st minus 3 months = October 1st plus 7 days = October 8th).

Naegele's method is good for a ball-park figure of a due date, but can be somewhat inaccurate because of assumptions it makes that are not always true. For instance, it assumes a regular 28-day cycle with ovulation occurring in the middle (day 14), and also assumes that a woman will remember the first day of her last menstrual period. Given these challenges, it is perhaps not surprising that using Naegele's Rule, less than 5% of births occur on the estimated due date.

The Mittendorf-Williams Rule: Given the fact that there is normal variation between women and even between pregnancies, and that other factors may affect the length of pregnancy, a new method was proposed in the 1990s called the Mittendorf-Williams Rule. This model considers 16 separate factors, including maternal age, pre-pregnancy weight, nutrition, hypertension, ethnic background, and alcohol and coffee use. For instance, Caucasian women tend to have longer pregnancies than non-Caucasian women (Mittendorf et all, Obstetrics and Gynecology, 1990; Vol. 75) and first pregnancies tend to be a little longer than subsequent ones (Mittendorf et al, 1993). With the added information factored in, the Mittendorf-Williams Rule is about twice as accurate as Naegele's Rule in predicting the due date. But this still means that it is inaccurate over 90% of the time.

THE SECOND MONTH

Maternal and Embryo Size

During the second month the embryo/fetus goes through an amazing growth spurt, beginning the month at .2 of an inch long and ending the month somewhere in the vicinity of 1.6 inches long (crown to rump). She has gone from being almost negligible in weight to about 5 grams (or .2 of an ounce) and is the size of a small plum.

Most women begin the month not showing at all, with perhaps a few pounds gained (or lost if morning sickness is more of an issue). By the end of the month, many women may just barely be "showing" with the addition of perhaps a couple more pounds. The uterus has certainly grown in size and by the end of the month is the size of a grapefruit, having grown from the pre-pregnancy size of an apple.

The end of the second month (the 10th week) concludes the embryonic phase, a stage of development in which the embryo is more vulnerable and susceptible to things that could interfere with its development. The majority of congenital malformations occur before the end of week 10. Thus, eating well and avoiding anything that is potentially harmful is particularly crucial during this period.

Weight Gain During Pregnancy

Because women and their individual pregnancies vary normally, the range of weight gain among women varies from weight loss of a few pounds to gains of over 60 pounds. "Ideal" weight and ideal weight gain are different for everybody, but the research does show that pregnancy problems are more likely to occur at the extremes of either gaining too little or too much weight (Fagin, 1995; Naeye & Chez, 1981).

Distribution of Pregnancy Weight	
Source of Weight	*Pounds*
Uterus	2-2 ½
Breast enlargement	2-2 ½
Amniotic fluid	2-2 ½
Placenta	1 ½ -2
Increased fluid volume	4-5
Increased maternal stores (fat, protein, & other nutrients)	7-8
Baby	7 ½
TOTAL	**27-31**

Generally speaking, if a woman is of normal pre-pregnancy weight, the ideal weight gain is considered to be between 25 and 35 pounds. This breaks down to a gain of about 2-5 pounds in the first trimester, and then about 1 pound per week in the second and third trimesters. A twin birth should result in an approximately 35-45 pound gain.

If a woman begins pregnancy as underweight, her ideal weight gain may range from 28-40 pounds. If she is overweight prior to pregnancy, the ideal may be in the 15-25 pound range.

As can be clearly seen from the table to th left, most of the weight gain (all but about 8-10 pounds) will be lost during the actual birth process. Breastfeeding also facilitates weight loss.

Diet During Pregnancy

Given the importance modern culture places on women's physical appearance, many women are concerned about weight gain in pregnancy. But pregnancy is rarely the appropriate time to diet, although awareness of what one is eating is advised. In general, women need to eat approximately 300-800 more calories per day than the normal 1500-2000 (which is NOT eating for 2!). If these extra calories are not there, a woman's body may metabolize protein for energy leaving less protein available in her blood for the baby to utilize in building muscle and other body tissues. They key is not how MUCH a woman is eating, but WHAT a woman is eating. Avoidance of "junk" and overly-processed food is critical. Getting enough of the right foods is important to insure that the baby has the "raw materials" with which to grow.

Protein: Adequate protein is particularly important during pregnancy. It is used by both the mother's and baby's bodies to grow and repair. Since most proteins (and the best for amino acid combinations) come from animal sources such as meat, milk, eggs, cheese, poultry and fish, pregnant women who are vegetarians or vegans need to be particularly attentive to adequate protein sources. Pregnant women need 6 to 7 ounces of protein each day. Non-animal sources of protein include beans and nuts of all kinds.

While fish are a healthy source not only of protein, but of pregnant women's increased need for fats, most fish also have traces of mercury which can be harmful to fetal brain development. Thus, the FDA encourages pregnant women to avoid certain types of fish known to be higher in mercury content (mackerel, swordfish, shark, and snapper) and to limit intake of other types of fish to 2 times per week (tuna, salmon, shrimp, catfish, etc.). Oysters and clams should be completely avoided due to other risk factors such as bacterial and viral pathogens.

Carbohydrates: Adequate carbohydrate intake is also important during pregnancy, as carbohydrates provide the fuel that both a mother and baby need to function. Generally speaking, about 60% of calories should be in carbohydrate form (Carbohydrates, 2006).

The best sources of carbohydrates are fruits, vegetables and whole grains because they also contain numerous essential vitamins, minerals and fiber. These carbohydrates are also categorized as having a low glycemic load (meaning they don't cause a spike in blood sugar), unlike high glycemic load carbohydrates such as candy, potatoes, processed white flour products and sugars (Jenkins et al, 2002). Diets rich in high load glycemics are associated with heart disease (Liu & Willett, 2002; Pereira & Liu, 2003) and diabetes (Schulze et al, 2004; Willett, Manson & Liu, 2002), whereas low glycemic load carbohydrates are associated with the prevention of such diseases (Brand-Miller et al, 2003).

Lack of adequate carbohydrate intake is associated with the production of ketones in the blood stream, which are potentially harmful to growing babies in utero. Some studies have shown that high prenatal ketone exposure is associated with later learning problems and reduced IQ (Churchill, Berendes, & Nemore, 1969; Rizzo et al, 1991), but other studies have not found this outcome (Knopp, Magee, & Raisys, 1991).

Fats: The need for fat consumption increases during pregnancy and continues as long as a mother is breastfeeding. Given the modern American diet, lack of adequate fat intake is almost never a concern. But very low fat levels in pregnancy are associated with birth damage and other birth defects (Edison & Muenke, 2003; Hatchey, 1994).

But all fats are not created equal. Fats promoting "good" cholesterol (HDL, or high-density lipoproteins) are preferable to those promoting "bad" cholesterol (LDL, or low-density lipoproteins). Generally speaking, monounsaturated fats (contained in olives, cashews, almonds, peanuts, and avocados) and polyunsaturated fats (contained in corn, soybean, and cottonseed oils and fish) lower LDL and increase HDL cholesterol and are generally beneficial. Saturated fats (contained in whole milk, butter, cheese, ice cream, red meat, chocolate and coconuts) raise both HDL and LDL. Trans fats (contained in most fast foods and commercial baked goods) are the least healthy because they decrease HDL and raise LDL (Fat & Cholesterol, 2006).

Since pregnancy itself causes cholesterol changes to occur in response to higher hormone levels, it is best for pregnant women to decrease their intake of foods which promote higher levels of LDL and increase intake of foods which cause higher levels of HDL cholesterol. Overall cholesterol levels fall during the first trimester and then rise throughout the rest of pregnancy. Normal pre-pregnancy levels for total cholesterol (between 120 and 190 mg/dl) rise dramatically (between 200 and 325 mg/dl) during pregnancy and the period of breast-feeding. While this is normal and expected, exacerbating cholesterol levels through a diet rich in trans fats may put a developing baby at risk, since higher levels of cholesterol are associated with higher levels of pre-eclampsia (Enquobahrie et al, 2003), hypertension (Thadhani et al, 1999) and atherosclerosis (Palinski & Napoli, 2002). Evidence has found that taking adequate amounts of vitamins C and E significantly help to mitigate any negative effects of cholesterol during pregnancy (Enquobahrie et al, 2003).

Nutrients and Minerals

Folate: Other dietary nutrients and minerals are important for ideal fetal development. Folate (also called folic acid and one of the B vitamins) is among the most important, not only during pregnancy but prior to conception as well. Inadequate amounts of folate are associated with neural tube defects such as spina bifida. Taking a folate supplement has been correlated with heavier birth-weight babies (Relton et al, 2005; Relton, Pearce & Parker, 2005). Pregnant women who smoke, drink moderately to heavily and/or have Crohn's or Celiac disease are particularly prone to low folate and iron levels (Annibale et al, 2001).

Good sources of folate can be found in collard greens, spinach, kale, broccoli, asparagus, beans, oranges, strawberries, and squash. Because folic acid is so crucial for development, pregnant women are encouraged to take a supplement with higher folic acid levels. Prior to pregnancy, women should get at least 400 micrograms, rising to at least 600 once pregnancy begins (many prenatal vitamins have 1000 micrograms). Folate is water-soluble and is flushed from the body each day making it difficult to take too much.

Iron: Adequate iron levels are also crucial during pregnancy, when iron requirements increase significantly because blood volume increases by about 50%. Iron is used to produce these extra blood cells and as the baby gets bigger, the need for extra iron also increases to a peak of about 30 mg. per day. Deficiencies in iron may have long-term negative effects for the baby (Blot, Diallo, & Tchernia, 1999).

Large women and women carrying multiples may need more than 30mg. With a healthy diet, most women don't need to take an iron supplement in the first trimester. But since many women don't eat a healthy diet, as many as 12-30% of women are iron-deficient even before pregnancy (Cogswell, Kettel-Khan & Ramakrishnan, 2003; Cogswell et al, 2003). But even for women who are not anemic, an iron supplement is recommended to avoid anemia during the second and third trimesters. Foods rich in iron include red meats, chicken, pork, fish, liver, kidneys, beans, eggs, and green, leafy vegetables.

Calcium: Adequate amounts of calcium are also important for fetal bone and teeth formation, as well as the control of blood pressure and reduction of the risk of pre-eclampsia. Milk, yogurt and cheese are the most readily available sources of calcium. Calcium supplements are often recommended to insure the required 1200 to 1500mg a day (about 4 glasses of milk!). Further, some substances, particularly salt, coffee and tea, interfere with calcium absorption and thus intake of these should be minimized when drinking milk or taking a supplement.

Foods to Avoid: The discussion of the effects of teratogenic agents such a alcohol and drugs will be discussed in a later chapter. But certain foods should also be avoided or their intake greatly reduced due to potential harmful effects. These include the previously mentioned mercury-prone fish, oysters, clams, and caffeine-laden food and drinks (energy drinks, coffee, tea, sodas, chocolate). All herbs and herbal teas should also be avoided due to the unknown and possibly negative effects on pregnancy. Some studies have connected certain herbs (cohash, ephedra, St. John's wort, rosemary, and peppermint) with uterine contractions and thus premature labor and delivery (Drugs and Herbs, 2006).

Unpasteurized soft cheeses (feta, Brie, Camembert, and Roquefort) and unpasteurized milk increase chances of a listeria infection during pregnancy (CDC, 2005) and should also be avoided. Due to risk of salmonella poisoning, fresh raw vegetables (such as sprouts or spinach) should also be avoided.

Lastly, the research data on artificial sweeteners is still somewhat unknown. Some studies have found Aspartame (sold as *Nutrasweet* and *Equal*) to be safe (London, 1988; Sturtevant, 1985) and saccharin (sold as *SweetNLow*) to be questionable at best and possibly associated with fetal bladder problems or bladder cancer (West et al, 1986). Thus, the aspartame sweeteners are much preferable to the saccharin ones. Some experts recommend avoiding both in the absence any clear studies indicating safety.

Food Cravings: Food cravings are one of the most commonly reported phenomena of pregnancy. Studies have found that between 38% (al-Kanhal & Bani, 1995) and 84% (Walker et al, 1985) of women reported distinct cravings for particular foods (Bailey et al, 2002; Wijewardene, Fonseka, & Goonaratne, 1994). While no one has yet clearly identified why such cravings exists, several theories have been articulated, including changes in gustatory thresholds resulting from biochemical changes of pregnancy (Persinger, 2001). Others have noted that such cravings may be an adaptive response to addressing deficient levels of certain vitamins or nutrients (Mercer & Holder, 1997). In the majority of cases, such cravings are harmless (pickles and ice cream, anyone?) and non-problematic.

Pica: Cravings for, and the ingestion of non-edible substances, however, is potentially harmful and is called pica. Prevalence ranges widely as a function of culture and socioeconomic background, from .02% (Mikkelsen, Andersen & Olsen, 2006) to 65% (Lopez, Ortega Soler & dePortela, 2004). The ingestation of dirt (Luoba et al, 2005), soft stone (Luoba et al, 2004), clay (Ukaonu, Hill & Christense, 2003), baking soda (Grotegut et al, 2006), and feces (Heger, 2002) all have the potential for harm to the mother and the fetus. While some studies have found minimal negative outcomes (Corbett, Ryan, & Weinrich, 2003), problems resulting from pica may include lead poisoning (Shannon, 2003), bacterial infections (Luoba et al, 2005) and other complications (Heger, Teyssen & Lieberz, 2001) and thus should be avoided.

THE THIRD MONTH

Maternal and Fetal Size

During this month, the first of the fetal stage, the crown-to-rump length of the fetus will double in length, from approximately 2 to 4 inches. She will also triple her weight, from about 0.3 of an ounce to 1 ounce.

Most women will have gained enough weight to begin clearly showing and may begin to need maternity clothes. Women who have previously been pregnant will often show sooner due to the stretching of muscles and skin that occurred in the previous pregnancy.

The uterus continues to expand to accommodate the growing fetus and placenta. During this month it grows large enough to fill the pelvic area and starts to expand into the abdominal area. In a non-pregnant state, the uterus is almost solid and weighs about 2.5 ounces. As pregnancy continues, it stretches enough to increases its capacity to between 500-1000 times its pre-pregnancy capabilities. By the time the baby is born, the uterus has gotten 16 times heavier (to 40 ounces) and yet, it will return back down to 2.5 ounces within a few weeks after birth.

Physical Changes and Conditions

Skin Conditions

Linea Alba and Linea Nigra: Because of the increased production of various hormones (George et al, 2005) during the first few months of pregnancy, this in turn causes an increase in the pigment called melanin. The result, particularly among women with darker pigmentation (Beischer & Wein, 1996), is often a line which appears on the skin from the belly button down to the pubis. One study found that it occurred in 75% of women (Esteve et al, 1994). It often appears as a faint white line (*linea alba*) and then gradually turns darker into a brownish line (*linea nigra*). These lines tend to appear at the end of the third month and usually (but not always) disappear after birth. Research has pointed to a connection between linea nigra and deficiencies in folic acid.

Palmar Erythema and Vascular Spiders: Often occurring together and the result of increased estrogen production, palmar erythema and vascular spiders are relatively common (Sodhi & Sausker, 1988), seen in 65% of Caucasian women and 35% of African-American women. Palmar erythema is a reddening of the palms and bottom of the feet and vascular spiders are small areas of reddish, raised skin with tiny branches typically appearing on the face, neck, arms and chest areas (James & Odom, 1979). Both vascular spiders and palmar erythema are temporary and disappear after birth.

Chloasma: Another result of the increased presence of progesterone and estrogen in pregnant women systems is a condition called "mask of pregnancy" or chloasma (or melasma). It is seen most commonly in women who have light brown skin and live in areas where significant sunlight exposure is likely. Like linea nigra, chloasma is caused by increased melanin production and appears as patches of discoloration on the face. These tend to fade or disappear within weeks after birth. Occurring in approximately 15% of pregnancies (Schmultz, 2003), it can be minimized by reducing skin exposure to sunlight.

Acrochordons: Also called skin tags, acrochordons are small benign tumors that grow on the face and in areas of the body where the skin forms creases (such as the neck, armpits and groin). They are bits of skin that grow out into a stalk and are harmless. While influenced by genetic predispositions and age, the hormonal changes caused by pregnancy also stimulate skin tag growth (Ellis, Nanney & King, 1990).

Pruritus Gravidarum: Occurring at any time during pregnancy, but particularly in the third trimester, pruritus gravidarum is the name for itching skin during pregnancy. It is a common phenomenon (Weisshaar et al, 2005), affecting about 5 to 20% of all pregnancies (Shanmugam, Thappa, & Habeebullah, 1998). There are no lesions or bumps in the skin and the condition is harmless with no negative outcome for the baby. Studies have found that it tends to occur more commonly in pregnancies with multiples, and in pregnancies of women who have had fertility treatments and diabetes mellitus. Because of these correlations, women with pruritus gravidarum are more likely to give birth via cesarean delivery (Sheiner et al, 2006).

Striae Distensae: Also called stretch marks, striae distensae are common in varying degrees in pregnancy and for many women are a cause of aesthetic concern both during, and after pregnancy. Stretch marks can appear early in pregnancy and most often appear on the parts of the body most "stretched" by pregnancy, the abdomen, breasts, hips and buttocks. They often fade to the same shade as the rest of skin after pregnancy, but do not disappear.

Stretch marks occur in a little over half of pregnancies (Esteve et al, 1994), but in most of these cases (88%) they are relatively minor. There are factors which seem to increase the likelihood of stretch marks, including significant weight gain during pregnancy and/or giving birth to a large baby. Most surprising is that stretch marks are most likely to occur with teenage mothers and least likely to occur in women over age 30 (Atwal et al, 2006).

Breast Changes: By the third month of pregnancy, there have been significant changes in most pregnant women's breasts, particularly in size. Prior to pregnancy, the average breast weighs approximately 7 ounces and gets progressively larger and heavier until birth, when each breast may range from 14 to 28 ounces in size. This doubling, tripling or quadrupling in size and weight is a by-product of the breasts getting ready to be able to produce milk.

While size is the most obvious and observable difference in the breast, the hormones that produce these changes also produce other changes. For many women, tingling, tenderness, soreness, itchiness, and sensitivity to touch are also present. Because larger breasts need to be nourished by an increased blood supply, bluish veins may be observable in the breasts. Further, the areolas and nipples darken in color and may thus act as a more pronounced visual signal for the newborn. Glands on the areolas become raised and a bit bumpy, producing an oily substance to prevent the nipples from drying and cracking.

During the 3rd month, some women also find that their breasts begin to leak. This fluid is the colostrums, the first type of breast milk women produce for their babies in the first few days after birth. Early in pregnancy, colostrums are thick and yellowish in color, but as birth approaches, it turns less viscous and paler in color. This leakage is harmless; some women have it and others do not.

Couvade Syndrome

The word *cauvade* comes the French word meaning "to hatch" and refers to a psychosomatic condition (Masoni et al, 1994) in which potential fathers evidence pregnancy-like symptoms, including indigestion, morning sickness, food cravings, and weight gain (Klein, 1991; Lipkin & Lamb, 1982). Also called "sympathy pregnancy", it seems to occur as a function of the over-identification of some men with their pregnant spouses and studies have found between 20% (Bogren, 1984) and 65% (Masoni et al, 1994) of men have some couvade-type symptoms.

Most typically emerging toward the end of the first trimester, it has been observed in various cultures (Khanobdee, Sukratanachaiyakul, & Gay, 1993; Mayer & Kapfhammer, 1993) and particularly among men who are highly emotionally involved with the pregnancy (Conner & Denson, 1990). Recent studies indicate that there may be an underlying physiological cause to cauvade syndrome. Research has found higher levels of prolactin and estadiol and lower levels of cortisol and testosterone in expectant fathers' blood when compared to non-expectant men. The same hormonal fluctuations occur in pregnant women (Storey et al, 2000; Wynne-Edwards, 2001; Wynne-Edwards & Reburn, 2000).

THE FOURTH MONTH

Maternal and Fetal Size

At the beginning of the fourth month, the fetus weighs about 1.75 ounces, but by the end will triple in weight to 5.25 ounces. The fetal crown-to-rump length will go from about 4.3 inches to about 5.5 inches. Most women will have gained from 10-12 pounds by the end of the fourth month and will be clearly "showing". **Exercise During Pregnancy** Because of general ignorance about female anatomy and physiology historically, recommendations regarding exercise for women have often been inaccurate. As recently as the end of the 19th century, exercise was generally discouraged, even for women who were not pregnant. It was thought by the "experts" (most of whom were male) that the reproductive process, especially menstruation, was central to understanding women's physical capabilities. Women were thought to be limited, even handicapped, by the monthly "illness" of menstruation. Thus, exercise was strongly and "logically" (if you believed this) discouraged, as it would also be for anyone who has an illness (Vertinsky, 1994).

If this was true for non-pregnant women, it was even more so for women who were pregnant. Women were encouraged to "take it easy" and reduce extraneous activity to ensure a healthy pregnancy (McCool & Simeone, 2002; Vertinsky, 1988). Attitudes towards exercise and pregnancy slowly and gradually changed (Artal & Gardin, 1986), but it wasn't until 1985 that the American College of Obstetrics and Gynecology (ACOG) first approved limited aerobic exercise for pregnant women. Even then, the ACOG suggested that the limit should be 15 minutes in length and no higher than 140 beats per minute in intensity (Goralski, 2006). These limits were modified in 1994 to encourage more vigorous and regular exercise (ACOG, 1994). As evidence continued to accrue that exercise, far from being harmful in pregnancy, is generally beneficial (Sternfeld, 1997), the ACOG again changed recommendations in 2002 and encouraged approximately 30 minutes of moderately intense exercise per day (ACOG, 2002; 2003; Artal & O'Toole, 2003).

Given the anatomical, physical, and hormonal (Calguneri, Bird, & Wright, 1982) changes that occur during pregnancy, especially weight gain and the increased pressure this places on joints (Karzel & Friedman, 1991), low-impact activities such as swimming, yoga, Pilates, walking, and cycling are recommended, with avoidance of high-impact sports such as strenuous running, skiing, horseback riding, spinning and intense aerobic dance activities. Generally, any activity that has an excess of bouncing, jarring, leaping and/or potential for physical contact is potentially problematic.

Most experts also recommend that after the first trimester, pregnant women avoid weight training and sit-ups. Weight lifting reduces the blood flow to the kidneys and uterus, while exercises done on the back tend to cause the heart rate to drop, which decreases blood flow to the baby. Because of blood pressure issues, scuba diving is also discouraged.

The benefits of regular exercise in pregnancy include a general increase in health throughout pregnancy, the prevention of excessive weight gain, the reduction of back pain and general swelling (Horns et al., 2000), constipation, improved sleep, increased energy, shorter and less painful delivery as well as fewer complications (Clapp, 1990). Studies have found that women who exercise during pregnancy experienced less stress, insomnia, anxiety, and depression, as well as a better overall sense of well-being throughout pregnancy and more positive attitudes regarding their body image (Brown, 2002; Hartmann & Bung, 1999; Goodwin et al., 2000).

Some studies, however, have connected vigorous exercise and/or work with lower birth weight (Clapp & Capeless, 1990; Launer et al, 1990; McDonald et al, 1988; Naeye & Peters, 1982). But further data have suggested that this is the case only in women who are restricting dietary intake. If a pregnant woman is eating well, there appears to be no reduction in birth weight for exercising mothers (Alborg, Bodin, & Hogstedt, 1990; Saurel-Cubizolles & Kaminski, 1987; Sternfeld B et al, 1995) and there may actually be an increase in birthweight (Hatch et al, 1993). Overall, exercise in pregnancy has not been correlated with any appreciable decrease in infant birthweight (Leet & Flick, 2003).

There are some risks, however, that pregnant women should attend to. Women should avoid or limit exercise if they have an incompetent cervix, vaginal bleeding, placenta praevia, pregnancy-induced hypertension, severe anemia, are extremely over-weight or under-weight, or are heavy smokers (Artal & O'Toole, 2003). Women should stop exercising if any of the following occurs: dizziness, headache, chest pain, muscle weakness, calf pain or swelling, preterm labor, decreased fetal movement, or amniotic fluid leakage (Davies et al., 2003; Paisley, 2003).

Excessive (over 102 degrees Fahrenheit) temperature increases are also potentially problematic, especially during the first trimester. Thus, exercise on very hot days or in places where there is little or no ventilation should be avoided. The fetal heart rate does increase in response to his mother's increased heart rate (Carpenter et al, 1988; Clapp, 1985; Collings, Curet, & Mullin, 1983; Wolfe et al, 1988), but no negative or long-term results seem to result.

Sleep During Pregnancy

Sleep disturbances are a relatively common occurrence during pregnancy. The huge hormonal changes coupled with the fatigue of producing a new human being, mean that sleep while important, will often be interrupted. Early in pregnancy, women may often feel sleepier, particularly in the day. While taking a nap might seem to be the perfect solution, this can disrupt the circadian rhythms of sleep potentially resulting in nighttime insomnia.

As the pregnancy proceeds, and the fetus grows larger, bringing more and more significant physical changes to the mother's body, sleep is often disturbed by various and sundry aches and pains and by the inability to find a comfortable position. Sleeping on one's stomach becomes impossible and undesirable by the 2nd or 3rd month. Experts recommend women avoid sleeping on their back as well, because this puts the weight and pressure of the fetus, placenta, and entire uterus on the spine, back muscles, and intestines. Thus, back-sleeping increases the likelihood of backaches (see below), hemorrhoids and digestive problems. Back-sleeping also puts pressure on both the aorta and the inferior vena cava (the main vein going from the lower body to the heart), and the result can be lowered blood pressure and dizziness. The best position is lying on the left side (although the right is almost as good) because it tends to maximize ease of breathing, blood flow and kidney function, which in turn reduces ankle, feet and hand swelling.

The growing fetus and placenta within the uterus causes pressure on the bladder, reducing its capacity to hold urine. The result is that sleep is quite often disturbed by the need to get up and urinate. Reducing overall intake of fluids is not advisable due to the need for adequate fluid for both mother and baby.

While sleep is often disturbed by these factors and others (vivid dreams, congestion, heartburn), the second and third trimesters also bring fetal movement into the picture. Pregnant women often find that just as they want to quiet down and sleep, their babies want to start doing gymnastics and kicking vigorously. The resulting lack of sleep is compounded by fatigue from carrying an extra 20-30 pounds around all day and being the conduit for the food and oxygen of a growing human being. Some women find that full-size pillows allow for a greater comfort level (see right and left).

Backache During Pregnancy

Backache is another common problem that may or may not be aggravated by poor sleep. That over half of pregnant women experience backache is not surprising given the gradual increase in weight that women's' bodies have to support as pregnancy proceeds. In addition to the sheer addition of weight, the growing uterus sticks out in front, changing the center of gravity forward. In an effort to compensate, extra pressure is often put on the spine and back muscles, causing the pain. The ligaments and joints of the body become looser and stretch in response to hormonal changes and in preparation for labor and delivery. But this also provides women with less structural support, and hence the prevalence of back aches.

Research has found that women who have consistent and regular exercise regimens are less likely to suffer from backache due to the increased strength in their muscles. In addition, exercises that put less pressure on the body (swimming) are particularly beneficial. Women who have appropriate weight gain are also less likely to have back ache.

THE FIFTH MONTH

Maternal and Fetal Size

The fifth month begins a huge burst of weight gain for the fetus. She goes from weighing 7 ounces at the begging of the month to a little over 12 at the end of the month. She grows (crown-to-rump) from being a little over 5 inches to around 7.5 inches.

Most pregnant women have gained approximately 12-15 pounds by the end of the fifth month, with much less than a pound the baby herself. Walking is still relatively comfortable and bending over is still quite possible. For most women, morning sickness has ended completely.

Fluid Intake During Pregnancy

As the fetus and placenta grow and their needs for nutrients and oxygen also grow, a pregnant woman's body increases blood flow by as much as 50%. This increased blood flow requires increased fluid in the body. Thus adequate fluid intake is crucial. The side effect, however, is the increased need to urinate we noted earlier in this chapter. Due to the pressure the growing uterus places on the bladder, its capacity for urine containment is greatly reduced.

The hassle-factor of the seemingly constant need to urinate should not be "solved" by reducing fluid intake. Pregnancy increases the likelihood of urinary-tract and bladder infections and one can minimize the chances of infection by frequent urination and adequate fluid intake, especially cranberry juice.

Urinary Tract Infections: Symptoms of urinary tract infections include frequent and "burning" urination, often combined with feeling the need to urinate but having nothing "come out" (Sheffield & Cunningham, 2005). In more severe cases, there may be blood in the urine. These infections are caused by bacteria and can be treated relatively easily with an antibiotic.

However, if left untreated, urinary-tract infections can get worse and have been implicated as a possible cause of premature labor, low-birth-weight delivery (Herraiz et al, 2005; Millar & Cox, 1997), and as a contributing factor in the development of pyelonephritis.

Pylonephritis: Often requiring hospitalization, pyelonephritis is a kidney infection (most often affecting the right kidney) which affects between 1% to 2% of all pregnant women. Symptoms are similar to those of urinary tract infection, with the addition of chills, fever, and back pain. It is treated with intravenous antibiotics (Gaither, Ardite & Mason, 2005).

Dizziness During Pregnancy

Another common symptom reported by pregnant women is a feeling of dizziness. Depending on the cause of the dizziness, it may or may not be something to be concerned with.

Hypotension: Low blood pressure, also known as hypotension, is a common source of dizziness in the second and third trimesters and is often caused by the growing and thus enlarging uterus putting pressure on the on the aorta and/or vena cava. Called supine hypotension , it most often occurs when someone is lying on their back and can thus be generally avoided by lying and sleeping on one's side. Postural hypotension is caused when someone rises quickly from a sitting or lying-down position. Gravity causes blood pressure to drop, inducing dizziness. This type of hypotension can be minimized by getting up slowly from a sitting or lying position.

Blood-sugar Levels: Dizziness can also be caused by pregnancy-induced fluctuations in blood-sugar levels. Both high blood sugar (hyperglycemia) and low blood sugar (hypoglycemia) can causes dizziness. In most cases this can be minimized by eating small and balanced meals to regulate levels of blood sugar.

Anemia: During pregnancy, there is a significant increase in the number of red blood cells needed to adequately supply oxygen and nutrients to both the woman herself and her growing baby. When there is an inadequate number of these red blood cells, the result is anemia, a relatively frequent occurrence (approximately 15-20% of pregnant women) in pregnancy (Dairo & Lawoyin, 2006; Lee et al, 2006; Van Bogaert, 2006) and another potential source of dizziness. The most common cause of anemia in pregnancy is iron-deficiency, often due to the baby using a mother's iron stores for his own physical development, effectively depleting the available iron for red blood cell production. The normal recommended daily intake of iron for an adult woman is 18mg per day, increasing to 27mg per day during pregnancy.

For most women, preventing iron-deficiency anemia is as simple as taking prenatal vitamins. But even with such supplements, anemia can occur and various factors can increase the likelihood of its occurrence, including bleeding during pregnancy, multiple fetuses, antacid use, and poor eating habits.

Because iron-deficiency anemia has such subtle symptoms, it is easy to miss and ignore in the midst of the more obvious changes which occur in pregnancy. But the possible consequences of anemia include growth retardation, premature birth, and even miscarriage.

THE SIXTH MONTH

Maternal and Fetal Size

As the sixth month begins, the fetus is closing in on weighing almost 1 pound and will be almost 2 pounds by the end of the month. The change in length is less noticeable, with the baby beginning the sixth month having a crown-to-rump length of 8 inches and ending this month at about 9.2 inches. Maternal weight gain by the end of the 6th month should be between 16 and 23 pounds.

Sex During Pregnancy

Numerous misconceptions have arisen regarding sexual activity during pregnancy. The research evidence is quite clear that for the majority of women, sexual intercourse and orgasm do not increase risk for miscarriage, premature birth (Kurki & Ylikorkala, 1993; Yost et al, 2006), premature water breaking, birth defects or any other negative outcome (Sayle et al, 2001). This is true even for sexual activity in the last few months of pregnancy (Ekwo et al, 1993). Some studies have shown the opposite to be true; that women who have sex in the third trimester, even in the last 2 weeks before birth, appear to have lower rates of premature babies that those that avoided sexual activity (Brown, 2001). This does not apply to sexual behavior during pregnancy that involves the contraction of a sexually transmitted infection such as Chlamydia or syphilis, both of which are correlated with increased rates of premature delivery (Jancin, 2000).

The baby is surrounded and protected by umbilical fluid within the umbilical sac, as well as the mucous plug that blocks the cervical opening. But as the baby gets bigger, sexual activity may have to change to accommodate the changes in a woman's body. Sexual positions that include front-entry and lying flat on the back (i.e. the "missionary" position) are often uncomfortable, especially in the third trimester of pregnancy. Woman- on-top and rear-entry positions tend to be more comfortable.

Many women may lose some of their interest in sex during pregnancy due to feelings of exhaustion, nausea, morning sickness, and self-consciousness about the changing shape of their bodies. Coupled with significant and drastic hormonal changes, the result may be a temporary decrease in sex drive. These same hormonal changes may have the opposite effect for some women, significantly increasing sex drive. Generally speaking, research has found that sexual activity during pregnancy tends to decrease from pre-pregnancy levels and gradually decreases in frequency as the pregnancy proceeds (Aslan et al, 2005; Sayle et al, 2003).

For some women in particular situations, however, sexual intercourse during pregnancy may be problematic. For women who are at risk for premature labor due to non-sexual causes, exposure to the prostaglandins contained in semen could trigger preterm labor. Sexual intercourse should also be avoided when there is vaginal bleeding, incompetent cervix or placenta previa. Many experts also encourage pregnant women who are having multiples to avoid sex during the last several months of pregnancy. While no research data have indicated clear risks, the recommendation is one of caution. In all of the above cases, it is only intercourse that is potentially problematic. Other sexual activities have not been implicated as risky and are thus acceptable.

The research evidence is clear that contrary to popular belief, having an orgasm will not hasten the onset of labor and delivery (Schaffir, 2006). Regular intercourse in the third trimester is also associated with a decreased risk of being overdue and having to induce labor and delivery artificially (Tan et al, 2006).

Pulmonary Function During Pregnancy

As we noted earlier, the increased blood flow required by pregnancy is necessary for healthy fetal growth. But there are several "side effects" to this increased blood flow which are common, if unpleasant, consequences that most pregnant women experience.

Hemorrhoids: When the blood vessels around the anal area dilate and remain so, the result is often hemorrhoids. Pregnancy increases the changes of hemorrhoids because the increased blood flow and pressure in the anal area are combined with the increasing weight of the uterus, which exacerbates the congestion and blockage of circulation (Wald, 2003).

Hemorrhoids tend to worsen as pregnancy proceeds and women who are pregnant more than once tend to experience worse hemorrhoids with each subsequent pregnancy (Hasse, 2001). Drinking plenty of fluids and eating a diet with adequate amounts of fiber both help reduce hemorrhoidal symptoms, as does alleviation of weight on the vaginal/anal area by resting with the feet and legs elevated and avoiding sitting for long periods of time (Abramowitz & Batallan, 2003).

Varicose Veins: Varicose veins appear to be caused by increased blood pressure and pregnancy increases blood pressure significantly. Appearing mostly in the legs (but also the vulval area), varicose veins occur in almost half of pregnancies (Krasinski et al, 2006). Risk factors such as family history, previous pregnancy and increased age enhance the likelihood and severity of varicose veins (Jukkola et al, 2006). They also tend to be more prevalent as pregnancy proceeds and women gain weight, as well as standing for long periods of time (Tuchsen et al, 2005).

Blood Clots: A potentially serious pulmonary complication of pregnancy may be a blood clot in the legs or groin. It is among the commonest causes of maternal mortality (Tan, 2002). Referred to as venous thrombosis or thrombophlebitis, blood clots are made more likely by pregnancy due to the constriction of blood flow in the legs and groin area caused by the growth of the uterus. Pregnancy also increases the clotting mechanisms in the blood. Inherited predisposition for blood clots is called thrombophilia (Nelson & Greer, 2006), which along with advanced maternal age, obesity and pre-eclampsia (Greer, 2003; Tan, 2002), are the major risk factors for blood clotting problems during pregnancy.

THE SEVENTH MONTH

Maternal and Fetal Size

The seventh month begins the third and final trimester. The baby will go from 2 pounds to 3 pounds during this month and will grow from a crown-to-rump length of about 9.6 inches to almost 11 inches. Overall length at the beginning of the seventh month is a little over 15 inches and will increase to about 17 inches by the end of the month. Maternal weight gain continues, making the seventh month and the third trimester ever more challenging for the mother. Standing up, lying down and movement in general are often somewhat restricted by the bulging baby and uterus in the abdomen.

Braxton Hicks Contractions

Named after the English obstetrician John Braxton Hicks (right) who first described them in 1872 (Dunn, 1999; Longo, 1975), these contractions appear primarily in the last half of pregnancy. Also known as "false labor", Braxton Hicks contractions can begin as early as 6 weeks, and are almost always relatively mild, infrequent, irregular and painless in the early to middle part of pregnancy (MacKinnon & McIntyre, 2006), lasting between 30 and 60 seconds and occurring less than 4 times in an hour. Further, they seem to have no adverse effect on the fetus (Mulder & Visser, 1987) even though fetal breathing patterns and movement often change in response to Braxton Hicks contractions (Wilkinson & Robinson, 1982). These contractions are thought to be "practice runs" which function as preparation of the uterine muscles for the birth contractions when they finally arrive. Not all women experience Braxton Hicks contractions and in women who do experience them, they may misidentify them as fetal movements (Schmidt et al, 1982).

There are usually identifiable differences between the two types of contractions (see table at right). But in some women, it may be more difficult to distinguish between Braxton Hicks and "real" contractions (Day, 1990), particularly toward the latter part of the pregnancy. They can be intense and in some cases may assist in the process of effacement, the thinning and dilation of the cervix. Sexual activity, particularly orgasm, and dehydration are among the factors which have been identified as

True Labor	Braxton Hicks
Contractions gradually get stronger	Contractions remain approximately the same
Contractions are felt all over the body	Contractions are felt only in the front of the body
Contractors gradually get closer together	Contraction stay similarly spaced
Walking making contractions stronger	Walking reduces or has no effect on the contractions
Contractions last longer	Contractions don't last longer

prompting or increasing Braxton Hicks contractions. Thus avoiding sexual activity and/or drinking several glasses of water may help avoid or dispel the contractions.

Premature Labor

In some cases, what may initially appear as Braxton Hicks contractions because they are earlier in pregnancy than might be expected, are real contractions and indicate potential premature labor, defined as the onset of labor prior to 37 weeks. While premature labor does not always result in premature birth, the two are very much connected. The signs of premature labor include regular contractions spaced 10 minutes apart or shorter, cramping, vaginal discharge (blood or amniotic fluid), pelvic pressure, and low dull backache (Prematurity, 2005).

Any pregnancy can result in premature labor and/or delivery. Numerous causes have been identified as risk factors for premature labor, but few of these inevitably cause premature delivery. Among the most common risk factors include pregnancy with multiples, a previous premature delivery and the presence of uterine abnormalities. While premature labor does seem to have a genetic predisposition (, pregnancies with placenta previa, incompetent cervix, pre-eclampsia, premature rupture of membranes and/or fetal abnormalities are also all associated with greater likelihood of premature labor.

Further, lifestyle habits such as smoking, drinking, drug use, physical, emotional or sexual abuse, lack of social support, and stress (Coussons-Read, Okun & Nettles, 2006) all increase the chances of premature labor. A personal and/or medical history with any of the following factors also increases risk: being younger than 17 or older than 35, being African-American (Howard et al, 2006), being obese or underweight before pregnancy, having experienced a urinary tract infection, vaginal infection, sexually transmitted infection, diabetes, high blood pressure, thrombophilia, vaginal bleeding, or a short time period between pregnancies (Prematurity, 2005).

The particular cause of premature labor is often very difficult to identify, but an attempt is usually made to insure that treatment, if any, is maximally effective. In the majority of cases, arresting labor and prolonging the time in utero prior to birth is most beneficial for the health of the fetus. Usually, the best place for a fetus is in his mother's womb. But in some cases, premature birth is inevitable and even advisable.

Treatment options include bed rest and drugs which suppress labor contractions by relaxing the uterus. The most commonly prescribed is ritodrine (brand names Yutopar and Anpo), which can be taken orally, as an injection and intravenously. While this drug is effective, side effects can be severe and include tachycardia (rapid heartbeat), hypotension, feelings of apprehension or fear, chest pains, pulmonary edema (fluid in the lungs), headaches, vomiting, fever and hallucinations. Some of these symptoms may also be seen in the baby both prior to and following birth. Due to the severity of the side effects, premature delivery may be preferable.

THE EIGHTH MONTH

Maternal and Fetal Size

By the beginning of the eighth month most women have gained between 21 and 27 pounds. This additional weight and the change in the center of gravity it produces can make everyday movement and functioning more of a challenge than has previously been the case. The baby herself will go from about 3 pounds in weight and 18 inches in length to almost 5 pounds and 19.8 inches by the end of the eighth month.

Preeclampsia

Pre-eclampsia is a disorder unique to pregnancy and the postpartum period. It affects both the mother and her baby, and is a rapidly progressive condition characterized by a variety of symptoms, most commonly hypertension and proteinuria (the presence of protein in the urine). Edema (swelling) and hyperreflexia (a change in reflexes) are among the most observable signs, along with sudden weight gain, visual change and headaches. But some women report few and/or very subtle signs which may make the condition easy to miss.

Affecting between 5-8% of all pregnancies (Ngoc et al, 2006), preeclampsia typically occurs after 20 weeks gestation (in the late 2nd or 3rd trimesters), although it can occur earlier. Pre-eclamosia can, if untreated, progress to eclampsia, which includes seizures and/or convulsions along with the symptoms of preeclampsia. Pregnancy Induced Hypertension (PIH) (high-blood pressure but without the proteinuria) is a closely related condition, and essentially treated the same way. Together these disorders are among the leading causes of maternal and infant death, responsible for over 75,000 deaths each year.

Most likely to occur in older women, those who are obese (Villamor & Cnattingius, 2006), and during a first (vs. subsequent) pregnancies, the definitive cause or causes of preeclampsia remain unknown and unclear. Placental hormonal dysfunctions, perhaps caused by different factors, seem to play a role (Andrews et al, 2006; Maynard et al, 2003; Venkatesha et al, 2006), as does exposure to some bacterial agents (Ponzetto et al, 2006). These "causal" factors seem to constitute a first stage, the second being the subsequent symptomology. Preeclampsia is also more likely to occur in women who have or have had hypertension, diabetes, lupus, thrombophilia, and are pregnant with multiples (Kamath, 2006).

The goal of treatment with preeclampsia is to avoid the seizures and convulsions of eclampsia. Thus, monitoring blood pressure, diet, and weight gain are important, along with bed rest, particularly on the sides and not on the back. This position is the most effective for allowing maximal blood flow to the uterus and insuring optimal kidney function. In cases where symptoms get worse, hospitalization may be needed. Finally, early delivery may be necessary to prevent harm to both mother and baby.

Vitamin (Rumbold et al, 2006) and calcium(Villar et al, 2006) supplements, and moderate exercise (Meher & Duley, 2006a), all recommended by some experts in the past as having a potential preventative effect, have not been found to make much of a difference. Some preliminary studies have found that regular rest (Meher & Duley, 2006b) and aspirin ingestion (Duley et al, 2004) may be prophylactic in reducing the risk of preeclampsia.. Somewhat surprisingly, exposure to tobacco may also reduce risk due to the positive benefit that nicotine may provide in preventing the initial hormonal dysfunctions that occur at the onset of preeclampsia (Cohen et al, 2001; Lain et al, 1991).

THE NINTH MONTH

Maternal and Fetal Size

The beginning of the final month of pregnancy finds the average baby at a little over 20 inches in overall length and weighing about 5 ½ pounds. At birth the average baby will weigh about 7 pounds and will be about 21 inches long. Most women have gained somewhere in the vicinity of 25 to 35 pounds and often just want the baby to be born. Due to this extra weight, every normal task becomes increasingly difficult.

Lightening

Sometime during the ninth month, the baby begins to settle or "drop" into the mother's pelvic area. It is often referred to as "lightening" because the sensation of being pregnant often changes a bit and becomes "lighter". This sensation is not a good predictor of labor and may occur 4 weeks (or even earlier) prior to actual labor. In first-time mothers, this lightening tends to occur earlier than in subsequent pregnancies. In women that have had several pregnancies, the dropping may occur immediately prior to labor beginning.

Some women note that after lightening occurs, they find it easier to breathe and that heartburn, if present, diminishes and occurs less often if at all. This is because there is a bit more room in the upper abdomen. The downside is that the "dropped" baby tends to put pressure on the bladder, increasing the urge to urinate.

This descent into the pelvis is measured in "stations". When the baby's head is still "out of the pelvis", she is at the −3 station. This gradually changes to -2 and then -1. When the baby's head is at the bottom of the pelvis, the position is the 0 station. The stations then increase to +1 and then +2, and when the head begins to emerge into the birth canal and crowning is occurring, the baby is at the +3 station.

Rupture of Membranes

More commonly referred to as "water breaking", the rupture of membranes refers to the amniotic sac beginning to leak amniotic fluid and usually indicates the onset of labor. In 75% of pregnancies, this doesn't occur until a woman is well into labor. But in 13% of pregnancies, the water breaks prior to labor.

Amniotic fluid can usually be distinguished from urine because it is clear. But occasionally it may have a yellowish or greenish tinge or may be combined with blood. Distinguishing between amniotic fluid and any other fluid isn't always obvious and so a test may need to be done on the discharged fluid to accurately ascertain if the rupture of membranes has begun.

Nitrazine Test: One test is called the nitrazine test. It utilizes small strips of paper which chemically change color in response to the acidity (or pH) of the fluid. Because amniotic fluid is acidic, its presence will produce a change in the color of the paper. A negative test results in a yellowish color (a pH of 5 or so), while a positive test produces a purple color (a pH of 7 or so). But since the presence of blood will also affect the pH level, the nitrazine test can produce a false positive result, indicating a rupture of the amniotic sac when a rupture has not occurred.

Ferning Test: Another more accurate test may need to be done that is less likely to give a false result. Amniotic fluid is swabbed from the back of the vagina and placed on a slide for examination under a microscope. As the amniotic fluid dries, it takes on the appearance of a fern (hence, the "ferning" test) or a pine branch.

Cervical Dilation

Prior to the onset of labor, the cervical opening has a mucous plug which has accumulated in the early part of pregnancy and serves as a protective barrier between the baby and the "outside" world, preventing infection. As labor approaches and then begins, this thick mucous plug begins to thin out. This thinning process is called effacement and corresponds to the dilation of the cervical opening.

This dilatation of the cervix (measured in centimeters) needs to occur to allow the baby to pass into the birth canal and eventually be born. At the onset of labor, the cervix is usually closed or minimally dilated (1 centimeter). One of the results of labor is the gradual dilation of the cervix to 10 centimeters.

The station is also determined. Station describes the degree to which the presenting part of the baby has descended into the birth canal. If the baby's head is at a -2 station, it means the head is higher inside you than if it were at a +2 station. The 0 point is a bony landmark in the pelvis, the starting place of the birth canal.

CONCLUSION

The baby is now ready to make the incredible transition from the protected "world" of the womb to the "world" of the rest of her life. The foundation of the structure of the rest of her life is done. In the great majority of cases, the process has gone relatively smoothly. But in about 5% of pregnancies, there is a problem of some sort and these potential "problems" are the topic of our next chapter.

9

TERATOGENS

It is said that the present is pregnant with the future.

Voltaire

INTRODUCTION

The study of non-genetic causes of birth defects is called teratology and comes from the two Greek words, τέρᾰς (meaning "monster") and λόγος (meaning "word" or "knowledge"). While the "study of monsters" is not a very eloquent way of describing the field, it does adequately convey the essential meaning of the field, which is the study of any agent which causes structural abnormalities following fetal exposure during pregnancy. There are over 2000 known or suspected causes of birth defects that are not genetic in origin (Lewis, 2005). Also called dysmorphology, the field is relatively new because it was long assumed that the embryo and fetus were essentially protected from the maternal environment by the placenta.

The discovery of a particular teratogen almost always occurs not as a result of an epidemiological study, but because birth defects appear in a cluster of children. For example, in the years following World War II in the Minamata Bay area of Japan, there appeared to be an increase of encephalopathy in newborn babies similar to cerebral palsy. Called Minamata disease, it was eventually traced to an increase in methyl mercury, discharged into the water as waste by a local factory. The fish became contaminated, and some were eventually caught and eaten by the local population, including pregnant women. Similar results occurred in Iraq and Mexico, the result of a fungicide used agriculturally that contaminated grain with mercury (Teratogens, 2006).

ETIOLOGY OF CONGENITAL MALFORMATIONS IN HUMANS	
Cause of Congenital Malformations	% of All Defects
Single Gene Disorders	20%
Chromosomal Disorders	10%
Teratogens Types	
Infections	1%
Maternal Disorders	1-2%
Radiation	<1%
Drugs & Chemicals	2%
Unknown Causes	65%
Total	**100%**

Cases of physical deformity in Australia and Germany in the 1960's eventually identified Thalidimide as a teratogen.

The official criteria for determining whether an agent is teratogenic or not is based upon Koch's Postulates (Medical Genetics, 2006; Shepherd, 1982; Walker, Levine & Jucker, 2006) and include the following:

1. The agent must be present during the critical stage of development.
2. The agent produces a particular pattern of birth defects in animal studies.
3. The agent crosses the placenta and there is a dose-response relationship.
4. There is an abrupt increase in the frequency of a particular defect or group of defects (syndrome).
5. The increase of defects is associated with the use of a new drug or the widespread exposure to a chemical or environmental change.
6. There is an absence of other factors to explain the observations.
7. The mechanism of teratogenesis makes biological sense.

Animal studies have also been invaluable in the study of teratology, particularly regarding drugs. But the human response to drugs is not always the same or similar to animal models and so animal studies are sometimes problematic as a predictive tool.

Even with the huge increase of research and study on teratogenesis, known teratogens only account for approximately 5-6% of all birth defects (Bertollini, Pagano & Mastroiacova, 1993). Thus, the causes for the majority of birth defects remain unknown. Approximately 3-5% of babies have some defect caused by teratogen (Leen-Mitchell et al, 1995).

PRINCIPLES OF TERATOLOGY

The study of teratology is complicated because there are no absolute teratogens that cause defects in every baby and in every situation. Rather, various factors influence the likelihood of teratogenic effect. Originally developed by James Wilson, there are several principles of teratology that co-determine the likelihood of any particular exposure resulting in a malformation (Wilson & Warkany, 1985).

Dose Response.

The amount of exposure of a particular agent will influence the outcome of the teratogenic effect. Generally speaking, the greater the exposure, the more likely the chances are for a negative outcome. For instance, the child of a pregnant woman who drinks an average of 7 ounces of alcohol per day during pregnancy is more likely to suffer adverse consequences than the child of a mother who averaged 2 ounces of alcohol per day.

Duration of Exposure

Generally speaking, the longer the exposure, the greater the likelihood of negative effects. A mother who is exposed repeatedly to radiation is more likely to give birth to a child with birth defects than one exposed only once or twice during pregnancy.

Multiple Exposure

Generally speaking, exposure to multiple teratogens may produce an interactive effect greater than the expected sum of their parts. For instance, a woman who uses alcohol and a tranquilizer runs the risk of increased adverse effects because both are depressants.

Time of Exposure

The particular time of exposure during pregnancy is also a significant factor in the outcome of teratogenic effect. Since different organs of the body are forming at different times, the sensitivity to a particular teratogen and the affected organ will vary.

Generally speaking, there is little if any risk prior to implantation. Risk appears to be most pronounced during the earlier part of pregnancy, and much less so during the second and third trimesters. Prenatal exposure to the drug Thalidomide provides a good example. Exposure during the 35-37th day results in no ears, while exposure during the 39th to 41st days results in the absence of arms, with malformations in the tibia and thumbs resulting from exposure during the 45-47 day span and 47-49 day span respectively (Teratogens, 2006).

Genetic Susceptibility.

Every child inherits chromosomes from his parents and his particular genotype may be more or less affected by an interaction with any particular teratogen. For instance, some babies may be hardier and others may be more predisposed to the effect of any particular teratogen. In the same way, maternal genotype may result in variations in maternal metabolism of a particular drug which in turn influences how much exposure the baby has to the drug. Variations in placental function and rates of excretion may also have an effect on the outcome of exposure. The ingestion if alcohol provides a good example of an individual's variable susceptibility. Large amounts appear to have little effect on some fetuses, while others appear to be adversely affected by very small amounts.

TYPES OF TERATOGENS

The consequences of various teratogens range from relatively mild (stained teeth and skin discoloration) to severe (including physical deformities, blindness, deafness, central nervous system damage, prematurity, low birth weight, micrencephaly, miscarriage, and fetal death). They are often organized not by effect, but by cause. In this chapter we will examine the teratogenic effects of medications, substance abuse drugs, and common infections. In the next chapter we will examine environmental pollutants, malnutrition, radiation, hyperthermia and maternal stress.

Medications

Over 8,000 legal drugs are available for prescription in the United States, in addition to various illegal drugs. This represents a huge increase over the past 40 years. For instance, in 1961, only 656 drugs were available for prescription (Hazard Database, 2006). Over 26,000 drugs have been evaluated for potential teratogenic effects (Lewis, 2005) and have been classified by the FDA into categories with the designations of A, B, C, D, and X. The A and B categories show no evidence of risk, with C, D, and X indicating successively increased risk to the baby.

Some common drugs that pose no risk for the mother may have a potentially devastating impact on her baby because it stops or slows down the development of fetal organs. Further, a mother's body is more efficient than her baby's in the excretion of drugs from her system. Finally, two medications may be relatively harmless to the baby if taken alone, but together may produce an interaction which is harmful. Below are some of the more common medications which are teratogenic. This list is by no means exhaustive.

FDA CATAGORIES	
Category	**Description**
A	Medication has not shown an increased risk for birth defects in human studies.
B	Animal studies have not demonstrated a risk and there are no adequate studies in humans, OR animal studies have shown a risk, but the risk has not been seen in humans.
C	Animal studies have shown adverse effects, but no studies are available in humans, OR studies in humans and animals are not available.
D	Medications are associated with birth defects in humans, however, there may be potential benefits in rare cases that outweigh their known risks.
X	Medications should not be used because of known fetal abnormalities that have been demonstrated in both human & animal studies.

Accutane: Accutane (generic name = isotretinoin), a synthetically-produced type of vitamin A, is a commonly prescribe oral medication for the treatment of cystic acne. Also sold under the brand names of Amnesteem, Claravis and Sotret, it is completely excreted by the body after about 10 days. (Accutane & Pregnancy, 2006). Women are advised to stop using Accutane at least 1 month prior to becoming pregnant. Topical use of the drug, however, is not associated with increased risk (Loureiro et al, 2005).

Taken during the first trimester, the risk of miscarriage may be as high as 40% and the risk of birth defects as high as 35% (Dai, LaBraico & Stern, 1992; Lammer et al, 1985). Common birth defects include small or absent ears, visual and hearing problems, microencephaly, cleft palate, thymus gland defects, and heart problems (Adams & Lammer, 1991; 1993; Lammer et al, 1987). Further, many children exposed to accutane prenatally will be moderately to severely mentally retarded (Adams, 1996; Rosa, 1983).

While there are no studies indicating the presence of isotretinoin in breast-milk, and if so, the consequences for breast-feeding babies, similar medications are known to be passed on in breast milk. Thus, Accutane use should be avoided until breast-feeding ends.

Anticonvulsants: Anticonvulsant drugs are used to treat the seizures common in epilepsy, but are also utilized in the treatment of bipolar disorder and schizophrenia. There are several classes of drugs under the anticonvulsant category, including phenytoin (brand name Dilantin), phenobarbital, carbamazepine (brand name Tegretol), and valproic acid (brand names Depakote & Depakene). Because the liver breaks down these drugs, individual differences in metabolism differ from person to person. Thus, women should stop taking these drugs at least several weeks prior to becoming pregnant (Tegretol & Pregnancy, 2003).

These drugs do cross the placental barrier and are associated in some studies with birth defects, including neural tube defects such as spina bifida (Kallen, 1994; Rosa, 1991), microencephaly (Holmes et al, 2001), heart defects, and cleft lip (Canger et al, 1999; Gladstone et al, 1992; Jones et al, 1994; Nulman et al, 1996; Samren et al, 1994; Scolnik et al, 1994; Wide et al, 2000). While these drugs are excreted into breast milk, the amount is low and at this point is not associated with any increased risk to the baby (Nau et al, 1982).

Antidepressants: The antidepressant medications can be organized into several types, the most popularly prescribed being the SSRI (selective serotonin reuptake inhibitors) medications paroxetine (brand name Paxil), sertraline (brand name Zoloft) and fluoxetine (brand name Prozac). Other types of medications include the tricylclics (brand name Elavil). These medications are used to treat not only depression but anxiety, obsessive-compulsive, post-traumatic stress, panic, and eating disorders.

A large study found that 2% of all pregnant women took some type of antidepressant in the first trimester and this number decreased to 1.8% during the second and third trimesters. Almost 60% of women taking antidepressants prior to pregnancy stopped taking them once pregnancy began (Ververs et al, 2006). While the teratogenic risk of these medications is generally considered low (Addis & Koren, 2000; Casper et al, 2003; Goldstein, Corbin, & Sundell, 1997; Kulin et al, 1998; Nulman et al, 1997), several studies have found potential problems, including evidence of withdrawal symptoms for newborns whose mother's were taking antidepressants, particularly in high dosages, during the third trimester (Costei et al, 2002; Hendrick et al. 2001; Levinson-Castiel et al, 2006; Sanz et al, 2005). Small increased risks for heart defects and pulmonary hypertension have also been found (Chambers et al, 2006), as have greater risks for miscarriage and premature delivery (Pastuszak et al, 1993).

Several studies have shown that for both Paxil and Zoloft, one to two percent of the amount of medication that the mother that the mother takes passes into breast milk (Begg et al, 1999). Given the minimal level, there appeared to be no short-term harmful effects in breastfed infants in several studies (Misri et al, 2000; Ohman et al, 1999; Stowe et al, 2000).

But for Prozac, ten to twenty percent of the amount of the drug in the mother's blood seems to be passed on to infants in breast milk. (Burch & Wells, 1992; Isenberg, 1990). While some studies have found no problems in these babies (Taddio, Ito, & Koren, 1996; Yoshida et al, 1998), other studies have shown increased irritability, vomiting, diarrhea, and/or decreased sleep in breastfed newborns (Kristensen et al, 1999; Lester et al, 1993) as well as decreased weight gain (Chambers et al, 1999).

Benzodiazepines: Benzodiazepines are a group of medicines used to treat a variety of conditions, including anxiety, sleeplessness, and seizures. Among the more commonly prescribed are diazepam (brand name Valium), alprazolam (brand name Xanax), clonazepam (brand name Klonopin) and lorazepam (brand name Ativan).

Data on the teratogenic effects of these drugs is mixed, with some studies indicating small increased risks of cleft palate and cleft lip (Laegrid, 1990; Shino & Mills, 1984), but most studies have not found serous increases of adverse risk (Czeizel, 1988; Dolovich Eros et al. 2002; Ornoy A, et al.1998). In cases where pregnant mothers used these drugs throughout the entire pregnancy, some children did have minor withdrawal symptoms (Perault et al, 2000) and studies have shown an interaction effect between temazepam and the allergy medication diphenhydramine (Brand name Benadryl) that may cause an increase risk for stillbirths (Kargas et al, 1985). Since the benzodiazepines are secreted into breast milk, their use during breastfeeding is generally discouraged (McElhatton, 1994).

Lithium: Sold under the brand names Eskalith, Lithane, Lithobid and Lithonate, Lithium is a medication primarily used to treat bipolar disorder and is completely excreted from the body within 3-4 days. The teratogenic risk of lithium has been found primarily within the first trimester when the heart is forming and is associated with a small increase in the chance for heart defects (Cohen, 1990; Shepherd et al, 2002). In addition, lithium use in the second and third trimester is associated with a small increase in the development of both maternal and fetal goiters (Lithium & Pregnancy, 2004).

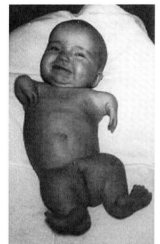

Because lithium readily passes through to break milk (Morrell et al, 1983; Schou, 1990), the American Academy of Pediatrics does not recommend the use of lithium to breastfeeding mothers (Lithium & Pregnancy, 2004).

Thalidomide: Thalidomide was one of the first drugs definitively associated with birth defects when used by pregnant women. Discovered in Germany in 1955, and sold widely around the world as a sedative (but not in the United States), severe birth defects began to be connected with its use in the early 1960s in Germany (Lenz, 1961) and Australia (McBride, 1962). Not sold in the United State until 1998, it has been identified as a treatment for leprosy (Sheskin, 1966) and tumors (D'Amato et al, 1994) and more recently as a promising medication for the treatment of auto-immune disorders and cancer (Stephens & Brynner, 2001).

However, it remains very teratogenic when used in pregnancy (Castilla et al, 1996), especially the first trimester and is associated with a 20% or higher risk for serious birth defects (Smithells & Newman, 1992). Depending on when thalidomide is used during pregnancy, birth defects include missing ears and deafness, missing eyes and blindness, missing or very short arms and legs, heart and kidney abnormalities, mental retardation and a fetal death rate as high as 40% (Silverman, 2002; Thalidomide & Pregnancy, 2003).

Substance Abuse Drugs

Many of the substance abuse drugs are legal and have a number have legitimate uses in treating various conditions. Some, such as alcohol, are widely used recreationally. Others are illegally produced and used. These distinctions are meaningless, however, when considering their potentially negative effects on babies in utero. Because many of these drugs have addictive qualities, their use by potentially pregnant and pregnant women can be difficult to curb and often results in unhealthy choices even when women become aware of their pregnancies. Further, use of these drugs by sexually active women may cause birth defects in their babies even before they know they are pregnant, since the embryo and fetus are most vulnerable to teratogens in the first trimester when organs are developing. Below are the most common of these potentially harmful substances.

Alcohol: Alcohol is arguably the most common preventable known cause of post-birth problems in children, and the third leading cause of mental retardation (Streissguth, 1997) in the United States. The problem is compounded because the most profoundly negative effects of alcohol on babies often occur in the first few weeks of pregnancy, when many women are not yet aware that they are pregnant (Naimi et al, 2003). Even among women who are aware of their pregnancies, 1 out of 30 continues risk drinking (more than 7 drinks per week and/or 5 or more drinks in any one occasion) (Craig & Dunn, 2007) and upwards of 30% continued to drink some alcohol during pregnancy (Goransson et al, 2003).

The teratogenic effects of alcohol have been divided into fetal alcohol effect (FAE) for mild to moderate exposure, and fetal alcohol syndrome (FAS), for moderate to severe exposure. Although the consequences of alcohol consumption during pregnancy are manifested along a continuum of effect and are somewhat dependant on mitigating factors (May et al, 2004), particularly stress (Schneider, Roughton & Lubach, 1997), generally FAE does not have the distinct facial features clearly seen with FAS.

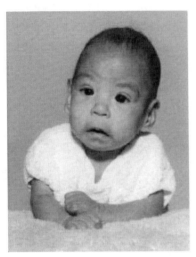

Although some studies have shown otherwise (O'Callaghan et al, 2003), most research studies have shown that even small amounts of alcohol exposure are associated with increased risk of miscarriage (Abel, 1997) and other structural and behavioral effects (Astley et al, 1992; Nugent, Green & Mazor, 1990). Studies have generally found, however, that the more alcohol a woman consumes during pregnancy, the more profound the adverse effects. But binge drinking is particularly harmful on long-term cognitive and psychological prognosis, even if the overall average consumption is not severe (Bailey et al, 2004; Barr et al, 2006: Maier & West, 2001).

Occurring in as many as 2 out of 1000 births (May & Gossage, 2001), babies with fetal alcohol syndrome have distinct facial feature, including a thin upper lip, a smooth filtrum (space between the lip and the nose), flat cheekbones, a small and upturned nose, a wide space between the margins of the eyelids, and microencephaly (a small head). Babies are often born small and remain that way for the duration of their lives. FAS babies are more likely to have respiratory and heart defects (Streissguth, 1997). Significant deficits in cognitive comprehension and functioning (Goldschmidt, Richardson & Cornelius, 2004), attentiveness, and increases in hyperactivity (Mattson & Riley, 1998), learning disabilities (Newman & Buka, 1991), speech difficulties, behavioral problems, and sensory abnormalities are all characteristic of children with FAS. Further, these problems do not go away but continue into childhood, adolescence and adulthood (Steinhausen & Spohr, 1998; Streissguth et al, 1999). These children also have social attachment deficits and other social problems that extend into adulthood (Kelly, Day & Streissguth, 2000).

Alcohol consumption by mothers does appear in human milk and appears to cause sleep disturbances in breastfeeding newborn (Mennella & Garcia-Gomez, 2001) and disruptions in early gross motor development (Mennella, 2001). Further, drinking also reduces a mother's ability to produce adequate amounts of milk (de Araujo Burgos, Bion & Campos, 2004).

Amphetamines: Dextroamphetamine is a legally prescribed stimulant medication used to treat ADHD and as an appetite suppressant. A chemically similar drug, methamphetamine, is illegal and can be snorted, swallowed or smoked. Both drugs are very addictive.

The most common adverse result of amphetamine use in pregnancy is prematurity and/or low birth weight (Naeye, 1983; Smith et al, 2003). Depending on how early and how small these babies are at birth (Felix et al, 2000), they are at risk for long-term breathing, visual, auditory and learning problems, as well as increased risk for neonatal death (Stewart & Meeker, 1997).

Further, there are studies that have connected prenatal methamphetamine exposure and increased risk for sudden infant death syndrome (SIDS) (Stewart & Meeker, 1997).The research data on birth defects and amphetamine use are mixed (Chang et al, 2004), as are studies linking amphetamine use and long-term school and behavioral problems (Cernerud et al, 1996).

Infants born to mother's using amphetamines can be born addicted and may have to suffer through withdrawal symptoms, including neurological, sleep, feeding, and muscular abnormalities (Sherman & Wheeler-Sherman, 2000). Withdrawal is usually complete within a few weeks, but tremors and other neurological symptoms may remain for several months, and may be severe and persistent enough to require infant stimulation therapy or physical therapy. Breast milk does contain measureable levels of the drug in using mothers and therefore the American Academy of Pediatrics recommends that amphetamines not be used while breastfeeding (Methamphetamines & Pregnancy, 2005).

Caffeine: Caffeine is a mild stimulant found naturally in over 60 different plants and in numerous beverages and foods, as well as some medications (Caffeine and Pregnancy, 2006). Most commonly associated with coffee, but present in soda, tea, and chocolate, caffeine does cross the placental barrier and has a stimulating effect on the fetus.

Low to moderate caffeine consumption (below 300 mg./day; approximately 3 cups of coffee) is considered safe during pregnancy (Christian & Brent, 2001; Larroque et al, 1993; Mills et al, 1993). But higher amounts (over 800 mg./day) may be associated with an increased risk of miscarriage (Cnattingius et al, 2000; Klebanoff et al, 1999; Signorello et al, 2001) and low birth weight (Matijasevich, Santos, & Barros, 2005; Parazzini et al, 2005; Santos et al, 1998), although not all studies have shown this association (Shu et al, 1995). The difficulty in regulating intake of caffeine is partially due to its presence in so many foods and beverages. In addition, caffeine functions as a diuretic, eliminating fluid and calcium from the body, both of which are important for good fetal growth and placental functioning. Caffeine is excreted in breast milk and may cause irritability and sleeplessness in babies, so consumption should also be limited during the breastfeeding period (Caffeine and Pregnancy, 2006).

Cocaine: Cocaine is a central nervous system stimulant that is inhaled in a powder form (see photo at right) or smoked in a crystal form as "crack" (see photo below). It remains in the adult body for up to 4 days after being used. Cocaine does cross the placental barrier and can be found in the blood, urine and hair follicles of babies exposed to its use in utero. Because the fetus is smaller and her excretion system is less efficient than her mother's, cocaine stays in the baby's body longer than in the mother's. Cocaine and crack use, especially heavy use, are associated with increased rates of microencephaly, prematurity, miscarriage and birth defects of the brain (Doering et al. 1989), eyes, heart, skull, face, limbs (Behnke et al, 2001), intestines, genitals, and urinary tract (Chavez, Mulinare, & Cordero, 1989). Since cocaine reduces the supply of oxygen and nutrients to the fetus (Hoyme et al, 1990), babies are often born with lower birth weights (Little et al, 1989; Neerhof et al, 1989) and thus have all the risks attendant with being born small, including increased risk of breathing difficulties, stroke, and neonatal death (Chasnoff et al, 1987).

Babies born to addicted mothers are also addicted and go through withdrawal. They tend to have sleep-pattern abnormalities, irritability, hyperactivity, tremulousness, muscular rigidity (Napiorkowski et al, 1996), and often evidence poor sucking ability that hampers feeding. The symptoms often begin 1 day or so after being born and become most severe by days 2 and 3. They may have sensory complications for as long as 10 weeks after birth. Long-term effects of cocaine-exposed children include developmental cognitive delays, learning disabilities (Singer et al 2004), language problems (Singer et al 2001) and visual and hearing problems (Arendt et al, 1998; 2004; Chasnoff et al, 1998; Lewis et al, 2004; Minnes et al, 2005; Noland et al, 2002; Singer et al, 2002). Cocaine is also found in the breast milk of mothers who are users (Briggs, Freeman & Yaffe, 1998) and so cocaine use after pregnancy can also have a deleterious effect of neonates.

Marijuana: Recent studies have shown rates of 7% (Brazil; Mitsuhiro et al, 2006) to 13% (Scotland; Williamson et al, 2006) of pregnant women use marijuana and or its derivatives at some point during pregnancy. The active ingredient in marijuana, and the one which causes the sensation of being "high", is tetrahydrocannabinol (THC), which crosses the placental barrier and is measurable in fetal tissues, urine and mecomium.

While the teratogenicity of marijuana has been debated and some have minimized its negative effects, particularly in comparison to heroin and cocaine, some recent studies have raised serious concerns about prenatal exposure of infants. For instance, studies have found that exposure during pregnancy tends to slow down fetal development and restrict weight gain (Davitian et al, 2006) and length (Hurd et al, 2005), negatively alters the neurobehavioral performance of newborns (Bada, Ryenolds & Hansen, 2006; de Moraes Barros et al, 2006) and is correlated with increases in birth defects (Forrester & Merz, 2007), a type of tumor called a neuroblastoma (Bluhm et al, 2006). Exposure is associated with attention deficit problems (Huizink & Mulder, 2006), memory difficulties (Noland et al, 2005) and impaired decision-making ability in children aged 3-12 (Karila et al 2006). Even after 20 years, prenatal marijuana exposure is associated with alteration in the neural functioning of the working memory of young adults (Smith et al, 2006). Interestingly, prenatal exposure to marijuana is a predictor of depression at 10 years of age (Gray et al, 2005) and marijuana use at 14 years of age, indicating some predisposing mechanism (Day, Goldschmidt & Thomas, 2006).

Narcotics: The various narcotics, some legally prescribed and others illegally procured, tend to depress fetal respiration, slow down growth (Rommelspacher, 1991) and often result in babies born less responsive and small in birth weight (Hulse et al, 1997; Little et al 2003). Babies also have greater risks for neonatal mortality (Hulse et al, 1998). Narcotics-using mothers are at greater risk for preeclampsia, anemia and placenta problems (Thangappah, 2000).

Codeine, morphine, dilaudid, heroin (Kandall et al, 1976), and methadone (Hulse & O'Neill, 2001) are all addictive (Volpe et al, 1983) and will result in babies having to go through withdrawal (Berghella et al, 2004; Kempley, 1995; Rahbar, 1975; Rao & Desai, 2002). These withdrawal symptoms included shaking, vomiting, irritability, difficulty in feeding and sleeping (Hulse et al, 2001; O'Brien & Jeffrey, 2002). These drugs also pass through to human milk and are thus potentially problematic for infants (Bar-Oz et al, 2003). Long-term effects have been seen at 4 months and 12 months and longer-term deficits in language and attention persist well into childhood (Craig & Dunn, 2007).

Tobacco: Among the most studied teratogens is smoking. The active ingredient in tobacco is nicotine, but tobacco smoke also contains numerous other substances, including various carcinogens, carbon monoxide, hydrogen cyanide, tars, and resins. These may be more harmful than nicotine itself (Bainbridge & Smith, 2006). Clearly, smoking in pregnancy is teratogenic (Dempsey & Stewart, 2006) and is associated with greater rates of miscarriage (George et al, 2006), stillbirths and prematurity (Mill, 1999; Ness et al, 1999), as well as low birth weight (on average about 7 ounces less) and retarded growth (Streissguth et al, 1989). Long-term effects have been noted on children exposed prenatally and include both cognitive and behavioral deficits (Fried, Watkinson & Gray, 1998; Olds, 1997; Sexton, Fox, & Heber, 1986), including recent evidence pointing to a correlation between smoking and ADHD (Schmitz et al, 2006). The strong connection between prenatal exposure to smoking and sudden infant death syndrome (SIDS) has also been noted in several studies (Adgent, 2006; Shah, Sullivan & Carter, 2006).

Smoking causes problems in various ways, including the constriction of blood vessels in the placenta. This in turn restricts the amount of oxygen and nutrient availability (particularly vitamins B, C and folic acid) to the fetus (Naeye, 1981), particularly as a function of the effect of carbon monoxide (Ernst & Zibrack, 1998: Longo, 1977; Salam et al, 2005). Withdrawal symptoms, including sleeplessness, irritability and tremors have been observed in the infants of heavy smoking mothers (Pichini & Garcia-Algar, 2006).

Ongoing debate about the negative effects of nicotine replacement therapies (gum, patches) continues, but it generally not recommended. However, experts have noted that such inventions, although less than ideal, have significantly less risk than smoking (Jimenez Ruiz, 2006; Price, Jordan & Dake, 2006).

Infections

Various disease infections in a mother are known to cause birth defects or are associated with prematurity, miscarriage and long-term cognitive, sensory, neurological and behavioral problems. Some can be passed on to the child and this can occur in variety of ways. For instance, HIV and rubella can be passed through the placenta, gonorrhea and syphilis can be passed on through the amniotic fluid, herpes can be acquired by the baby through exposure in the birthing process and HIV can be acquired through contact with blood and by breastfeeding.

Not all diseases are teratogenic. The placental barrier blocks many, particularly bacterial infections. Viruses such as rubella, HIV, herpes, and many colds and flus are structurally smaller organisms, and therefore the placenta is much less effective in protecting the baby. The consequences for the fetus often depend on the timing of the infection, with first trimester exposure usually producing the most profound consequences. Below are some of the more common and potentially harmful infections, but the list is by no means exhaustive. Some diseases that may be potentially harmful (i.e. malaria and West Nile virus), have been effectively controlled in developed countries, and so are a minimal risk to women in these countries. This is not true for many pregnant women in less developed areas of the world.

Cytomegaloviris (CMV): Cytomegalovirus is a virus similar to herpes and is most often contracted through sexual contact. Since it is present in blood, breast milk, and vaginal secretions (in addition to semen, tears and saliva), it can also be transmitted congenitally from a mother to her child. Two types of CMV infections exist, primary and recurring (Cytomegalovirus & Pregnancy, 2001).

A simple initial blood test can determine whether a woman has a CMV infection, with more complex follow-up tests given to determine if it is the primary or recurrent type. While the recurrent type appears to be less of a problem (Boppana et al, 1999), long-term effects did occur (Ahlfors et al, 1981; Ahlfors, Ivarsson & Harris, 1984; 1999; Casteels et al, 1999; Peckham et al, 1983). The primary type is more problematic and occurs in 0.7 to 4.0% (Gaytant et al, 2003) of pregnancies, with transmission rates to the fetus between 23 (Azam et al 2001) and 75%, averaging about 40% (Cytomegalovirus & Pregnancy, 2001). Of these, approximately 10% will evidence symptoms at birth, with blood, spleen, liver, brain ,and eyes at risk (Ramsey, Miller & Peckham, 1991). Long-term effects may include visual and hearing impairment, mental retardation and developmental delay (Nelson & Demmler, 1997). Of the remaining 90%, no symptoms will be evident at birth, but 5-15% may be at risk for long-term effects (Ivarsson, Lernmark & Svanberg, 1996).

While the gestational age of the fetus has no influence on the risk of transmission, symptoms tend to be worse for first trimester vs. later exposure, particularly for primary CMV. Amniocentesis is initially used to determine fetal infection, with an ultrasound follow-up to determine visible symptoms such as growth retardation and a decreased amount of amniotic fluid. While there are drugs (forscarnet and ganciclovir) to treat maternal CMV, there are at present no interventions for fetal CMV (Piper & Wen, 1999).

Fifth Disease: Parvovirus, also called Fifth disease, because it was the fifth disease to be described with a certain kind of rash, is a viral illness most commonly found in school-age children because the classroom setting is particularly amenable to its airborne means of infection (Fifth Disease & Pregnancy, 2005). It sometimes produces a mild fever, sore throat, and flu-like symptoms and a rash of reddened skin that fades and recurs and lasts up to a month, but some individuals are asymptomatic. About 50% of adults have had the infection and have antibodies which make them immune to a second infection (Fifth Disease & Pregnancy, 2005).

For the majority of pregnant women who contract fifth disease, there is no negative impact on their baby (Ergaz & Ornoy, 2006). But a first-trimester exposure has a risk of approximately 10% for problems (Miller et al, 1998), including miscarriage (Candotti et al, 2006). But even third trimester infections increase risk, including fetal death (Leung, 2000; Skjöldebrand-Sparre et al, 2000).

The virus can be problematic because it can damages the bone marrow, thereby interfering with the production of red blood cells. This in turn can causes anemia and inflammation of the heart (myocarditis) (Soulie, 1995; von Kaisenberg et al, 2001). If this is severe, the result is excessive fluid in the fetal tissues (called hydrops) (Anderson et al, 1988; Cameron, Swain & Patrick, 1997), potentially resulting in miscarriage (Anderson, 1990; Anderson & Hurwitz, 1988). No treatment is available at the present, with the exception of a fetal transfusion (Fairley et al, 1995) and an induced premature delivery (de Jong et al, 2006; Koga, 2001) in very serious cases.

Rubella: First described in 1941, rubella is also known as German measles and is indeed a mild form of the measles virus (Cooper, 1985). Spread by contact with the airborne virus (coughing or sneezing) or physical contact with an infected person or their contaminated items, rubella incubates for between 2 to 3 weeks before symptoms appear. These symptoms may include headache, sore throat, fever, temperature, swollen lymph glands, and a mild rash that disappears after a few days. In some people the symptoms may be very mild, to the point that a person may not know they have experienced a rubella infection.

Immunity from a vaccination lasts for up to 16 years while immunity from having a rubella infection lasts longer, but is not necessarily life-long (Robinson et al, 2006). For the 11 % of women of childbearing age (Eisele, 1993) who have never been vaccinated or had a rubella infection, the risk is most critical in the first trimester of pregnancy. Babies born to women infected in the first 8-10 weeks of pregnancy have a 90 percent chance of developing abnormalities (Miller, Cradock-Watson, & Pollock, 1983), while the risk rate decreases to 10-20 percent between weeks 10 and 16. Problems in the 16 to 20 week gestational age range are rare (Grillner et al, 1983), and the baby is at no risk in the second half of the pregnancy (Robinson et al, 2006)..

The effect of a rubella infection is very much a function of when in pregnancy the infection occurs. The most profound consequences occur when infection is prior to 8 weeks, with a subsequent reduction in the severity of the symptoms. Potential result may include mental retardation, deafness, blindness, heart defects, inflammation of the brain, liver, lungs and bone marrow.

Sexually Transmitted Infections (STI): Over 15 million individuals in the United States contract a sexually transmitted infection (STI) each year and many of these are pregnant women. The CDC estimates that each year there are 200,000 chlamydia, 40,000 gonorrhea, and 8,000 syphilis infections among pregnant women (CDC, 2004). While we have previously discussed how some of these infections are associated with pelvic inflammatory disease and ectopic pregnancy, these infection are also associated with increased rates of miscarriage, prematurity, birth defects and neonatal death (Goldenberg et al, 1997). The largest risk to babies, however, is an infection during the birthing process. These infections may be caused by bacteria, parasites, or viruses.

Bacterial Infections

Chlamydia: One of the most common STIs is a bacterial infection called Chlamydia, affecting approximately 10% of pregnant women. Left untreated, Chlamydia is associated with increased risk of miscarriage and premature rupture of the amniotic sac (Andrews et al, 2000), as well as the risk of infection to the baby during delivery. The result could be an eye infection or pneumonia (Pokrzywnicka, Krajewski, & Kwiatkowska, 2005) that must be treated with antibiotics.

Gonorrhea: Gonorrhea is another bacterial infection similar in its consequences to Chlamydia. Risks likewise include increased rates of miscarriage, premature delivery, low birth weight (Elliot et al, 1990) and premature rupture of the membranes (Alger et al, 1988; Donders et al, 1993). As with Chlamydia, infection of the baby in the birth process can result in an eye infection called gonorrheal ophthalmia, as well as joint and blood infections, necessitating treatment with antibiotics.

Syphilis: Syphilis is a much less common bacterial infection than Chlamydia or Gonorrhea but is potentially much more dangerous because it can cross the placental barrier in the second half of pregnancy and directly infect the fetus. Left untreated, syphilis is associated with prematurity (Tridapalli et al, 2006), miscarriage and infant death in up to 40 percent of cases (Woods, 2005). In some cases, infected infants may show no symptoms at birth and if untreated with antibiotics, can develop brain damage, deafness, blindness (Sangtawesin et al, 2005), bone and tooth abnormalities and other problems. In addition, syphilis tends to increase the chances of a woman passing on HIV to her child (Mwapasa et al, 2006).

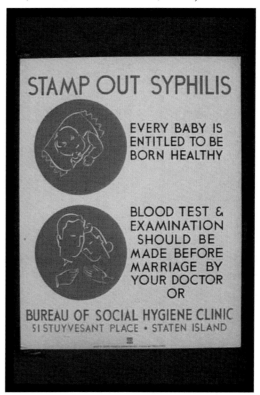

Bacterial Vaginosis (BV): Bacterial vaginosis (BV), is among the most common STIs, affecting approximately 16 percent of pregnant women. It is caused by an overgrowth of normally occurring bacteria in the vagina. Because it is often symptomless, it is frequently undetected and left untreated (Goldenberg, Culhane & Johnson, 2005). It is associated with increased risk of prematurity and low birthweight (Svare et al, 2006) and treatment with antibiotics seems not to reduce risk (Klebanoff et al, 2001).

Parasitic Infections

Trichomoniasis: Trichomoniasis affects approximately 80,000 pregnant women each year, and is caused by a parasite. It is associated with increased risks for prematurity and premature rupture of the amniotic sac (Azargoon & Darvishzadeh, 2006). Very rarely, it can be contracted during delivery and if so, the baby develops a fever. It can be treated with a drug called metronidazole (Nanda et al, 2006).

Viral Infections

Herpes: A common STI, there are several types of herpes which cause periodic outbreaks resulting in blisters, and occasionally a fever, fatigue, body aches and swollen glands. The virus remains permanently in the body. If the infection is in the vaginal area, the major risk is to pass on the infection to the baby in the birthing process, particularly if a pregnant women has an outbreak immediately prior to labor and delivery (Khandelwal, 2006). The risk seems to be highest for women who contract herpes for the first time during the third trimester. An infected infant can develop the herpes sores on the skin (Diguet et al, 2006). Anti-viral drugs are usually successful in treating the virus, but it can sometimes spreads to the brain (Duin et al, 2007) and internal organs (Verma et al, 2006), causing serious damage, including blindness, brain damage, mental retardation and even death (Chen et al, 2005; Kimberlin, 2005). In cases where a woman has a herpes outbreak near delivery, a cesarean delivery is often done to protect her baby (Meylan, 2005).

Human Immunodeficiency Virus (HIV): Human immunodeficiency virus (HIV) is a virus which can be acquired by means of sexual intercourse or exposure to bodily fluids of an infected individual (including breast milk). Women make up one of the fastest growing groups infected with the human immunodeficiency virus (HIV) and since most affected women are of childbearing age, the result is approximately 8,000 pregnant women per year in the United States who are HIV positive (CDC, 2004). While these numbers are troubling, they pale in comparison to HIV rates among pregnant women in areas of sub-Saharan Africa, particularly southern Africa, where up to 43% of pregnant women test positive for HIV (WHO, 2005). Every day 1700 HIV-positive babies are born in Africa. Of the approximately 2.3 million children with pediatric AIDS, 2 million are in Africa (WHO, 2006), most of whom have no access to medications to treat the virus.

HIV can spread from a mother to her child by crossing the placental barrier, through exposure to maternal bodily fluids at birth, and through breastfeeding (Nduati et al, 2000). Left untreated, approximately 25% of babies will get HIV from their HIV-positive mothers (Keenan-Lindsay & Yudin, 2006). This rate of transmission increases in mothers with syphilis (Mwapasa et al, 2006) and with poor nutrition (Dreyful & Fazwi, 2002). But when treated with antiretroviral drugs, this transmission rate has been cut to less than 2% (Giaguinto, Rampon & De Rossi, 2006). In some cases, a caesarian section is recommended to further reduce the likelihood of transmission, as well as the utilization of infant formula as an alternative to breast milk (Petropoulou, Stratigos, & Katsambas, 2006).

HIV-positive mothers, even when they don't pass on the virus to their babies, are more likely to have babies with intrauterine growth retardation, premature delivery, and be of low birth weight (Brocklehurst & French, 1998; Coley et al, 2001). When HIV is passed on from mothers to their babies, the eventual result may be acquired immune deficiency syndrome (AIDS), a disease which leads to a progressive debilitation of the immune system, greatly increasing vulnerability to numerous infections and other negative outcomes (Lee et al , 2006), including cognitive deficits (Willen, 2006). But treatment of infants with antiretroviral drugs has greatly reduced the negative outcomes associated with being HIV-positive (Gona et al 2006; Resino et al, 2006).

Toxoplasmosis: Toxoplasmosis, an infection caused by a parasite (*Toxoplasma gondii*), can be contracted through handling dirt or cat feces containing the parasite (Kapperud et al, 1997), but especially by ingestion of infected and undercooked meat (Cook et al, 2000). It can result in a mononucleosis-type (fever, fatigue, sore throat, swollen lymph nodes), but some adults are asymptomatic. After an initial infection, adults are immune from subsequent infections. Most women have not had a toxoplasmosis exposure and thus are at risk during pregnancy, and should avoid all raw or uncooked meat and avoid exposure to cat feces (Toxoplasmosis & Pregnancy, 2002).

Congenital toxoplasmosis can only occur if a mother is infected during pregnancy, and the result is that approximately 40% of the time the baby is also infected. This parasite can cross the placental barrier, and 1 or 2 out of 1000 babies born in the United States have congenital toxoplasmosis (Toxoplasmosis & Pregnancy, 2002). This condition is associated with eye, heart, kidneys, blood, liver, spleen and brain problems, especially if exposure is between 10 and 24 weeks gestation (Koppe et al, 1986). Exposure later in pregnancy results in minimal risk for adverse consequences. Symptoms are often absent at birth, and can emerge months or years later. Thus, exposed infants are treated in infancy in an effort to reduce long-term symptoms (Christoph et al, 2004).

Amniocentesis or chorionic villi sampling (CVS) is used for initial diagnosis (Foulon et al, 1990a; 1990b), with a follow-up ultrasound to check for further birth defects (Couvreur, 1993; Daffos et al, 1988). Treatment is with antibiotics and the earlier the infection is diagnosed and treated, the greater the likelihood for preventing birth defects (Robert-Gangneux et al, 1999).

Environmental Pollutants

Numerous animal studies have found that maternal exposure to a wide variety of chemicals and pollutants can have an adverse effect on offspring. These include cadmium (Mori et al, 2006), manganese (Dorman et al, 2005), DEHP (Andrade et al, 2006), arsenic (Wang et al, 2006) and many others. Human studies have identified air pollution as a correlational factor for increased rates of prematurity and low-birth weight in babies (Hansen et al, 2006; Leem et al, 2006; Rogers & Dunlop, 2006) and exposure to various other chemical toxins have been connected to increases in childhood brain cancers (Anderson, 2006; Choi et al, 2006) and are assumed to cause other neurological problems (Hass, 2006). There are literally thousands of chemicals which may affect humans (Tuomisto, 2006), and the potentially teratogenic effects for many remain unknown. Potential but still unknown dangers include pesticides (Eskenazi et al, 2004; Ma et al, 2002), and hair dye and straightening treatments (Blackmore-Prince et al, 1999; John, Savitz & Shy, 1994; Rylander et al, 2002). Because exposure may be airborne or the result of diet, and because the effects of many chemicals may be multi-generational due to genetic damage (Cherry et al, 2002), determining the exact risks for many pollutants is extremely complicated. The risks for lead and mercury exposure, however, are clearly evident.

Lead: Previously used in paint and gasoline, lead is a heavy metal still used industrially in the production of many products), including batteries, construction materials, dyes and wood preservatives. Since it is present in polluted air, soil and water, most adults have some level of lead in their systems. Further, a diet poor in calcium, iron and zinc has been associated with increased levels of lead absorption (Lead & Pregnancy, 2005), increasing the prophylactic necessity of prenatal vitamins.

Lead does cross the placental barrier after 12 weeks gestational age and like many other pollutants, is primarily associated with increased rates of miscarriage, prematurity and low birthweight (Bellinger, 2005; Ernhart, 1992). While not associated with birth defects, increased lead levels in children are correlated with cognitive and learning problems, including reduced IQ levels (Dietrich et al, 1993; Tong et al, 1996). Maternal lead levels are also reflected in lead levels in human milk (Rothenberg et al, 2000).

Mercury: Mercury comes from a variety of natural sources. The toxic form is known as methylmercury and can be found in the air, soil and water. The primary danger of mercury poisoning comes from industrial pollution released into the water and subsequently found in fish. Almost all fish have small amounts of methylmercury and when eaten in limited quantities is not toxic to humans and is not teratogenic. But larger amounts are toxic. Fish that are long-lived (i.e. shark, swordfish, and mackerel) and have thus had longer exposure to methylmercury are most problematic. According to the Food and Drug Administration (FDA), pregnant women and even women who are planning to become pregnant should thus avoid eating these types of fish (FDA, 2002). Small amounts (limited to 2 or less servings per week) of other types of fish (salmon, pollock, catfish & tuna) and shellfish (crab & shrimp) are considered safe (Koos & Longo, 1976). These same guidelines should be followed during breastfeeding as mercury does appear in breast milk (Hale, 2002).

Higher levels of methylmercury cross the placental barrier, and are particularly harmful to the developing brain. Problems include mental retardation, microencephaly, cerebral palsy and seizures (Marques et al, 2006; Rodier, Aschner & Sager, 1984). These problems are often long-term (Debes et al, 2006; van Wijngaarden et al, 2006).

Hyperthermia

Normal body temperature fluctuates somewhat, but always near 98.6 degrees Fahrenheit or 37 degrees Celsius. Hyperthermia is thus an abnormal elevation of body temperature. Small increases are not usually problematic, but when a pregnant women's temperature exceed 102 degrees F or 38.9 C, especially for an extended period of time, there is an increased risk to her baby of potential damage (Edwards et al, 1995; Morishima et al, 1975). The potential causes of hyperthermia are variable and include fevers from infections (Spragget & Fraser, 1982a), exercise (Lomax, 1987; Morris & Johnson, 2005), prolonged hot baths (Ridge & Budd, 1990), the use of hot tubs (Chambers, 2006; Harvey, McRorie, & Smith, 1981) or saunas (Lipson, Webster & Edwards, 1985; Saxen et al, 1982; Spragget & Fraser, 1982b). As with most other teratogens, all hyperthermia is not equally risky; rather, the timing during pregnancy (Lecyk, 1966) and the duration (Germaine et al., 1985) and intensity (Harvey et al., 1981) of the heat are variable factors that influence the severity of potential negative outcomes.

As with other teratogens, various animal models have clearly indicated that the central nervous system is at risk from hyperthermia during early pregnancy (Pergament, Schechtman, & Rochanayon, 1997). Other abnormalities include eye, limb (Edwards, 1968; Skreb & Frank, 1963), kidney and palate abnormalities, microencephaly (Harding & Edwards, 1993; Hartley, Alexander, & Edwards, 1974) and learning impairment (Angles et al, 1990; Kimmel et al, 1993).

Exposure to severe temperatures early on in pregnancy (Shiota, 1982) is clearly associated with increased risk of neural tube defects (Christo et al, 1987; Hunter, 1984; Layde, Edmonds, & Erickson, 1980). In a very large study of over 23,000 women, Milunsky and his colleagues (1992) found very strong evidence for first-trimester hyperthermia and neural tube defects, even after controlling for other potential causes of neural tube defects such as maternal age, folic acid supplements, and family history of neural tube defects.

A second potentially negative outcome of hyperthermia during pregnancy is miscarriage. Studies have found clear correlations (McDonald 1958; 1961). Kline and his colleagues (1985) found that the risk of miscarriage during pregnancy decreases over time from any particular incident of hyperthermia. The odds ratio of miscarriage happening in the month following a high fever was 6.04. The ratio was 3.28 for between 1 month and 2 months, and 1.41 after 2 months.

As with the animal studies noted above, numerous studies have also connected hyperthermia with abnormalities in addition to neural tube defects and miscarriage. These include cardiovascular defects (Tikkanen & Heinonen, 1991), congenital heart disorders (Fraser & Skelton, 1978), seizures, spinal cord defects (Chance & Smith, 1978), facial malformations (Pleet, Graham & Smith, 1981), abdominal wall defects (Little et al, 1991), occipital lobe brain damage (Fisher & Smith, 1981), limb defects (Firth et al, 1994; Webster, Lipson & Brown-Woodman, 1987), and microencephaly (Hartley, Alexander & Edwards, 1974).

While the evidence generally points to hyperthermia as a potential serious teratogenic cause, several large studies have found countervailing evidence (Kleinebrecht et al, 1979; Smith, Claren & Harvey, 1978) Studying over 55,000 pregnancies, the Collaborative Perinatal Project did not find any statistically significant increase in negative outcomes from fever-induced hyperthermia during pregnancy during the first trimester (Claren et al., 1979).

Pregnant women should not be concerned about short-term baths and showers or the use of electric blankets and heated waterbeds. There is no evidence that there is any potential harm from theses sources as they do not significantly raise maternal body temperature (Wertheimer & Leeper, 1986).

CONCLUSION

While the numerous possible risks of pregnancy are disconcerting to anyone contemplating pregnancy, that is just one small part of the larger picture. What is truly amazing and quite surprising is sophisticated the preborn baby is psychologically. Our next and final chapter takes up this question of the cognitive, emotional and psychological skills of a fetus.

10

FETAL PSYCHOLOGICAL DEVELOPMENT

When Elizabeth heard Mary's greeting, the baby leaped in her womb, and Elizabeth was filled with the Holy Spirit. In a loud voice she exclaimed: "Blessed are you among women, and blessed is the child you will bear! . . . As soon as the sound of your greeting reached my ears, the baby in my womb leaped for joy."

Luke 1: 41-42; 44
NIV Bible

INTRODUCTION

With the advance of technology, babies born as early as 28 weeks have survived outside the womb, presenting opportunities for "external" observation of the 28th through the 40th weeks of gestation. In addition, ultrasound technology now allows for the "natural" observation of babies in the womb while they are behaving. These technological advances have drastically changed our view of prenatal babies and their quite amazing physical and psychological capabilities. Studies that have examined the systematic development of fetal growth have found that there tends to be great similarity of development between babies regardless of whether they are in or outside the womb (Gesell, 1945). Further, there seems to be a regular advance in detectable development every 4 weeks in terms of "strength of responses, the degree of muscle tone and endurance, more regular waking and sleeping patterns and a more definite cry" (Chamberlain, 1983, p. 5). EEG results have confirmed this similarity. There is an ongoing pattern throughout the fetal period of increasing organization, ever-steadier activity, the development of more regular sleep-wake cycles, and greater synchrony within and between hemispheres.

MOVEMENT

One of the first indications of a functioning nervous system is the response of movement, which seems to begin at around 8 weeks (Liley, 1991). The movements of 8-20 week-old fetuses obtained by hysterectomies have been described as slow and "wormlike" (Goodlin, 1979). Tactile stimulation seems to elicit more rapid and forceful movement than occurred spontaneously. An early study by Preyer (1885) is described by Goodlin:

> In 1885, Preyer recorded movements of the extrauterine human fetuses, apparently from therapeutic abortions. He concluded that spontaneous fetal movements could occur before they are felt by the gravida, that fetal movements continued for a considerable time even when the fetus was without oxygen supply, that fetal movements were affected by temperature, that they could be elicited by stimulus (such as touching with a feather), and that these fetal movements were apparently independent of the mother's condition" (Goodlin, 1979, p. 3).

While some studies have found "rolling movements" as early as 6 weeks (Goodlin, 1979), others have found that up until the middle of the 7th week, embryos appear incapable of movement (Hooker, 1952; Humphrey, 1978). The first reflex movement, contralateral (moving away) head flexion, appears at 7.5 weeks with a second, ipsilateral (moving toward) head flexion coupled with mouth opening appearing a week later). Hooker writes that numerous studies, beginning around 1920, looking at movement in 7-8 week old embryos did find some movement among some embryos of this age but ran into several problems, among them the "progressive anoxic condition of the embryo, maternal anesthesia, and a group of physical factors" (Hooker, 1952, p. 57). He began his studies in 1932 and attempted to deal with these problems in the following manner:

This team worked with over 140 human embryos and fetuses of various ages obtained by caesarian delivery in cases where therapeutic abortion was deemed necessary by a committee of obstetricians. Within two minutes of delivery they were placed in an isotonic fluid bath at body temperature and stroked gently with a fine hair to test for reactions (Chamberlain, 1983).

While "spontaneously executed activity" (Hooker, 1952) is apparent at 8.5 weeks, others have found that by this time, not only is the fetus moving his head, trunk, and arms, but "he has already fashioned these movements into a primitive body language-- expressing his likes and dislikes with well-placed jerks and kicks" (Verny, 1981, p. 37). Using ultrasound technology, some have observed that as early as the end of the first trimester, regular exercise patterns have been observed including rolling, turning, leg kicks, flexing, and waving of arms" (Van Dongen & Goudie, 1980). Others have observed that fetal movement becomes sufficiently pronounced in the 10th or 11th week to allow for a change in the position of the fetal body (Goodlin, 1979). The fetus will changes positions constantly in reaction to the intra-uterine environment. Propelling himself by means of his arms and legs is the mechanism by which he changes "ends" in the uterus while the mechanism by which he switches "sides" in the uterus is a little more complex. According to Liley, the fetus employs a "longitudinal spiral roll [which] at the midpoint of his turn has a 180 degree twist in his spine" (Liley, 1991, p. 193). He continues by describing the method of turning:

> He [the fetus] first extends his head and rotates it, next his shoulders rotate and finally his lumbar spine and legs-- in fact, he is using his long spinal reflexes. Insofar as this is the obvious way to turn over, there would be nothing remarkable about it except that according to textbooks of neonatal and infant locomotor function the baby does not roll over using his long spinal reflexes until 14-20 weeks of extra-uterine life. However, we have unequivocal films of the fetus using this mechanism at least as early as 26 weeks gestation, and it is apparent that the reason we do not see this behavior in the neonate is not that he lacks the neural co-ordination but that a trick which is simple in a state of neutral buoyancy becomes difficult under the newfound tyranny of gravity (p.194).

By 15 weeks, 16 distinct movement patterns in pre-term infants that resemble those of post-term infants are clearly distinguishable (de Vries, Visser & Prechtl, 1982). Studies of fetuses in the third trimester show that they rarely go more than 10 minutes without some "gross motor activity including breathing spurts during REM sleep" (Roberts, Griffin, Mooney & Cooper, 1980, p. 482).

As to whether movement itself can be considered significant psychologically to the embryo or fetus, various studies have certainly shown that such movement is very psychologically important for pregnant mothers. Perceived attachment to the developing fetus is greatly enhanced following the first sign of movement (Grace, 1989; Heidrich & Cranley, 1989). Further, numerous studies (Comparetti, 1981, 1986; Comparetti & Gidoni, 1967, 1976; Ianniruberto & Tajani, 1981; Valentin & Marsal, 1986; Van Woerden, Van Geijn, Caron & Swartjes, 1989) have correlated fetal movement and lack of movement to other fetal variables. Accordingly, researchers have stated that "alternation of movement and immobility in the fetus is in itself an expression of an existing organization" (Gidoni, Casonato & Landi, 1988, p. 349). Further, movement in utero has been correlated with later neonatal behavior (Ishikawa & Minamide, 1984).

THE SENSES

The Tactile Sense

As noted above, movement is often in response to tactile stimulation, or the sense of "touch". This sense is really a combination of three different sensory capabilities; those of pressure, temperature and pain. All three develop simultaneously so that by the 32nd week, "tactile responsivity can be demonstrated for all parts of the fetal body" (Chamberlain, 1983, p. 5).

The position of the fetus in utero is often in response to the tactile environment within the womb. According to Liley, many changes in the environment provoke movement, including Braxton-Hicks contractions, maternal movements, and external palpation. The fetus will repeatedly and purposefully move to avoid a knuckle on the prominences or the "sustained pressure of a microphone or phonendoscope" (Liley, 1991, p. 194). By the second month, the embryo will kick and jerk if poked at, and by the fourth month the stroking of the eyelids will result in squinting instead of a violent jerking movement; indeed stroking the lips results in sucking behavior (Verny, 1981). Tickling the scalp of the fetus at the surgical induction of labor will result in movement. Liley (1991) writes that "stroking the palm of the prolapsed arm elicits a grasp reflex, and to plantar stimulation the footling breech obliges with an upgoing toe" (p. 195) and by the fifth or sixth month, the fetus is "as sensitive to touch as any one-year old" (p. 37).

In addition, the fetus will respond with "violent movement" to a needle puncture. Goodlin reports that during the performance of "hundred of amniocenteses" normal, healthy, near-term infants would invariably respond to "needle sticks" with movement and drastic fetal heart-rate changes. For some of these fetuses, he reported that prior to performing the amniocentesis, he recorded the fetal heart-rate up to five minutes. He writes "if we obviously stuck the fetus with the needle during the amniocentesis, we invariably found the FHR (fetal heart-rate) abruptly changed" (Goodlin, 1979, p. 193). This change was usually in the direction of acceleration, but on occasion, deceleration occurred, or as other researchers have discovered, "a sudden crash" to a silent pattern of non-movement. In one study (Neldam and Peterson, 1980), six of seven of these "silent" fetuses did not move for two minutes. Goodlin reports that during amniocenteses where there was no feel of puncture by the fetus, there was no observable change in FHR, suggesting to him that the fetal responses to the needle were those of pain.

Interestingly, many have denied the sensation of pain in the fetus based upon an incomplete understanding of the process of myelinization of the neurons in the central nervous system. DeMause (1987) has pointed out that this has occurred because of an uncritical acceptance of a faulty study by J.R. Langeworthy in 1933 titled "Development of Behavior Patterns and Myelinization of the Nervous System in the Human Fetus and Infant." This study made the assertion that "incomplete myelinization of sensory tracts" resulted in the inability of the fetus to receive neural messages from its specialized sense receptors.

As has clearly been shown in numerous subsequent studies (i.e. Anand & Hickey, 1987; 1988), this is untrue. According to Larrouche (1966), the cranial nerve roots are myelinated very early, preceded only by myelinization in the spinal cord at about the 22nd week after conception. Almost concomitant with cranial myelinization is that in the medulla and pons, followed quickly by the cerebellum and the cerebral hemispheres (Larrouche, 1962). While full myelinization, which occurs only after birth, does increase the rapidity of conduction, it is not essential for sensory functioning. Well-organized neural activity and sense receptivity, including pain, occurs long before the nerve fibers are completely myelinated (Bekoff & Fox, 1972). As Windle (1979) has written:

In a general way the functional development and acquisition of myelin by certain fiber tracts are related. Nevertheless much well-organized activity of animal fetuses is present before there is any myelin. There are no myelin sheathe on fibers of the peripheral nerves, spinal cord, or brain of cat fetuses prior to the last third of prenatal life, but many coordinated movements can be elicited reflexively before the middle of gestation (p. 71).

Using multiple fetal x-ray films, Liley described the process of birth and particularly contraction as one of "frantic" flailing fetal movement, with the arms and legs being thrown about and what appeared to be an active resistance to each contraction. He observed that this behavior is characteristic of the reaction of a post-birth human being to severe pain:

If one attempts to reproduce in the neonate by manual contraction a mere fraction of the cranial deformation that may occur in the course of a single contraction the baby protests violently. And yet, all that has been written by poets and lyricists about cries of newborn babies would suggest that newborn babies cried for fun or "joie de vivre"-- which they never do afterwards-- and in all the discussions that have ever taken place on pain relief in childbirth only maternal pain has been considered (Liley, 1991, p.196).

Further, studies have found that in the early stages of labor, healthy in utero fetuses will often respond with FHR changes or movement of some kind in response to various noises and sounds produced outside the intra-uterine environment. But as the labor continues, this reaction will cease. While some have described this as an instance of fetal habituation, others state that it is rather a response to the distraction of the overwhelming fetal pain associated with labor (Goodlin, 1979). Liley notes that the first sleep of neonates after birth is "more profound than any subsequent sleep" based on the strength of the stimuli needed to awake them, thus perhaps testifying to the ordeal that labor has indeed represented.

Normally, the fetus will not experience temperature less than his mother's because he lacks a truly "external" surface. In fact, the placenta acts as a heat exchanger which keeps the fetal temperature a constant .5 to 1.5 degrees Celsius above the mother's. Should she run a temperature, so will the fetus within her. However, experimental studies have shown that the fetus will respond to temperature changes. Goodlin reports that the fetus will respond to cold saline flushed into the amniotic space at 18-20 weeks with fetal heart rate changes and movement. He concludes that these responses reflect intact temperature receptors in the skin. The fetus does not, however, have the sensation of "wetness" due to her constant and total immersion in the amniotic fluid.

The Vestibular Sense

Of the "senses" of the body, the vestibular apparatus appears first, at around 9.5 weeks (Chamberlain, 1988a), with morphological maturity at 14 weeks (Goodlin, 1979). It is unknown how

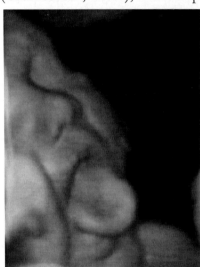

early the sense of balance is functioning, but Hooker has reported 25 weeks as the earliest "definite human vestibular response" (Hooker, 1952, p. 70). As early as 1927, Galebsky had shown that by birth the semicircular canals are functional to the extent that the neonate experiences any type of sudden movement, including rotatory, vertical and horizontal.

The Gustatory Sense

The "sense" of taste also appears quite early in the fetal period, with microscopic analysis of fetal tongues finding that taste "buds" are present at 8 weeks, morphologically mature by 12 weeks (Goodlin, 1979), with all the necessary components such as the pores and hair cells present by 14 weeks. Thus, researchers have concluded that the gustatory sense is functional by 15 weeks (Bradley & Stern, 1967). Since amniotic fluid begins entering the mouth at 9.5 weeks and the fetus begins swallowing at 12 weeks (Chamberlain, 1987b), it is likely that the fetus is tasting the glucose, fructose, citric, lactic, uric, fatty and pyruvic acids, amino-acids, phospholipids, creatinine, urea, polypeptides, proteins, salts, and other chemical agents in the amniotic fluid for up to 28 weeks prior to birth (Misretta & Bradley, 1977). Thus taste preferences at birth are related to the fetal experience with various tastes during the intra-uterine period.

The fetus drinks amniotic fluid regularly, reaching a rate of 15-40 ml per hour during the third trimester. Research modifying the taste of amniotic fluid produces dramatic results. An early study done by de Snoo in 1937, found that the injection of saccharin increased the rate of fetal swallowing in 34-38 week

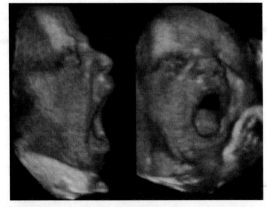

fetuses. Liley confirms this, stating that the rate usually doubled. However, some conversely drank less. An almost total cessation of fetal drinking occurs with the injection of Lipidol, a foul-tasting iodinated poppy seed oil which will also cause a newborn to grimace and cry if placed in their mouths. The fetus digests the constituent components of the amniotic fluid and this caloric intake may reach 40 calories a day (Liley, 1991).

Swallowing, tongue and lip movements all originate between the 10th and 12th weeks followed by a gag reflex apparent in the 18th week. Sucking and puckering are present in the 22nd, with the possibility of audible crying occurring between the 21st and 23rd week. Fetal hiccups occur and are fairly common. Indeed, they can be induced by "irrigating the amniotic cavity with cold solutions" (Ridgeway, 1987, p. 74).

Not only is the fetus an experienced swallower by the time birth occurs, but in many cases it also has extensive sucking experience. Obstetric sonography and radiography has produced images of thumbsucking as early as 9 weeks. The sucking of fingers and toes, which is a common occurrence in the fetal period, seems to be an early manifestation of the "rooting" reflex common among neonates (Liley, 1991).

The Olfactory Sense

While no evidence exists which allows one to conclusively state that human fetuses smell, this is not all that surprising given the absence of air within the uterus. Without the airborne particles needed to stimulate the specialized receptors within the olfactory epithelium, smell is impossible.

However, some animal studies have found evidence of olfactory function in utero (Petersen, Stewart, Greer & Shepherd, 1983) and have connected odors with aversion conditioning (Smotherman, 1982).

Research done with neonates immediately following birth, however, clearly demonstrates that the sense of smell is present and functional at birth (Schaal, 1988). Research has shown behavior indicating "acceptance and satisfaction" to the odors of bananas, strawberries and vanilla while indicating "rejection" to the odors of rotten eggs and fish (Steiner, 1977; 1979). In a similar study, babies from 1-6 days old turned away from the smell of ammonia on either the left or right indicating the ability to spatially orient the source of the smell and react accordingly (Rieser, Yonas & Wikner, 1976).

Other researchers have demonstrated learning behavior related to the sense of smell. Studies have shown habituation and dishabituation to various smells (licorice, garlic, vinegar and alcohol) by neonates with the clear ability to distinguish between pairs of smells (Engen & Lipsitt, 1965; Engen, Lipsitt & Kaye, 1963). Newborns between 2 and 7 days can also quickly distinguish between their mother's used breast pad and an unused one, and within several days distinguish between their mother's used pad and another woman's (Macfarlane, 1975). Breast-fed neonates also learn very quickly to discriminate their mother's underarm odor from that of other women (Cernoch & Porter, 1985).

The Auditory Sense

The morphological structures which would allow hearing to occur are present and functional in the fetus from 20 weeks on (Eisenberg, 1969). Due to the presence of fluid in both the middle and external ear, there has been some debate among researchers as to sound levels actually reaching the fetus. Research does indicate that hearing does indeed take place through bone conduction (Jensen

& Flottorp, 1982), and thus is mostly at the higher-frequency levels (Tomatis, 1987). Regarding fetal hearing, Liley (1991) writes:

> [The] averaging of foetal electroencephalographic records with repeated stimuli shows sound-evoked cortical potentials and demonstrates as does experience with deaf mothers that the foetus is responding directly. . . . Higher frequencies suffer less loss than low frequencies in transmission though tissues and fluid. Therefore, it is probable that with sound, unlike light, intrauterine spectra are similar to extrauterine. Further, it is worth noting that, unlike most foetal organs which start off in miniature, the structures of the inner ear are very nearly of adult size from initial development. This magnitude of course is necessary because cochlear spectral response obeys simple physical laws dependent on cochlear dimensions. If, for instance, the cochlear grew in proportion to the rest of the body, babies and children would hear in a different frequency range from adults and the communication gap between generations would be even wider than it is already (p.199).

Other research has shown that from the 24th week on, fetal listening is quite constant (Wedenberg & Johansson, 1970). One study examining fetal movement of the eyes, arms, legs and head in response to sound found that responses first occurred between the 24th and 25th weeks, with consistent response following the 28th week (Birnholz & Benacerraf, 1983).

That this is true is not surprising given the noise level inside the uterus. Utilizing an intrauterine photocatheter, noise as loud as 85 decibels reaches the fetus (Liley, 1991), mostly from the mother's bodily internal activity. Less noisy, but still around 55 decibels are the intermittent sounds of voices, including the mother's and father's, and the more regular sounds of the flow of blood in synchrony with the mother's heartbeat. Research done by Salk (1970; 1973) and others (Chamberlain, 1987b; Vitz, 1972) has shown that this early fetal hearing is "remembered" after birth. With reference to the constant sound of the mother's heartbeat in utero, Liley (1991) writes:

> Does this long exposure explain why a baby is comforted by holding him to your chest or is lulled to sleep by the old wives' alarm clock, or the magnetic tape of a heartbeat? Does this experience explain why the tick of a grandfather clock in a quiet study or library can be a reassurance rather than a distraction, why people asked to set a metronome to a rate which "satisfies" them will usually chose a rate in the 50-90 beat per minute range -- and twins show a strong concordance in independent choice (pp. 199-200)?

Using recordings of heartbeats at an "ideal" 72 per minute, Salk played these for a group of newborns while a similar "control" group heard no recordings. Even though both groups recorded the same amount of food intake, the experimental group gained more weight and gained it quicker. The difference in time spent crying was also significant with the control group spending 60% vs. 38% for the experimental group in time spent crying (Salk, 1973).

Any sudden noise in a room will cause a startle response in a fetus lined up under an image intensifier. Further, when fetuses are tonally stimulated, their heart rates changes immediately and they begin to move (Bernard & Sontag, 1947; Lecanuet, Granier-Deferre, Cohen & le Houezec, 1986). Indeed, the simple observation of fetal reactions to tones of sound are quite predictive of deafness (Granier-Deferre, Lecanuet, Cohen & Busnel, 1985). As the decibel level of sound increases, so does the activity and heart rate of the fetus (Bartoshuk, 1962). Using the fetal heart rate as a measure of response, 40 decibels in amplitude and 300 milliseconds in duration seems to be the parameters of auditory sensation (Eisenberg, 1965). Thus, many of the normal sounds of life are within the auditory scope of sensation and some studies seem to indicate a "remembering" of familiar noises, particularly their mother's voice (Ockleford, Vince & Layton, 1988).

Research has also shown that four and five month-old fetuses will respond differently to various types of music (Olds, 1989), quieting down to Mozart and Vivaldi and exhibiting "violent kicking and movement" to the music of Beethoven and Brahams and rock music of every type (Clements, 1977). Olds relates the account of a pregnant woman who attended a rock concert and came home with a broken rib due to the violent kicking of her fetus in response to the music (Olds, 1979). From about 25 weeks on, infants will "jump" in synchrony with the beat of an orchestral performance.

Using sophisticated technology (acoustic spectrograms and sonocineradiographic tracings), researchers (Truby, 1975; Truby & Lind, 1965) have found that fetuses in utero were, through hearing of some sort, receiving and "remembering" various maternal speech features. Interestingly, Truby found similar correspondences of the infant cry related to the speech rhythms and intonations of the mother in extremely premature neonates (900 grams). The fact that newborns of mute mothers do not cry at all, or if so, cried in a very peculiar manner, lead Truby to speculate that the reception of incoming maternal speech is necessary for the production of speech. Further, confirming other studies related to fetal crying, Truby noted that fetuses seemed to be practicing the neuromuscular gestures of crying and vocalization.

Much research has also focused upon the ability of newborns to apprehend various sounds. Using brainstem electric response audiometry (BERA) it has been shown that normal neonates hear as well as adults (Schulman-Galambos & Galambos, 1979). While newborns seem to be especially responsive to sound frequencies within which the human voice falls, namely in the 500-900 Hertz range, they seem to prefer higher rather than lower frequency noises (Chamberlain, 1987b). Newborns can distinguish the directions of sound sources (Wertheimer, 1961) and they consistently respond to various noises when awake and asleep as measured by brain-wave patterns (Goodman, Appleby, Scott & Ireland, 1964; Weitzman, Fishbein & Graziani, 1965). They react to recorded infant cries by crying themselves (Simner, 1971; Sagi & Hoffman, 1976), but to their own recorded cry by ceasing to cry, perhaps indicating a recognition of their own familiar voice (Martin, 1981).

The Visual Sense

Vision is the most complex of the specialized senses and in some ways has proven to be the most difficult to determine as it relates to fetal visual acuity. Chamberlain notes that even up until the middle 1960's, pediatric textbooks were reporting that newborns were virtually blind (Chamberlain, 1987b). Allik and Valsinger (1980) note humorously that infants seemed to develop new visual capabilities with each improvement in the ingenuity and methodology of the researchers. Although the womb is quite dark, light can and does pass through to the fetus (Weaver & Reppert, 1989). Research has shown that from the 16th week on, the photoreceptors in the fetal eye are sensitive to light (Prechtl & Nijhuis, 1983). Flashing light applied to the maternal abdominal wall produces fluctuations in the fetal heart rate (Smythe, 1965) and will cause a startle response often followed by a turning-away of the head (Verny, 1981).

Research done with premature infants has shown that the papillary reflex is present and functions variably given the intensity of light present. The same response that occurs in utero to flashing light occurs in these premature infants, including changes in heart rate and the rate of respiration, the eye-blink reflex and the startle response often accompanied by "the eye-neck reflex involving a backward thrust of the head" (Chamberlain, 1987b, p. 38). The ability to both horizontally and vertically track movement has also been demonstrated in preterm babies between 31-32 weeks (Dubowtiz, Dubowtiz, Morante & Verghote, 1980).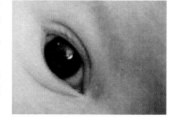

As with the auditory sense, much research has been done on the visual abilities of newborn infants. The first few months of post-natal

life bring about great maturation in vision, but even at birth vision, movement and object perception are coordinated, cross-modal and meaningful (von Hofsten, 1983). At birth the neonate has a visual acuity of between 20/500 and 20/150 (Dayton, Jones, Aiu, Rawson, Steele & Rose, 1964), but he can still make out most of the features of his mothers face if she is 6-12 inches away and can spot the outline of a finger as far as 9 feet away (Verny, 1981). Infant acuity is more or less adult-like by 8 months (Norcia & Tyler, 1985). At birth neonates will track attractive moving targets with their eyes (Aslin, 1981; Dayton, Jones, Steel & Rose, 1964; Wolff & White, 1965). Likewise, enough rods and cones are present at birth to permit the perception of various colors and hues (Werner & Lipsitt, 1981; Dobson, 1976). Differential electroencephalograph responses indicate neo-natal responses to different wavelengths in the color spectrum (Chamberlain, 1987b). Likewise, research has shown that infants as early as 1-2 weeks old indicate a rudimentary depth perception (Ball & Tronick, 1971; Bower, 1974; Bower, Broughton & Moore, 1970).

Research done with neonates as young as 10 hours old also indicates various preferences in their visualization. They prefer patterns to plainly colored surfaces (Fantz, 1961, 1963, 1964, 1965) as well as showing preferences for curved vs. straight lines, chromatic vs. achromatic stimuli, three-dimensional vs. two dimensional objects, complex vs. simple patterns, and faces vs. non-faces (Cohen, 1979).

Thus, to summarize the fetal period regarding the senses, deMause (1982) writes this regarding the 3rd to the 6th month:

> The fetus . . . now floats peacefully, now kicks vigorously, turns somersaults, hiccoughs, sighs, urinates, swallows and breathes amniotic fluid and urine, sucks its thumb, fingers, toes, grabs its umbilicus, gets excited at sudden noises, calms down when the mother talks quietly, and gets rocked back to sleep as she walks about (p. 253).

By birth the summary of behavior is a little more elaborate, but not substantially. From the first minute after birth the newborn has the ability to suck, swallow, get rid of wastes, look, hear, taste, smell, turn the head, and signal for help (Caplan, 1973). As Chamberlain (1983) summarizes, "all sensory systems are functioning; many have been functioning for some time" (p. 6).

INTERMODAL FLUENCY

As with so many of the other areas of fetology, the integrative capabilities of the fetus and the neonate between sense modalities have been grossly underestimated. Much of the research already cited assumes a certain level of intermodal fluency and coordination between the senses and motor movement. For instance, the fact that the auditory and visual systems work together with motor control when a neonate looks at the source of sound is evidence of these capabilities (Bower, 1974). The same can be said of the fetus, with motor movement coordinated with the tactile, visual, auditory, gustatory, and olfactory sense modes.

Research on premature and full-term newborns specifically illustrates the capabilities that exist at birth, thus allowing for the assumption that these capacities existed in some approximate form prior to birth. Many of the findings of the research studies cited above require motor and sense coordination. For instance, the ability to both horizontally and vertically track movement with the coordination of the visual and motor spheres in preterm babies between 31-32 weeks (Dubowtiz, Dubowitz, Morante & Verghote, 1980) indicates this ability so that at birth, vision, movement and object perception are "coordinated, cross-modal and meaningful" (von Hofsten, 1983, pp. 241-242).

Sander's research between newborns and their fathers, utilizing slow motion film, showed that motor synchrony with the visual sense mode took place to allow for anticipation of movement. As fathers moved their heads to look down at the neonate, the baby's head and eyes began to look up. This occurred repeatedly, as did the synchrony of the father's and infant's hands. When the father's right hand moved up, the neonates left hand moved up and grabbed the father's finger (Sander, 1981).

Using frame-by-frame microanalysis of the body movements of newborns as they relate to adult speech patterns shows that infant movement became synchronized with adult speech, whether live or recorded, whether English or Chinese. Newborns did not react in the same way either to the broadcast of pure tones in a simulation of the rate of human speech or to a babble of disconnected vowel sounds (Condon, 1977; Condon & Sander, 1974). All 16 newborns in the study acted similarly, continuing to move through speeches of up to 125 words in length. Given the sophistication of this behavior, Condon has concluded that at birth the neonate has "an ability to steadily track auditory speech variations with almost as great an ability as that of an adult" (Condon, 1977, p. 167).

In an experiment using smooth and nubby pacifiers, researchers illustrated the transfer of information from one modality (tactile) to another (visual). A pacifier of the smooth or nubby variety was placed in the mouth of blindfolded newborns and they were later able to identify by sight the type of pacifier which had been in their mouths (Meltzoff & Borton, 1979). Other research (Papousek, 1967; 1969; Papousek & Papousek, 1977) on newborn operant learning has connected head movement with the delivery of a squirt of milk if a bell sounded, thus linking the interoceptive, gustatory and auditory modalities. These researchers have concluded that learning and other such "conceptualizations" by their very nature are cross-modal and have stated that "in natural situations, stimulations effecting the newborn are almost by principle 'plurimodal', not only visual and auditory, but also tactual, thermal, olfactory, vestibular, and kinesthetic" (Papousek & Papousek, 1982, pp. 369-370). Thus the qualities of "perception, learning, and memory are implied . . . [which infer] such integrative processes . . . [as] sensory awareness, information processing, the organization of adaptive, behavioral responses, cognition, affect and memory--an integration basic to all interactions with the environment" (Papousek & Papousek, 1987). Specifically, Liley (1991) writes regarding the concept of sensory space:

> The subject has received some much-needed simplification by the evidence that the various sensory modalities all feed and share a common space, and that this space in fact is the effective motor space. . . . When does such a concept of space begin? Refined experiments on the neonate suggests that his sensory space is a little ball, that although he may receive visual and auditory signals from more distant sources he is not much interested in anything outside the sphere which extends just beyond his toes-- a restriction which very neatly corresponds to his recently vacated home (p. 200).

Beyond the evidence for the existence of the morphological "hardware" for movement and sense perception is the evidence that these capabilities allow for the "higher-level" processes of learning, habituation, conditioning, memory, affect, dreaming, cognition, and self-expression. And indeed, the existence of these capabilities in the fetal period allows for the inference of a still "higher-level" organization of them into what might tentatively be called "consciousness", or even a "psychology".

CRYING

Audible fetal crying is rare because it requires the presence of air in the fetal trachea. Called *vagitus uterinus*, it most often occurs after an air amniogram. Goodlin (1979) writes that "there is no way to prove the point, but presumably the normal fetus is frequently "crying in utero", but only the presence of air within the uterus   makes it obvious. . . . It therefore seems reasonable to assume that fetuses are often as uncomfortable (enough to cry) "in utero" as "extra-utero" (p. 193).

Chamberlain notes that various researchers have recorded the cries of abortuses from 21-24 weeks weighing 650-930 grams (Chamberlain, 1988b). One study discovered that early clamping of the umbilical cord resulted in much greater crying than late-clamping, "suggesting that babies were experiencing something that they did not like" (Greenberg, Vuorenkoski, Partanen & Lind, 1967, p. 64). In addition, spectrographic studies of the cry response after birth indicate meaningful expression of various pain states, including hunger, pain, loneliness or discomfort which are clearly distinguishable from each and correlatable to the neonatal state (Chamberlain, 1988b).

LEARNING

Having presented evidence that a variety of stimuli can be sensed by the fetus and can in turn be responded to, we have the rudiments of what might be termed learning. Since learning requires a rehearsal of what has been learned, we must also assume the rudiments of memory. Thus we could define learning as "a change in behavior that accrues over time as a result of experience" (Chamberlain, 1987b, p. 33). Chamberlain continues and states that "learning and memory are linked, behavior on later occasions being influenced by what happened in the past".

Much research has focused upon the learning capabilities of neonates (Brackbill & Koltsova, 1967; Lipsitt, 1969; Lipsitt & Kaye, 1977; Lipsitt & Werner, 1981; Trowell, 1982). The newborn is described as having exceptional abilities for "differential responding, discrimination learning, and conditioning, often achieved in a matter of minutes" (Siqueland & Lipsitt, 1966, 357-58) after birth. These capabilities, by extension, can be inferred in some measure to prenates (Kolata, 1984), at least late-term fetuses. Babies who have had as few as 10 heel punctures for blood samples in the first 72 hours after birth, for weeks or months afterwards will promptly cry if you thoughtlessly grasp their foot (Liley, 1991).

But, as Lipsitt has warned, learning and other abilities do not necessarily follow an ever-increasing straight line of accumulative skill. Rather, some abilities actually diminish rather than increase with time and he puts forth the thesis that it is "time for someone to present the thesis that the newborn human creature is about as competent a learning organism as he can become" (Lipsett, 1969, p. 228). The same can be said for the fetus at any given developmental stage, and indeed, some research has shown that prenatal intervention "enrichment" programs enhances the post-natal maturation process (Logan, 1987; 1988; 1991; van de Carr, van de Carr & Lehrer, 1988; van de Carr & Lehrer, 1986; 1988). Studies examining pre-natal "bonding" done through increased verbal communication from the mother to the fetus, found the positive effects of greater alertness and control at birth, earlier talking, independence and better concentration post-natally (Bowen, 1983; 1988; Jernerg, 1988; Lundington-Hoe & Galant, 1985; Thurman, 1988). Other research has indicated the positive effect of extra stimulation and attention on preterms even up to one year later (Bender, 1988; Field, 1985; Kramer & Pierpoint, 1976; Ray & Martinez, 1984; Rice, 1977; Trowel, 1982) and on full-term up to five years (Kennell & Klaus, 1983; Mustaph, 1988; Ringler, Trause, Klaus, & Kennell, 1978; Scarr-Salapatek & Williams, 1973), including improved disposition, language ability and intelligence.

When considering fetal "learning" a distinction perhaps can and should be made between the observation in utero of "normal" fetal learning that might take place and attempts to condition the fetus and thus introduce "non-normal" learning into the intrauterine environment (Hepper, 1989). Perhaps the first study that attempted to demonstrate fetal "conditioning" or habituation was that of Peiper in 1925. His somewhat crude methodology involved emitting the sound of a car horn several feet from a mother's abdomen during a late-term pregnancy. He noted that this resulted in marked movement by the fetus which upon repetition gradually diminished. He concluded that the fetus thus habituated to the noise.

The study of habituation, defined as "a decrease in response due to the repeated presentation of a specific stimulation" (Thompson & Spenser, 1966) in newborns (Hinde, 1970; Kessen, Haith, & Salapatek, 1970; Peek & Hertz, 1973) has found neonatal habituation in response to auditory (Bartoshuk, 1962), olfactory (Engen & Lipsitt, 1965; Engen, Lipsitt & Kaye, 1963), and visual (Friedman, Nagy & Carpenter, 1970) stimuli. Studies utilizing habituation as an measure of fetal learning have proven to be the easiest to do because of their lack of any invasive procedures and thus the majority of "fetal learning" research involves habituation. Habituation of fetal heart rate (Goodlin & Lowe, 1974; Granier-Deferre et al, 1985) and body movements (Leader, Baille, & Martin, 1982a; 1982b; Madison, 1986; Sontag & Wallace, 1934) in response to vibration and auditory tones has been clearly demonstrated in fetuses as early as 23 weeks after fertilization and seems to appear first in females (Leader, Baille, & Martin, 1984). Another study found true fetal habituation in fetuses aged 28-37 weeks (Madison, Adubato, & Madison, 1986).

Since true habituation implies abilities for learning such as "a certain level of sensory competence, associative and memory capabilities" (Hepper, 1989, 291) then it stands that those fetuses deficient in these qualities should have deficits in habituation. Research on post-natal subjects suffering from schizophrenia (Gruzelier & Venebles, 1972), Down's syndrome (Dustman & Callner, 1979) and hyperactivity (Hutt & Hutt, 1964) has shown this to be the case. Various studies have shown that future cognitive abilities and skills are predictable from habituation abilities during both the fetal period (Madison, Madison, & Adubato, 1986) and early infancy (Bornstein & Sigman, 1954). Other studies have shown this same predictability using prematurely born neonates (Rose & Wallace, 1985) and newborns whose mothers had received high doses of anesthetic during delivery (Bowes, Brackbill, Conway, & Steinschneider, 1970). Habituation deficits have also been shown in fetuses' suffering from brain disorders such as microcephalia and anencephalia (Leader, Baille & Martin, 1982).

An alternate methodology seeking to demonstrate fetal learning capabilities has used classical conditioning. Ray, in an early study from 1932, paired vibration as a conditioned stimulus with a loud bang as an unconditioned stimulus. While no data were reported by Ray as to the success of his experiment, the study was repeated by Spelt in 1948, who reported that after 15-20 pairings of the CS (conditioned stimulus) and UCS (unconditioned stimulus), the CS alone elicited a response among 16 fetuses in the last two months of pregnancy.

More recently, similar studies have found comparable results. In a series of studies (Feijoo 1975; 1981), fetuses ages 30-37 weeks were classically conditioned with the repeated pairing of music as the UCS with the mother's relaxation as a CS. After 24 pairings, fetuses stopped all movement upon hearing the music alone. Feijoo found that this "learning" was retained following birth for fetuses that had been conditioned between 22 and 36 weeks. These newborns stopped crying, opened their eyes and showed fewer clonic movements upon hearing the same music as early as 6 minutes after birth.

Studies examining the ability to classically condition preterms and neonates are numerous. In 1928, an early study of aversive conditioning was done by Aldrich. After twelve pairings of a bell with pricking the sole of a neonate's foot with a pin, the bell alone produced a reflexive response. A more recent study (Polikanina, 1961) on 2-week old preterms pairing the smell of ammonia with a tone produced the same result. Perhaps taking their cue from Pavlov, numerous studies conditioning neonates related to heart rate, pupillary dilation and constriction, eye blinks and sucking as well as various studies examining fetal conditioning have been done by Russian researchers from the early 1920's (Brackbill & Koltsova, 1967).

A third category of "learning" studies has examined more naturally occurring events in the fetal environment. For instance, several studies have examined a variety of fetal responses in connection with voices, particularly the mother's voice. Using 3-day old newborns as subjects, various researchers have shown that neonates will alter their sucking response (either increasing or decreasing it) in order to hear their mother's voice (DeCasper & Fefer, 1980) but will not do the same to hear their father's voice (DeCasper & Prescott, 1984). Presumably, the constant prenatal auditory contact with the mother's voice vs. the father's voice gives rise to these preferences.

Seeking to test the memory of auditory learning from the prenatal period vs. mere familiarity with the mother's voice, researchers had pregnant women read a story repeatedly to their fetuses. Newborns were found to alternate their sucking responses to this same story read by another woman but did not respond to a novel story read by the same woman (DeCasper & Spense, 1978). Thus, the conclusion was that "the fetus has learned and remembered something about the acoustic cues that specified the story read to them in the womb, and conclusively demonstrates prenatal learning of acoustic cues in the womb" (Hepper, 1989, p. 290).

One other study (Hepper, 1988) found that the newborn children of mothers who watched a particular soap opera during their pregnancy tended to stop crying and became alert when the theme song of the program was played. Infants of women who had not watched the same program showed no response to the music.

Numerous other studies have focused on the abilities of newborns to learn. For instance research has illustrated neonatal abilities to imitate behavior (Field, Woodson, Greenberg & Cohen, 1982; Meltzoff & Moore, 1977, 1983), to change sucking behavior in response to negative and positive pressure on the gums (Sameroff, 1972) in response to regular or blunt nipples (Brown, 1972), and in response to plain and sweet fluids (Kobre & Lipsitt, 1972). While these studies are quite simple, newborns have shown quick learning ability even in the mastery of complex and confusing sets of contingencies and even continue to learn when these contingencies are reversed (Siqueland & Lipsitt, 1966). Associated with these learning tasks, newborns have been found to have good memory associations, including procedural memory (Rovee-Collier, 1985; Tulving, 1985), semantic memory (Brody, Zelazo & Chaika, 1984; Ungerer, Brody & Zelazo, 1978), episodic memory (Slater, Morison & Rose, 1982; Werner & Siqueland, 1978) and emotional or affect memory.

MEMORY

But does this very early memory ability last beyond a few weeks or even months? Numerous individuals have reported memories of very early childhood, including birth and prenatal ones, but many others have no access to such memories. Many therapists, however, report that birth and pre-birth "memories" are quite pervasive, even if they themselves have grave doubts about their veracity and reliability. For instance, Freud encountered them in some of his subjects but interpreted them in the same light as many early memories; namely, as fantasies (Freud, 1933). He coined the term "childhood amnesia" (1951) to account for the paucity of conscious memories of early childhood. Indeed, several researchers have found that the mean age of subjects' earliest memories are between 39 (Cohen, 1989) and 42 months (Dudycha & Dudycha, 1941).

The key may lay in the distinction between types of memory. Researchers have suggested that "memory" is divided up into multiple systems, each operating according to separate principles. One early distinction between two types of memory was made by Tulving (1972), who distinguished episodic memory of an experiential nature from semantic memory involving language and information. Memory of a semantic type is dependant upon language and is described by Tulving as "a mental thesaurus, organized knowledge a person possesses about words and other verbal symbols, their meaning and referents, about relations among them and about rules, formulas, and algorithms for the manipulation of these symbols, concepts and relations" (p. 380).

Episodic memory, according to Tulving, is autobiographical and involves the particular combinations of sensations, feelings, thoughts and behavior unique to the individual. Included in this memory sub-system would be the further sub-systems of memory related to sensation, perception and affect. Episodic memory thus contains representations of an individual's experiences "according to their temporal and contextual relations to those of other events" (Gregg, 1986, p. 24). Tulving later added a third memory system, called procedural memory (Tulving, 1983), which consists of connections between stimuli and responses. Also included are various motor memory skills such as turning over, sitting up, and operating equipment.

When we examine prenatal, birth and infant memories, they mostly consist of the episodic type, although procedural memory is also present. For instance, Frank Lake reports that many persons "reliving" their prenatal and perinatal experiences, make various motor movements quite representative of those developmental periods. Very few memories of the semantic type are reported, this being consistent with the fact that the language skills necessary for encoding such memories are not yet present.

The evidence regarding the reliability and verity of autobiographical and episodic memories is mixed, even in adults. In one study, Field (1981) analyzed interviews of individuals carried out on people at age 30, and again at age 47, and lastly, at age 70. Regarding questions about education, family, occupation and relationships, the average correlation for factual questions over the 40-year span was .88, while questions regarding attitudes and emotions were less, .43.

Other studies have shown that episodic memories tend to be grouped together according to similarities, often forming a composite memory (Linton, 1982; Means et al, 1988) and that chronological information is thus often lacking (Wagenaar, 1986). Both recency (Rubin, Wetzler & Nebes, 1986) and primacy effects (Holding, Noonan, Pfau & Holding, 1986) have been observed with episodic memories, and research shows that they tend to get less accurate over time (Cohen & Faulkner, 1986; 1988a; 1988b). The major determinants of memorability seem to be the presence of a significant temporal event (Brown, Shevell & Rips, 1986; Loftus & Marburger, 1983), the relative emotionality and perceived importance of the event, and rehearsal (Rubin & Kozin, 1984). This might perhaps explain why such memories seem more prevalent in those in therapy. One would assume the greater prevalence of early traumatic "significant temporal events".

Whatever the type of memory, many have taken the reports of memories, whether obtained as spontaneous recollections, or through the mechanisms of hypnosis, "conscious imaging" (Neighbour, 1981), gestalt methodology, dream recollection, deep-breathing regression or LSD, more at face-value. Beginning with Rank's *The Trauma of Birth*, many have reported extensively on birth and pre-birth memories, including Nandor Fodor (1949), D.W. Winnicott (1957; 1958; 1972), Francis Mott (1964), Stanislav Grof (1975; 1977), Phyllis Greenacre (1945), Melanie Klein (1975a; 1975b), M.L. Peerbolte (1951; 1954), Arthur Janov (1970; 1971; 1972; 1983), Gustav Graber (1924), R.D. Laing (1978; 1982), and others (Chamberlain, 1981; Ducasse, 1961; De Rocha, 1911; Feher, 1980; Kelsey, 1953; Orr & Ray, 1977; Ploye, 1973; 1976). While the sheer quantity of reported birth and pre-birth material is not evidence of its credibility or reliability, it certainly raises questions as to why its report seems to be so ubiquitous.

Many of the above mentioned researchers have stumbled upon these reports quite reluctantly and only came to accept their basic reliability after correlating many of the reports with hospital records and reports from parents and other observers. For instance, Cheek, in a study using hypnosis with 10 subjects, reported that all were able to demonstrate the exact sequential movements of their heads and shoulders during birth. Cheek (1974) reported that none of the individuals involved had any conscious knowledge of the mechanisms and combinations of movement during birth usually known only to those with specialized obstetrical training.

In a series of studies designed to differentiate true "memory" from suggestion, Raikov (1980) examined the ability of adults under hypnosis to exhibit genuine neonatal reflexes. The results proved interesting: 100% of the subjects showed the typical uncoordinated eye movements and sucking reflexes typical of neonates, 60% demonstrated the foot-bending reflex, 50% displayed the Babinski reflex and tearless crying, and 40% manifested the grasping reflex and spontaneous movements of the arms and legs. In a follow-up study (Raikov, 1982), using suggestion alone without hypnosis on highly hypnotizable subjects, only a small number of "neonatal" behaviors could be observed. The same was true when professional actors attempted to duplicate neonatal behaviors, being correct only 15% of the time. Raikov concluded that "neither acting, suggestion nor imagination could account for all the phenomena observed" (p. 116), and that the information acted out in the original subjects was being recalled from memory.

In a similar study designed to shed light on the reliability of birth memory retrieved in hypnosis, Chamberlain (1986) studied 10 mother-child dyads. The children, who ranged in age from 9 to 23, all stated that they had no conscious memories of their births, while the mothers all claimed that they had never shared details of their children's births with them. Chamberlain reported that the "mother and child reports were remarkably detailed and reflected individual interests, experiences, and perceptions. Their two stories interlocked and formed a coherent whole rather than veering off in different directions. Stories matched or dovetailed at as many as 24 different points while direct contradictions of fact in the separate narratives where quite rare. Children correctly reported many details such as "time of day, locale, persons present, instruments used, position of delivery, behavior of nurses and doctors, first feedings of water or formula, room layouts and details of discharge and homecoming. Sequences were usually accurate: moving in and out of cars, rooms, on and off of certain beds or equipment, nursing from the bottle and/or breast in correct order, and the appearance and disappearance of doctors and fathers" (Chamberlain, 1986, p. 34). Although Chamberlain did find one case of "a limited pattern of fantasy" he reports that "judging strictly from my sample of ten pairs, it appears that birth memories are quite likely to be real not fantasy, true not false and within reasonable limits, a reliable guide to what actually happened.

However, the fact remains that clear and certain falsehoods regarding early memories do often emerge under hypnosis, thus casting at least a hint of suspicion regarding the truth of such "data". One possible explanation for this was stumbled upon by Hilgard. He found evidence that in some cases, the "facts" about what happened can be known by one segment of "consciousness" but unknown by another, resulting in what Hilgard called "divided consciousness" (Hilgard, 1977). Thus, lack of memory about a certain event may indicate that the segment of consciousness under hypnotic consideration may be unaware of the memory, while another segment may have total recall.

Buttressing this contention was the discovery by Cheek (1959) and others (Bennett, Giannini & Kline, 1979; Levinson, 1965) that many patients under general anesthesia, who were supposedly unconscious, were indeed perceiving and reacting to comments made by medical staff. Indeed, researchers discovered that patients under general anesthesia were not only sensitive to the words spoken, but also to various nuances, inflections and tones in the voices.

The connection between early birth and pre-birth traumas and adult manifestations of psychopathology has been frequently observed. Leslie Lecron (1954; 1963) and David Cheek (1975), using an "ideomotor" technique in hypnosis, have connected early birth trauma with peptic ulcers, oesophageal spasms, spastic colon, asthma, emphysema, hyperventilation syndrome, sterility, dysmenorrhoea, failed analgesia in labor, premature labor, toxemia, frigidity and habitual abortion. Barnett (1979), using the ideomotor technique asked a series of questions of 876 different hypnotised patients and found that 28% reported negative birth experiences. Similar to Cheek, and Lecron, he found strong connections between these experiences and the presenting problems.

Cheek has found that under hypnosis, subjects have often also reported many prenatal "memories" (Cheek, 1986). Other "evidence" for the credibility of birth and pre-natal memories can be found in the spontaneous memories of children when asked about the circumstances surrounding their birth and pre-birth experiences (Chamberlain, 1988a; Rhodes, 1991). Given the limited vocabulary of younger children, many are able to point to parts of the body, act out, and give accurate motions and sounds of early experiences (Laibow, 1986).

One possible explanation of early implicit memory is found in the pioneering work of Karl Pribram. In several works (Miller, Galanter & Pribram, 1960; Pribram, 1969; Pribram & Broadbent, 1970), but particularly in *Languages of the Brain* (1971), Pribram has argued that long-term memory exists due to a two-process mechanism. The first is the neuron itself, while the second is the neural junction. The activity of the neural junction is part of an overall organization which is not specifically dependent upon any given single neuron. Pribram called this the "slow potential microstructure". This microstructure is composed of the "aggregate of slow potentials present over an extended location at any moment" (p. 19). Thus, the neural junctions are more than just merely transmitters of neural impulses, they can also serve as functional retainers of memory traces. Pribram writes that "it is in the junctional mechanism that the long lasting modifications of brain tissue must take place. . . . Long-term memory therefore becomes more a function of junctional structure than of strictly neural (nerve impulse generating) processes (p. 47).

The reason this is true is that the neurons themselves do not replicate, rather it is the neural junctions or synapses which not only multiply but are also replete with active chemical processes, any or many of which are candidates for the evanescent, temporary, and long term modification upon which memory must be based. What is significant is that the neural junctions or synapses can store hologram-like patterns which could provide the basis of a distributed memory system independent of particular neurons (Pribram, 1971, p. 143). It is said to be holographic due to the way optical holograms produced by laser light work. When a camera records a visual picture of an object, each point on the film records information which arrived from the corresponding point in the visual field and thus produces an image that "looks like" the object. But when properly exposed by a coherent light source, a holographic record results when an image is taken and information from each point of the visual field is stored throughout a filter. The information stored on this filter does not resemble the visual image at all since the information does not correspond directly to the various points in the image. Rather, "the optical filter is a record of the wave patterns emitted or reflected from an object". Thus, the filter serves to "freeze" the wave pattern, and it remains so "frozen" until the process is reactivated, and the waves are "read out of the recording medium" (Pribram, 1971, pp. 145-146).

The properties of holograms make them "potentially important in understanding brain function". Pribram 1971) cites Leith and Upatnicks (1965) when he writes that "first . . . the information about a point in the original image is distributed throughout the hologram, making the record resistant to damage. Each small part of the hologram contains information from the entire image and therefore can reproduce it" (p. 150).

The same would be true for a neural holographic process. Perceptions and memories can be stored as "spatial interactions among phase relationships of neighboring junctional patterns" (Pribram, 1971, p. 166), thus allowing for the possibility of memory traces as early as synaptic junctions exist. Thus, there could be chemical storage of memory traces within the spatial junctions and this may account for memories from very early in pregnancy, even from the first trimester. These memories, stored holographically, are perhaps "unfrozen" in some persons by some post-natal process, including trauma, hypnosis or some psychopharmacological intervention.

EMOTION

Whether fetal or neonatal emotion exists in the same or similar manner of adults is impossible to determine due to its relatively inherent subjectivity. Research with both prenates and newborns, however, has shown clear evidence for at least the external behavior normally associated with internal emotion. For instance, crying, of both the intra-uterine and extra-uterine varieties, has been connected to the internal states of pain, anger and "rage".

As noted earlier, audible fetal crying is rare because it requires the presence of air in the fetal trachea. However, Ryder, after a comprehensive review of the literature from 1800-1941, reported 123 cases by 114 different observers (Ryder, 1943). More recent corroboration has presented three instances when fetal crying occurred in response to rupture of a membrane, manual displacement of the head or the attachment of electrodes for internal monitoring (Thiery, Yo, Vrijens & Janssens, 1973). Audible crying has been reported from infants weighing as little as 650 grams (Pieper, 1963) and Humphrey (1978) cites instances of 5 aborted fetuses from age 21-22 weeks audibly crying.

It has been argued that fetal crying is not indicative of any emotional state, but is undifferentiated. The same has been asserted with regard to neonatal crying. However, research has shown that crying of preterm and full-term infants is very differentiated, even from each other (Friedman, Zahn-Waxler & Radke-Yarrow, 1982). Utilizing spectrography to produce "cryprints", researchers have clearly distinguished various cries as communicating different emotional states (Lester & Boukydis, 1985; Truby & Lind, 1965) including between birth, pain and hunger (Wasz, Lind, Vuorenkoski, Partanen & Valanne, 1968). Spectrographic distinctions have been found in the cries of infants who are had been prenatally and perinatally chronically stressed (Zeskind & Lester, 1978), who have chromosomal aberrations (Vuorenkoski, Lind, Partanen, Lejeune & Wasz-Hockert, 1966), hyperbilirubinemia (Wasz-Hockert, Koivisto, Vuorenkoski, Partanen & Lind, 1971), and fetal malnutrition (Juntunen, Sirvio & Michelsson, 1978; Lester, 1976).

Other studies have also illustrated the range of communicatory cries possible with newborns.

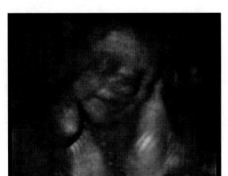

Using sonography and audio tape recordings before, during and after circumcision, one study (Porter, Miller & Marshall, 1986) demonstrated that certain distinctions in "cries" were definitely correlated to degrees of pain as measured by the relative degree of the invasiveness of the surgical procedure. Definite differences in pitch, temporal patterning and harmonic structure were discernible with various degrees of pain.

Another study (Izard & Read, 1986) with older infants aged 2-10 months was also able to sonographically distinguish various degrees of pleasure and displeasure. In this study, two month old infants showed emotional expression across the entire continuum of possible affect states, from extreme pleasure to extreme displeasure. Still another study (Papousek, Papousek & Harris, 1986) demonstrated easily discernible audible sounds of pleasure in child-parent interactions in infants from 2-4 months of age.

Another category of the external indication of internal affect states includes various facial expressions, particularly smiling. The earliest smiles occur during the REM stages of sleep (Reppert, Henshaw, Schwartz & Weaver, 1987; Reppert & Schwartz, 1983; Reppert, Weaver & Rivkees, 1988) perhaps indicating "expressions of private pleasure in dreams" (Roffwarg, Muzio & Dement, 1966, 610). What makes REM sleep so significant is the correlation of this stage with dreaming activity. The above study found that various measurable alterations in specific physiological systems (i.e.

gross motor movement) was identical for adults as for full-term and premature neonates, leading to the conclusion that even premature infants and fetuses dream. Whether this activity involves the full visual imagery and the other characteristics of adult dreaming is impossible to determine, but the REMs of neonates and adults are alike in every measurable way. The big difference has to do with the amount of time spent in REM vs. non-REM sleep. Those of old age spend less than 1 hour (13% of sleep time) in REM; adolescents 20%; full-term newborns 50%; 36-38 week preemies 58%; 33-35 week preemies 67%; and virtually 100% for 30 week-old premature infants. Interesting, this study noted many expressions of emotion on the faces of the various infants during REM sleep: grimaces, smiles, whimpers and even the nuances of affective expression such as perplexity, disdain, skepticism, and amusement.

Smiling has often been observed at birth (Leboyer, 1975; Star, 1986), but until recently it was thought to be a "physiological artifact" (i.e. caused by gas). However, research has identified neonatal smiling in response to specific tasks and also a wide variation in the frequency of smiling (Wolff, 1978).

Other facial expressions indicative of affect states have been clearly identified in newborns, including expressions that seem to indicate sadness, fear, disgust, happiness, surprise, anger, interest, distress, and shame (Emde, 1980). Using videotapes of neonates in the first week of life, Eisenberg and Marmarou (1981) revealed of full range of clear-cut expressions of emotion. Another study (Johnson, Emde, Pannabecker, Stenborg & Davis, 1982) examined neonatal affect states as perceived by their parents. Ninety-five percent reported seeing joy and interest, 78% saw anger, 68% surprise, 65% distress, 40% sadness, 40% disgust, and 35% fear in their babies during the first week of life. The introduction of new information resulting in the quick appropriate change of affect suggests the dependence of emotion upon cognitive beliefs and cognitive processes (Kagan, 1978).

THE INFLUENCE OF THE FETAL ENVIRONMENT

How does the emotional life of the mother effect the developing fetus? We noted earlier in our text that Frank Lake's understanding that "powerfully impressive experiences from the mother and her inner and outer world . . . reach the foetus, defining its relation to the intra-uterine reality in ways that persist into adult life" (Lake, 1981, 5) is analogous to Francis Mott's. Mott conceptualized a bi-directional flow of blood from mother to fetus as mediated by the placenta through the umbilical cord, which gives rise to various physical "feelings" that are the basis for subsequent psychological "feelings". Lake picked up on Mott's term "umbilical affect" to designate this exchange, defining it as the "feeling state of the fetus as brought about by blood reaching him through the umbilical vein" (Moss, 1987, 203). As both Lake and Mott define this exchange, the umbilical vein not only conveys nutritive resources and as such could be experienced as a "life-giving flow, bringing . . . renewal and restoration" but could also "be the bearer of an aggressive thrust of bad feelings into the foetus if the mother herself was distressed and 'feeling bad.'" If the mother felt emotionally unsupported , then "this feeling of deficiency, lack of recognition and the failure of looked-for support, would be just as specifically felt by the fetus. It became distressed by the failure of its immediate environment to provide the expected acceptance and sustenance, not so much at the level of metabolic input . . . but to nourish the earliest beginnings of the person in relationship" (Lake, 1976, S1).

Certainly the biological morphology for this exchange exists very early on, from about the fifth week after fertilization until birth. With the development of the placenta and umbilical cord

(Mulders, Muijsers, Jongsma & Nijhuis, 1986, 283-293), the embryo/fetus exchanges CO_2, water, urea, hormones and waste products for oxygen, water electrolytes, protein and lipid carbohydrates, vitamins, antibodies and other nutrients. But the morphological structures which allow this "natural" exchange to occur also allow for the passage through the placental barrier of various teratogens, particularly pharmacological agents and almost all viruses. As was noted in an earlier chapter, much research has been done on the deleterious effects of various teratogens and other prenatal "conditions".

The idea that the pregnant mother's emotional state during pregnancy might have a positive or deleterious effect on the developing baby within her is certainly not new (Van den Bergh, 1990). In an early study from 1941, Sontag found that pregnant women who were anxious, angry and/or afraid tended to have babies with higher heart rates, greater digestive problems, lower birth weight, and more hyperactivity. Numerous studies (Carlson & La Barba, 1979; Istvan, 1986; Van den Bergh, 1983) since have confirmed these findings, reinforcing Sontag's original results. For instance, emotionally disturbed women tend to have infants who are irritable (Dodge, 1972), poor sleepers (Ferreira, 1960), more prone to gastrointestinal difficulties (Glavin, 1984; Turner, 1956), have higher activity rates (Sontag, 1966), cry more (Farber, Vaughn & Egeland, 1981), are perceived by their parents as having a difficult temperament (Vaughn, Bradley, Joffe, Seifer & Barglow, 1987), and score lower on mental and motor skills tests (Davids, Holden & Gray, 1963).

Several studies have connected anxiety (Crandon, 1979; Grassi & Caracciolo, 1983) and/or various psychiatric diagnoses (Peterson, Mehl & McRae, 1988; Rider, Rosenthal, Wender & Blumenthal, 1975) in pregnant women with a much higher incidence of various birth complications.

For instance, Batchelor, Dean, Gray & Wenck (1991) examined 37 children with severe emotional/behavioral disorders vs. 119 children with severe emotional handicaps vs. 211 "normal" children. Using 26 items from Dean & Gray's (1985) Maternal-Perinatal Scale, this study found that the item with the highest correlation as a "predictive factor" of post-natal emotional and behavioral disorders was cigarette smoking, followed closely by maternal stress throughout pregnancy. Using an odds ratio developed by Mantel (1963), this study found, for instance, that maternal smoking throughout the pregnancy resulted in a odds ratio of 4.34 (i.e. mothers who smoked during pregnancy are 4.34 times more likely to have a child who eventually ends up being diagnosed as behaviorally or emotionally disordered. The score for stress throughout pregnancy was 4.22 and was higher than other factors such as low birth weight (3.37), preterm delivery (2.75), edema throughout the pregnancy (2.04), too little weight gain (1.74), hypoxia (1.18), mother over 35 years old (1.14) and maternal ingestion of alcohol (.63).

This study reinforced other studies that have connected maternal stress with general behavior problems (Cocchi, Felici, Tonni & Venanzi, 1984; De Sousa, 1974), attention deficit disorder (Varley, 1984), childhood autism (Finnegan & Quarrington, 1979; Foulatier, 1987; Gillberg & Gillberg, 1983; Mason-Brothers, Ritvo & Guze, 1987), psychosis (Torry, Hersh & McCabe, 1975), schizophrenia (Medick, Parnas & Schulsinger, 1987; Ritzman, 1989; Rutt & Offord, 1971), and psychiatric disorders in general (Huttunen & Niskanen, 1978).

Various studies have also correlated the likelihood of spontaneous abortions and birth complications with the level of fear, anxiety, and guilt in pregnant women (Golanska & Bacz, 1988) as well as disturbances in attitudes toward the child within them (Goshen-Gottstein, 1969; Laukaran & Van den Berg, 1980).

Research has also shown a connection between various psychological factors and preterm delivery (Blau, Slaff, Easton, Welkowitz, Springham & Cohen, 1963; Gunter, 1963). For instance, premature delivery is more likely to occur in women who have negative attitudes toward the pregnancy, were emotionally immature, had unresolved conflicts toward their mothers, a history of traumatic experience with a previous pregnancy, a high level of anxiety, feelings of inadequacy in female roles (De Muylder & Wesel, 1988), difficulty in accepting the pregnancy, poor "communication" with their fetus (Riley, 1988), lack of a spouse (Newton, 1988), husbands who offered little or no support, and an initial negative reaction to their first menses (De Muylder & Wesel, 1988). Another study (Iatrakis, Sakellaropoulos, Kourkoubas & Kabounia, 1988) found a significantly higher incidence of vomiting and nausea in the first 12 weeks of pregnancy in those women who had poor communication with their husbands and who had stress and doubts about the pregnancy.

Indeed, the sum total of research seems to indicate that potentially any emotional stress to the mother can lead to complications of various types (Laibow, 1988; Michel & Fritz-Niggli, 1978; Spielberger & Jacobs, 1979), not only after birth but even before birth. For instance, mothers under severe emotional distress are more likely to have hyperactive fetuses (Ferreira, 1965; McDonald, 1968; Montagu, 1962; Wolkind, 1981) and mothers who are anxious (Copher & Huber, 1967) or emotionally upset (Eskes, 1985) are likely to have fetus's suffering from tachycardia. One study illustrated the effects on 28 fetuses aged 18-36 weeks in response to their mother's reactions to an earthquake (Iannuruberto & Tajani, 1981). Using ultrasonography, the researchers were able to observe the intense hyperkinesia in all of the fetuses lasting from 2 to 8 hours. Other studies (Benson, Little, Talbert & Dewhurst, 1987; Van den Bergh, 1988; 1990) have also connected fetal behavior to maternal emotional state.

What allows the affect state of the mother to effect the child she is carrying are the neuroendocrinological interactions of the endocrine system and the nervous system, particularly a group of hormones called catecholamines (Lagercrantz & Slotkin, 1986; Moyer, Herrenkohl & Jacobowitz, 1978; Simkin, 1986), including epinephrine, norepinephrine and dopamine. Beginning in the 1925, W.B. Cannon found that fear and anxiety could be biochemically induced in animals. His method was simple; he withdrew the blood and thus the catecholamines of already fearful and frightened animals and injected them into calm and relaxed animals. Within seconds and in the absence of any fear or anxiety producing stimuli, these animals began to act fearful and anxious. Cannon discovered that the catecholamines acted like "a circulating fire alarm system," provoking all the physiological responses to fear and anxiety, particularly those of the sympathetic division of the autonomic nervous system.

This identical process allows the developing embryo and fetus to be affected by the mother's affective processes. When the gravida is anxious or fearful, various hormones, including adrenaline, flood into the blood stream and easily cross the placental barrier, thus provoking, biochemically, the physiological reaction to anxiety and fear in the fetus (Kruse, 1978; Peters, 1988). The mechanism that allows this process to work begins with the mother's brain, which is sensing and perceiving the environment. External circumstances, actions and thoughts are perceived in the cerebral cortex and subsequently affectively reacted to in the hypothalamus. The hypothalamus, in turn, directs the endocrine system and the autonomic nervous system to produce affect-appropriate physiological changes. For instance, sudden fear in a pregnant women quickly results in the hypothalamus directing the sympathetic division of the autonomic nervous system to make the heart beat faster, the palms to sweat, the blood pressure to rise, the pupils to dilate and the muscles to tense. The hypothalamus also directs the endocrine system to flood the woman's body with hormones, which as noted above, pass through the placenta to the fetus.

What is so important about this process is the effect it can have on the developing embryo and fetus. The various hormones released by the endocrine system, while variously reversible in adults, can be more-or-less irreversible at certain critical periods in development during the embryonic and fetal stages. What seems to be produced is a psychophysiological predisposition to respond that some researchers have traced into adulthood. While there is not yet a precise understanding as to how the psychological and physiological dimensions interact to cause long-term psychophysiological behavior changes, it is clear that something is going on. Recent evidence seems to indicate that the hypothalamus, as the "emotional regulator" of the body is key in this transaction.

Sontag, in an early study titled "War and the Maternal-Fetal Relationship" (1944), observed that the babies of women whose husbands were serving in the armed services and thus daily threatened with death tended to be crankier and have a greater array of physical problems. He theorized that the intra-uterine environment of constantly worryingmothers would have a deleterious effect on a whole generation of infants. Sontag coined the term "somatopsychics" to describe the way "basic physiological processes affect the personality structure, perception, and performance of an individual." This term infers the mirror process of "psychosomatics", which refers to the way in which psychological processes effect physiological ones (Verny, 1981). Thus, the developing fetal morphological apparatus is influenced by the intra-uterine environment in such a way as to predispose certain psychological processes following birth.

Among the most intriguing and yet controversial predispositions may be homosexuality. Several retrospective studies on human subjects (Dorner et al, 1975; 1980) have indeed found correlations between stressful maternal life events which occurred during pregnancy and the incidence of adult male homosexuality. Dorner and his colleagues found that out of 800 homosexual males, "highly significantly more homosexuals were born during the stressful war (World War II) and early post-war period than in the years before or after this stressful period. This finding suggested that stressful maternal life events, if occurring during pregnancy may represent in fact, an etiogenetic risk factor for the development of sexual variations in the male offspring" (Dorner, 1988, 426).

Another study (Dorner et al, 1983) compared the answers of 100 heterosexual men with 100 bi- and homosexual men of the same age to questions relating to maternal stress during their prenatal life. The highest significant correlation was found in homosexual men (followed by bi-sexual men) and maternal stress. One-third of the homosexual men reported severe maternal distress while they were in utero (i.e. death of someone close, rape, severe anxiety, abandonment by partner), and one-third reported moderate maternal stress. Compared with this data, none of the heterosexual men reported severe stress and only 10% reported moderate stress.

Animal studies done by Dorner (1967; 1968; 1969; 1970) and his colleagues (Dorner, Docke & Hinz, 1968; 1969; 1979; Dorner, Docke & Mustafa, 1968a; 1968b; Dorner & Fatschel, 1970; Dorner & Hinz, 1968; 1971; 1978; Dorner & Staudt, 1968; 1969) have found permanent alterations in adult sexual behavior were produced by neuroendocrine changes during critical brain organization stages during the embryonic period. Since the same basic neuroendo-crinological systems are functional in human beings as in the experimental animals, Dorner (1988) made the following hypothesis: "Primary hypo-, bi- or homosexuality produced by androgen deficiency in males and androgen excess in females during sex-specific brain differentiation might correspond etiologically to primary hypo-, bi- or homosexuality in human beings" (p. 423).

Thus, a neuropsychoendocrinological process occurs, whereby certain psychosocial influences in the mother's environment cause an intra-uterine environment that in turn causes hypothalamic predispositions in the fetal morphology to respond psychologically in particular ways. As this relates to sexuality, Dorner writes that "prenatal psychosocial influences, which are able to affect the levels of systemic hormones and/or neurotransmitters, should . . . be regarded as possible etiologic factors in the development of sexual deviations" (Dorner, 1988, 425). Other researchers have found the similar results (i.e. Stahl et al, 1978), particularly in rats, finding that prenatal stress tended to demasculinize males rats in terms of testosterone levels and observed behavior. Dorner (1988) cites another study that distinguishes the pre-natal stress as crucial:

We have observed bi- or even homosexual behavior in prenatally stressed male rats after castration plus estrogen treatment in adulthood, whereas prenatally non-stressed but later equally treated males displayed heterosexual behavior (Gotz & Dorner, 1980). Hence, prenatal stress can predispose to the development of bi- or even homosexual behavior in males (p. 425).

Research into other environmentally caused hormonal fluctuations in the prenatal period have also shown the deleterious effect of the post-natal predisposition. For instance, research on overnutrition (Franková, 1970; Dorner, Grychtolik & Julitz, 1977; Dorner, Hagen & Witthuhn, 1976) and undernutrition (Ravelli, 1976) resulting in changes in the insulin and/or glucose levels during critical periods of fetal brain development have been found to alter irreversibly the function and tolerance ranges of hypothalamic control centers for glucose metabolism (Dorner, 1988). This has been cited as a predisposing risk factor in obesity (Dorner, 1973; 1978), diabetes mellitus (Dorner & Mohnike, 1973; 1976; 1977; Dorner et al, 1973; 1975; 1984), and atherosclerosis (Dorner, Haller & Leonhardt, 1973).

Interestingly, the predisposing effects of neurohormones and other endocrinal effects does not end at birth. Rather, the source of the hormones changes from mother to child himself, but the effect can be just as profound. For instance, the postnatal psychosocial effects of extended handling, electric shocks (Denenberg, 1964), maternal deprivation (Dorner, Bluth & Tonjes, 1982), overnutrition (Dorner & Grychtolik, 1978), and malnutrition (Hinz, Hecht, Rhode & Dorner, 1976; Rodgers, 1978; Ryan, 1977), and the administration of various neurodrugs (Dorner, 1976; Dorner, Hecht & Hinz, 1976; Hecht et al, 1978; Hinz et al, 1978) all resulted in permanent neurochemical changes in the brain and/or permanent alterations of emotionality, exploratory behavior, learning capability and memory capacity.

Dorner (1988) has proposed two ontogenetic organization rules for the neuroendocrine system:

> During the pre- and/or early post-natal life, systemic hormones and neurotransmitters are capable of acting as organizers of the brain, which is the controller of the neuro-endocrine-immune system. Thus, the quantity of the systemic hormones and neurotransmitters co-determines during a critical period of brain development, the quality, ie. the responsiveness, of their own central nervous system controllers and hence the functional and tolerance ranges of their own feedback systems throughout life. . . . Abnormal levels of systemic hormones and neurotransmitters, which can be induced by abnormal conditions in the psychosocial and/or natural environment, can act as teratogens and lead to permanent physiological and/or psychological dysfunctions in later life. Thus many malfunctions of reproduction, metabolism, information processing, and immunity called up to now idiopathic, essential, cryptogenic, primary or genuine can be explained by pre- and/or early postnatal psycho- and /or physiological processes. Therefore, "structural teratology" (teratomorphology) . . . [must be] supplemented by [a] "functional teratology" (teratpsychophysiology) (p. 429).

Intriguingly, several other studies (Stott, 1973; Stott & Latchford, 1976) have found what seem to be discriminations of stressors by the maternal-fetal unit. Stott found that no negative effects, either physical or emotional, seemed to be present in the children of mothers who had suffered fairly intense, but brief stressors (i.e. witnessing a violent dog fight, suffering a scare at work, having an older child run away for a day). The argument that the brief exposure of the fetus to the "bath of neurohormones" necessarily limits the possibility of negative effect and this was true. But Stott and others have also found that intense, long-term stress did not always result in post-natal deficiencies. In 1983, Reading found that the impact of anxiety and stress is often moderated by other factors, such as attitudes toward the pregnancy, psychosocial support and appraisal of the threat of the stressor. Further, when prolonged stress did not directly threaten the mother (i.e. illness of a close relative) there seemed to be no ill effects, while stressors that did effect the potential well-being of the mother seemed to produce problems. Stott found that 10 out of 14 women suffering from personally threatening stressors which were long-term delivered babies with some physical or emotional problem. Two characteristics were deemed to be significant in the problem-causing stressors: "they tended to be continuous or liable to erupt at any time and they were incapable of resolution" (Verny, 1981, p. 46).

There seemed to be a pronounced effect when the source of the stress was a close family member, usually the husband. Stott found that a bad marriage or relationship was among the greatest causes of stress. Studying over 1300 children and their families, he estimated that a women trapped by a stormy marriage with an abusive or unsupportive husband runs a 237% greater risk of bearing a emotionally or physically handicapped child as opposed to a woman from a secure, nurturing stable marital environment. Further, Stott found that unhappy marriages tended to produce babies who were on average 5 times more fearful and "jumpy" than offspring from happy marriages (Stott, 1977). Verny (1981) writes that "these youngsters continued to be plagued by problems well into childhood. At four and five, Dr. Stott found them to be undersized, timid, and emotionally dependent on their mothers to an inordinate degree" (p. 50).

Several other studies have found different results regarding even short-term fetal behavioral response in reaction to induced maternal emotions. One study (Van den Bergh, Mulder, Visser & Poelmann-Wessjes, 1989) found no significant fetal response when their mothers watched a film on delivery, perhaps considered mildly stressing. Two other studies (Rossi, 1987; Rossi, Avveduti, Rizzo & Lorusso, 1989) found significant fetal movement in response to their mother's anticipation of an amniocentesis vs. a group of controls. A fourth study (Benson et al, 1987) found that fetuses' of anxious mothers, but not depressed or hostile mothers showed elevated heart rates.

Verny (1981), in commenting on Stott's study, writes:

> The only way to make sense of the difference [between the two groups subjected to long-term stress] is in terms of perception. In one case, the children were able to sense that while very real, their mother's distress was not threatening to her or them; in the other case, they sense, accurately, that her distress was a threat (p. 50).

Thus, some kind of fetal perceptual apparatus is assumed to enable the ability to distinguish between threatening and non-threatening neurohormones. One possible mechanism that might explain this is through a concomitant ongoing exchange between mother and fetus that communicates the positive vs. negative feelings of the mother herself to the child.

Numerous studies have examined the role of maternal attitudes (Ainslie, Solyom & McManus, 1982; Condon, 1985; Eggersten & Benedetti, 1984; Reading, Cox, Sledmere & Campbell, 1984), particularly attachment (Gaffney, 1986; Mercer, Ferketich, May & DeJospeh, 1988; Sjogren & Uddenberg, 1988; Stainton, 1985; Wu & Eichmann, 1988) toward the fetus growing within them. One study (Lukesch, 1975) examining 2000 pregnant women found that the single greatest factor in neonatal outcome was the attitude of the mother toward her child while the second most important variable was the quality of a woman's relationship with her spouse. The subjects in this study all had the same quality and quantity of prenatal care, were equally educated, and were of the same social and economic class. Lukesch and others (Condon, 1987) have found that the infants of mothers who were accepting of their pregnancies and who looked forward to the arrival of the baby were much more likely to give birth to an emotionally and physically healthy child than mothers who had negative attitudes towards the pregnancy and were "rejecting." Another study (Rottman, 1974) on 141 pregnant women duplicated Lukesche's results. Using various psychological tests, Rottman divided the pregnant women into 4 groups. Results with the two extremes were clear, with "Ideal" mothers (who both consciously and unconsciously wanted their unborn children) having the easiest pregnancies, the most trouble-free births, and the most physically and emotionally healthy infants. "Catastrophic" mothers (who both consciously and unconsciously were rejecting of their unborn children) "had the most devastating medical problems during pregnancy, and bore the highest rate of premature, low-weight, and emotionally disturbed infants" (Verny, 1981, p. 48).

Two other groups of mothers emerged, called "Ambivalent" (consciously wanting while unconsciously rejecting) and "Cool" (consciously rejecting while unconsciously wanting) mothers. The former gave birth to an unusually large number of neonates who suffered from behavioral and gastrointestinal problems, while the latter gave birth to babies who tended to be apathetic and lethargic. Verny hypothesizes that regardless of the various stresses that these women went through, the acceptance or lack of acceptance by the mother is somehow perceived by the fetus and that among those fetuses who felt accepted, a measure of maternal "support' and "acceptance" was evident enough which somehow enabled them to better cope with the stresses that emerged.

CONCLUSION

The evidence certainly appears overwhelming that a prenatal psychology exists. Prenates move and emote, hear and feel, taste and learn, all capabilities psychologists connect which the core of what it means to be human. The line separating a baby before birth and after birth is indistinguishable, psychologically-speaking. Technological advances such as 3D and 4D ultrasonography will only provide greater evidence that personhood and personality, indeed, psychology, exists far prior to birth for the human species. This accumulating evidence cannot be ignored. It speaks, indeed shouts, to the humanness of each embryo, of each fetus, and each neonate, indeed, each person.

King David's prayer from Psalm 139 (vvs. 13-16) is an appropriate epilogue:

You made all the delicate, inner parts of my body and knit me together in my mother's womb. Thank you for making me so wonderfully complex! Your workmanship is marvelous —how well I know it. You watched me as I was being formed in utter seclusion, as I was woven together in the dark of the womb. You saw me before I was born. Every day of my life was recorded in your book. Every moment was laid out before a single day had passed.

WORKS CITED

A

Abel, E.L. (1997). Maternal alcohol consumption and spontaneous abortion. *Alcohol and Alcoholism, 32,* 211-219.

Abramovich, D., & Gray. E. (1982). Physiological fetal defecation in midpregnancy. *Obstetrics & Gynecology, 60* (3), 294-296.

Abramowitz, L., & Batallan, A. (2003). Épidémiologie des lésions anales (la fissure et thrombosed le hemorroid externe) pendant la grossesse et après la mise bas. *Gynécologie, Obstétrique & Fertilité, 31,* (6), 546-549.

Accutane & Pregnancy (2006). Organization of Teratology Information Services. Retrieved on December 11, 2006 from http://otispregnancy.org/pdf/isotretinoin.pdf.

Adams, J. (1996). Similarities in genetic mental retardation and neuroteratogenic syndromes. *Pharmacology, Biochemistry, and Behavior, 55* (4), 683-690.

Adams, J., & Lammer, E.J. (1991). Relationship between dysmorphology and neuropsychological function in children exposed to isotretinoin "in utero". In T. Fujii & G.J. Boer (Eds.). *Functional Neuroteratology of Short Term Exposure to Drugs.* (pp. 159-170). Tokyo: Teikyo University Press.

Adams, J., & Lammer, E.J. (1993). Neurobehavioral teratology of isotretinoin. *Reproductive Toxicology, 7* (2), 175-177.

Addis, A. & Koren, G. (2000). Safety of fluoxetine during the first trimester of pregnancy: meta-analytical review of epidemiological data. *Psychological Medicine, 30* (1), 89-94.

Adgent, M.A. (2006). Environmental tobacco smoke and sudden infant death syndrome: a review. *Birth Defects Research. Part B, Developmental and Reproductive Toxicology, 77* (1), 69-85.

Adzick, N.S., & Kitano, Y. (2003). Fetal surgery for lung lesions, congenital diaphragmatic hernia, and sacrococcygeal teratoma. *Seminars in Pediatric Surgery, 12* (3), 154-167.

Adzick, N.S., Harrison, M.R., Crombleholme, T.M., Flake, A.W., & Howell, L.J. (1998). Fetal lung lesions: management and outcome. *American Journal of Obstetrics & Gynecology, 179* (4), 884-889.

Adzick, N.S., Harrison, M.R., Flake, A.W., Howell, L.J., Golbus, M.S., & Filly, R.A. (1993). Fetal surgery for cystic adenomatoid malformation of the lung. *Journal of Pediatric Surgery, 28* (6), 806-812.

Agarwal, K.N., Gupta, A., Pushkarna, R., Bhargava, S.K., Faridi, M.M., & Prabhuy, M.K. (2000). Effects of massage and use of oil on growth, blood flow and sleep pattern in infants. *Indian Journal of Medical Research, 112,* 212-217.

Agren, A., & Berg, M. (2006).Tactile massage and severe nausea and vomiting during pregnancy--women's experiences. *Scandinavian Journal of Caring Sciences, 20* (2), 169-176.

Ahlborg, G., Bodin, L., & Hogstedt, C. (1990). Heavy lifting during pregnancy: a hazard to the fetus? A prospective study. *International Journal of Epidemiology, 19,* 90-97.

Ahlfors, K., Harris, S., Ivarsson, S.A., & Svanberg, L. (1981). Secondary maternal cytomegalovirus infection causing symptomatic congenital infection. *New England Journal of Medicine, 305,* 284.

Ahlfors, K., Harris, S., Ivarsson, S.A., & Svanberg, L. (1999). Report on a long-term study of maternal and congenital cytomegalovirus infection in Sweden. Review of prospective studies available in the literature. *Scandanavian Journal of Infectious Diseases, 31,* 443-457.

Ahlfors, K., Ivarsson, S.A., & Harris, S. (1984). Congenital cytomegalovirus infection and disease in Sweden and the relative importance of primary and secondary maternal infections. Preliminary findings from a prospective study. *Scandanavian Journal of Infectious Diseases, 16,* 129-137.

Ainslie, R.C., Solyom, A.E., & McManus, M.E. (1982). On the infant's meaning for the parent: A study of four mother-daughter pairs. *Child Psychiatry and Human Development 13,* 97-110.

Aldrich, C.A. (1928). A new test for hearing in the newborn: The conditioned reflex. *American Journal of the Disabled Child 35,* 36.

al-Kanhal, M., & Bani, I. (1995). Food habits during pregnancy among Saudi women. *International. Journal for Vitamin & Nutrition Research, 65* (3), 206-210.

Allanson, J.E., & Graham, G.E. (2002). Sex chromosome abnormalities. In D. L. Rimoin, J. M. Connor, R.E. Pyeritz, & B. R. Korf. (Eds.). *Emery and Rimoin's Principles and Practice of Medical Genetics* (4th ed.). (pp. 1184-1201). London: Churchill-Livingstone.

Allbutt, C. (1921). *Greek medicine in Rome.* London: Macmillan.

Allik, J. & Valsiner, J. (1980). Visual development in ontogenesis: Some reevaluations. In H.W. Reese & L.P Lipsitt (Eds.). *Advances in Child Development and Behavior, Vol. 15.* New York: Academic Press.

Alter, B.P., Modell, C.B., Fairweather, D., Hobbins, J.C., Mahoney, M.J., Frigoletto, F.D., Sherman, A.S. & Nathan, D.G. (1976). Prenatal diagnosis of hemoglobinopathies: a review of 15 cases. *New England Journal of Medicine, 295,* 1437.

American College of Obstetricians and Gynecologists (ACOG). (2001). Prenatal Diagnosis of Fetal Chromosomal Abnormalities. *ACOG Practice Bulletin,* 27.

American College of Obstetricians and Gynecologists (ACOG). (2005a). *Your Pregnancy and Birth* (4th ed.). Washington, DC: ACOG.

American College of Obstetricians and Gynecologists (ACOG). (2005b). Diagnosing Birth Defects. *ACOG Educational Pamphlet,* AP164. Washington, DC: ACOG.

American College of Obstetricians and Gynecologists. (1994). Exercise during pregnancy and the postpartum period. American College of Obstetricians and Gynecologists Technical Bulletin No. 189. *International Journal of Gynecology and Obstetrics, 45,* 65-70.

American College of Obstetricians and Gynecologists. (2002). Exercise during pregnancy and the postpartum period. American College of Obstetricians and Gynecologists Committee Opinion No. 267. *Obstetrics and Gynecology, 99,* 171-173.

American College of Obstetricians and Gynecologists. (2003). Exercise during pregnancy and the postpartum period. *Clinical Obstetrics and Gynecology, 46* (2), 469-499.

Amniocentesis (2005). March of Dimes at marchofdimes.com. Retrieved October 26, 2006 from http://www.marchofdimes.com /professional/680AMNIO-CENTESIS.asp

Anand, K.J. & Hickey, P.R. (1987). Pain and its effects in the human neonate and fetus. *New England Journal of Medicine 317,* 1321-1329.

Anand, K.J. & Hickey, P.R. (1988). Pain and its effects in the human neonate and fetus. *Pre- and Peri-Natal Psychology Journal 3,* 103-123.

Anastasi, A. (1958). Heredity, Environment, and the Question 'How?' *Psychological Review 65,* 197-208.

Andersen, H., Ehlers, N., & Matthiessen, M.E. (1965). Histochemistry and development of the human eyelids. *Acta Ophthalmologica, 43* (5), 642-668.

Andersen, H., Ehlers, N., Matthiessen, M.E., & Claesson, M.H. (1967). Histochemistry and development of the human eyelids II. *Acta Ophthalmologica, 45* (3), 288-293.

Anderson, L.J. (1990). Human parvovirus B19. *Pediatric Annals, 19* (9), 509-513.

Anderson, L.J., & Hurwitz, E.S. (1988). Human parvovirus B19 and pregnancy. *Clinical Perinatology, 15* (2):273-286.

Anderson, L.J., Khousam, M.N., Maxwell, D.J., Gould, S.J., Happerfield, L.C., & Smith, W.J. (1988). Human parvovirus B19 and hydrops fetalis. *Lancet, 1* (8584), 535.

Anderson, L.M. (2006). Environmental genotoxicants/carcinogens and childhood cancer: bridgeable gaps in scientific knowledge. Mutation Research, 608 (2), 136-156.

Andrade, A.J., Grande, S.W., Talsness, C.E., Gericke, C., Grote, K., Golombiewski, A., Sterner-Kock, A., & Chahoud, I. (2006). A dose response study following in utero and lactational exposure to di-(2-ethylhexyl) phthalate (DEHP): reproductive effects on adult male offspring rats. *Toxicology, 228* (1), 85-97.

Andrews, W.W., Goldenberg, R.L., Faye-Petersen, O., Cliver, S., Goepfert, A.R., & Hauth, J.C. (2006). The Alabama Preterm Birth study: polymorphonuclear and mononuclear cell placental infiltrations, other markers of inflammation, and outcomes in 23- to 32-week preterm newborn infants. *American Journal of Obstetrics & Gynecology, 195* (3), 803-808.

Andrews, W.W., Goldenberg, R.L., Mercer, B., Iams, J., Meis, P., Moawad, A., Das, A., Vandorsten, J.P., Caritis, S.N., Thurnau, G., Miodovnik, M., Roberts, J., & McNellis, D. (2000). The Preterm Prediction Study: association of second-trimester genitourinary chlamydia infection with subsequent spontaneous preterm birth. *American Journal of Obstetrics & Gynecology, 183* (3), 662-668.

Ang, E., Gluncic, V., Duque, A., Schafer, M.E., & Rakic, P. (2006) Prenatal exposure to ultrasound waves impacts neuronal migration in mice. *Proceedings of the National Academy of Science, 103* (34), 12903-12910.

Angles, J.M., Walsh, D.A., Li, K., Barnett, S.B., & Edwards, M.J. (1990). Effects of pulsed ultrasound and temperature on the development of rat embryos in culture. *Teratology, 42,* 285-293.

Annibale, B., Capurso, G., Chistolini, A., D'Ambra, G., DiGiulio, E., Monarca, B., & DelleFave, G. (2001). Gastrointestinal causes of refractory iron deficiency anemia in patients without gastrointestinal symptoms. *American Journal of Medicine, 111,* 439-445.

Arendt, R., Angelopoulos, J., Salvator, A., & Singer, L. (1999). Motor development of cocaine-exposed children at age two years. *Pediatrics, 103* (1), 86-92.

Arendt, R.E., Short, E.J., Singer, L.T., Minnes, S., Hewitt, J., Flynn, S., Carlson, L., Min, M.O., Klein, N., & Flannery, D. (2004). Children prenatally exposed to cocaine: Developmental outcomes and environmental risks at seven years of age. *Journal of Developmental & Behavioral Pediatrics, 25* (2), 83-90.

Arey, L. (1954). *Developmental anatomy.* Philadelphia: W.B. Saunders Co.

Artal, R. & Gardin, K. (1986). Historical perspectives. In R. Artal & R.A. Wiswell. (Eds.). *Exercise in Pregnancy.* (pp. 1-6). Baltimore: Williams & Wilkins.

Aslan, G., Aslan, D., Kizilyar, A., Ispahi, C., & Esen, A. (2005). A prospective analysis of sexual functions during pregnancy. *International Journal of Impotency Research, 17* (2), 154-157.

Aslin, R.N. (1981). Development of smooth pursuit in human infants. In D.F. Fisher, R.A. Monty, & J.W. Senders (Eds.). *Eye movements: Cognition and visual perception.* Hillsdale, NJ: Lawrence Erlbaum Associates.

Astley, S.J., Clarren, S.K., Little, R.E., Sampson, P.D., & Daling, J.R. (1992). Analysis of facial shape in children gestationally exposed to marijuana, alcohol and/or cocaine. *Pediatrics, 89,* 67-77.

Atwal, G., Manku, L., Griffiths, C., & Polson, D. (2006). Striae gravidarum in primiparae. *Br.Journal of Dermatology, 155* (5), 965-969.

Augarten A, Yahav, Y., Kerem, B., Halle, D., Laufer, J., Szeinberg, A., Dor, J., Mashiach, S., Gazit, E., & Madgar, I. (1994). Congenital bilateral absence of vas deferens in the absence of cystic fibrosis. *Lancet, 344,* 1473-1474.

Auger, J., Kunstmann, J.M., Czyglik, F, & Jouannet, P. (1995). Decline in semen quality among fertile men in Paris During the past 20 years. *New England Journal of Medicine, 332* (5). 281-285.

Azam A-Z., Vial, Y., Fawer, C-L., Zufferey, J., & Hohlfeld, P. (2001). Prenatal diagnosis of congenital cytomegalovirus infection. *Obstetrics & Gynecology, 97,* 443-448.

Azargoon, A., & Darvishzadeh, S. (2006). Association of bacterial vaginosis, trichomonas vaginalis, and vaginal acidity with outcome of pregnancy. *Archives of Iranian Medicine, 9* (3), 213-217.

B

Babler, W.J. (1991). Embryologic development of epidermal ridges and their configurations. In C.C. Plato, R.M. Garruto, & B.A. Schaumann (Eds.) *Dermatoglyphics: Science in transition.* (pp. 95-112). New York: Wiley-Liss.

Bada, H.S., Reynolds, E.W., & Hansen, W.F. (2006). Marijuana use, adolescent pregnancy, and alteration in newborn behavior: How complex can it get? *Journal of Pediatrics, 149* (6), 742-745.

Bailey, B.N., Delaney-Black, V., Covington, C.Y., Ager, J., Janisse, J., Hannigan, J.H., & Sokol, R.J. (2004). Prenatal exposure to binge drinking and cognitive and behavioral outcomes at age 7 years. *American Journal of Obstetrics & Gynecology, 191* (3), 1037-1043.

Bainbridge, S.A., & Smith, G.N. (2006). The effect of nicotine on in vitro placental perfusion pressure. *Canadian Journal of Physiology & Pharmacology, 84* (8-9), 953-957.

Baker, D., Telfer M.A., Richardson, C.E. & Clark, G.R. (1970). Chromosome errors in men with antisocial behavior: comparison of selected men with "Klinefelter's syndrome" and XYY chromosome pattern. *Journal of the American Medical Association, 214,* 869-878.

Ball. W., & Tronick, E. (1971). Infant responses to impending collision: Optical and real. *Science 171,* 818-820.

Barber, T.X. (1962). Hypnotic age regression: A critical review. *Psychosomatic Medicine 24,* 286-299.

Barnard, K.E., & Bee, H.L. (1983). The impact of temporally-patterned stimulation on the development of preterm infants. *Child Development, 54,* 1156-1167.

Barnea,, E. (2001). Embryo maternal dialogue: Linking pregnancy recognition and proliferation control. *Early Pregnancy, 5* (1), 14-15.

Barnett, E.A. (1979). The negative birth experience in analytical hypnotherapy. Paper presented at the 22nd annual meeting of the American Society of Clinical Hypnosis, San Francisco.

Bar-Oz, B., Bulkowstein, M., Benyamini, L., Greenberg, R., Soriano, I., Zimmerman, D., Bortnik, O., & Berkovitch, M. (2003). Use of antibiotic and analgesic drugs during lactation. *Drug Safety, 26* (13), 925-235.

Barr, H.M., Bookstein, F.L., O'Malley, K.D., Connor, P.D., Huggins, J.E., & Streissguth, A.P. (2006). Binge drinking during pregnancy as a predictor of psychiatric disorders on the Structured Clinical Interview for DSM-IV in young adult offspring. *American Journal of Psychiatry, 163* (6), 1061-1065.

Bartoshuk, A.K. (1962). Human neonatal cardiac acceleration to sound: Habituation and dishabituation. *Perceptual and Motor Skills 15,* 15-27.

Batchelor, E.S., Dean, R.S., Gray, J.W., & Wenck, S. (1991). Classification rates and relative risk factors for perinatal events predicting emotional/behavioral disorders in children. *Pre- and Peri-Natal Psychology Journal 5,* 327-341.

Bates, B. (1987). *A guide to physical examination.* (4th ed.). Philadelphia: J.B. Lippincott.

Bayley, T.M., Dye, L., Jones, S., DeBono, M., & Hill, A.J. (2002). Food cravings and aversions during pregnancy:

relationships with nausea and vomiting. *Appetite, 38* (1), 45-51.

Begg, E.J., Duffull, S.B., Saunders, D.A., Buttimore, R.C., Ilett, K.F., Hackett, L.P., Yapp, P., & Wilson, D.A. (1999). Paroxetine in human milk. *British Journal of Clinical Pharmacology, 48*, 142-147.

Behnke, M., Eyler, F.D., Garvan, C.W., & Wobie, K. (2001). The search for congenital malformations in newborns with fetal cocaine exposure. *Pediatrics, 107* (5), E74.

Beischer, N.A., & Wein, P. (1996). Linea alba pigmentation and umbilical deviation in nulliparous pregnancy: the ligamentum teres sign. *Obstetrics & Gynecology, 87* (2), 254-256.

Bekoff, M., & Fox, M. (1972). Postnatal neural ontology. *Developmental Psychobiology, 5*, 323-341.

Bellieni, C.V., Buonocore, G., Bagnoli, F., Cordelli, D.M., Gasparre, O., Calonaci, F., Filardi, G., Merola, A., & Petraglia, F. (2005). Is an excessive number of prenatal echographies a risk for fetal growth? *Early Human Development, 81* (8), 689-693.

Bellinger, D. (2005) Lead. *Pediatrics, 113*, 1016-1022.

Bender, H. (1988). Psychological aspects of prematurity and of neonatal intensive care: A working report. In. P.G. Fedor-Freybergh & M.L.V. Vogel (Eds.). *Prenatal Psychology and Medicine*, (pp. 235-248). Park Ridge NJ: The Parthenon Publishing Group.

Bennett, H.L., Giannini, J.A., & Kline, M.D. (1979). Consequences of hearing during anesthesia. Paper presented at the Annual Meeting of the American Psychological Association.

Benson, P., Little, B.C., Talbert, D.G., & Dewhurst, J. (1987). Foetal heart rate and maternal emotional state. *British Journal of Medical Psychology 60*, 151-154.

Benzodiazepines & Pregnancy (2005). Organization of Teratology Information Services. Retreived on December 11, 2006 from http://?otispregnancy.org/pdf/ benzodiazepines.pdf.

Berghella, V., Lim, P.J., Hill, M.K., Cherpes, J., Chennat, J., & Kaltenbach, K. (2003). Maternal methadone dose and neonatal withdrawal. *American Journal of Obstetrics & Gynecology, 189* (2), 312-317.

Bernard, J., & L.W. Sontag, L.W. (1947). Fetal reactivity to tonal stimulation: A preliminary report. *Journal of Genetic Psychology 70*, 205.

Bertollini, R., Pagano, M., & Mastroiacovo, P. (1993). What is a human teratogen: clinical and epidemiological criteria. *Annali dell'Istituto superiore di sanità, 29* (1), 97-104.

Biard, J.M., Johnson, M.P., Carr, M.C., Wilson, R.D., Hedrick, H.L., Pavlock, C., & Adzick, N.S. (2005). Long-term outcomes in children treated by prenatal vesicoamniotic shunting for lower urinary tract obstruction. *Obstetrics & Gynecology, 106* (3), 503-508

Birnholz, J.C. & Benacerraf, B.R. (1983). The development of human fetal hearing. *Science 222*, 516-518.

Blackmore-Prince, C., Harlow, S.D., Gargiullo, P., Lee, M.A., & Savitz, D.A. (1999). Chemical hair treatments and adverse pregnancy outcome among black women in central North Carolina. *American Journal of Epidemiology, 149*, 712-716.

Blaschitz, A., Hutter, H., & Dohr, G. (2001). HLA class I protein expression in the human placenta. *Early Pregnancy, 5* (1), 67-69.

Blau, A., Slaff, B., Easton, K., Welkowitz, J., Springham, J., & Cohen, J. (1963). The psychogenic etiology of premature births. *Psychosomatic Medicine 25*, 201-211.

Blot, I., Diallo, D., & Tchernia, G. (1999). Iron deficiency in pregnancy: effects on the newborn. *Current Opinion in Hematology, 6* (2), 65-70.

Bluhm, E.C., Daniels, J., Pollock, B.H., & Olshan, A.F. (2006). Maternal use of recreational drugs and neuroblastoma in offspring: a report from the Children's Oncology Group (United States). *Cancer Causes Control, 17* (5), 663-669.

Blumenfeld, Z. (2001). The effects of fetal breathing movements on the utero-fetal-placental circulation. *Early Pregnancy, 5* (1), 41-42.

Bogren, L.Y. (1984). The couvade syndrome: background variables. *Acta psychiatrica Scandinavica, 70* (4), 316-320.

Boppana, S.B., Fowler, K.B., Britt, W.J., Stagno, S., & Pass, R.F. (1999). Symptomatic congenital cytomegalovirus infection in infants born to mothers with preexisting immunity to cytomegalovirus. *Pediatrics, 104*, 55-60.

Bornstein, M.H., & Sigman, M.D. (1954). "The Onset and Early Development of Behavior." In Manual of Child Psychology, 2d ed, ed. L. Carmichael, 60-185. New York: J. Wiley, 1954.

Borrelli, F., Capasso, R., Aviello, G., Pittler, M.H., & Izzo, A.A. (2005). Effectiveness and safety of ginger in the treatment of pregnancy-induced nausea and vomiting. *Obstetrics & Gynecology, 105* (4), 849-856

Bowen, E. (1983). *Pre-birth bonding.* San Diego: Heartstart/Lovestart.

Bowen, E. (1988). A program to facilitate pre-birth bonding. . In. P.G. Fedor-Freybergh & M.L.V. Vogel (Eds.). *Prenatal Psychology and Medicine*, (pp. 267-271). Park Ridge NJ: The Parthenon Publishing Group.

Bower, T.G.R. (1974). *Development in Infancy.* San Francisco: W.H. Freeman & Co.

Bower, T.G.R., Broughton, J.M., & Moore, M.K. (1970). Demonstration of intention in the reaching behavior of neonate humans. *Nature 228*, 5272.

Bowes, W., Brackbill, Y., Conway, E. & Steinschneider, A. (1970). The effects of obstetrical medication on fetus and infant. *Monographs of the Society for Research in Child Development 35*, 3-25.

Brackbill, Y., & Koltsova, M.M. (1967). Conditioning and learning. In Y. Brackbill (Ed.). *Infancy and Early Childhood* (pp. 207-288). New York: Free Press.

Bradley, R.M. & Stern, L.B. (1967). The development of the human taste bud during the foetal period. *Journal of Anatomy 101*, 743-752.

Bradley, R.M., & Mistretta, C.M. (1975). Fetal sensory receptors. *Physiological Review, 55*, 352-382.

Brand-Miller, J., Hayne, S., Petocz, P., & Colagiuri, S. (2003). Low-glycemic index diets in the management of diabetes: a meta-analysis of randomized controlled trials. *Diabetes Care, 26*, 2261-2267.

Briggs, G.G., Freeman, R.K., & Yaffe, S.J. (1998). *Drugs in Pregnancy and Lactation.* (5th ed.). Baltimore: Williams and Wilkins.

Britt, D.W., Risinger, S.T., Miller, V., Mans, M.K., Krivchenia, E.L., & Evans, M.I. (1999). Determinants of parental decisions after the prenatal diagnosis of Down syndrome: Bringing in context. *American Journal of Medical Genetics, 93* (5), 410-416.

Brocklehurst, P., & French, R. (1998). The association between maternal HIV infection and perinatal outcome: A systematic review of the literature and meta-analysis. *British Journal of Gynecology, 105*, 836-848.

Brody, L.R., Zelazo, P.R., & Chaika, H. (1984). Habituation-dishabituation to speech in the neonate. *Developmental Psychology 20*, 114-119.

Brown, B. (2001). Sexual intercourse and orgasm during late pregnancy may have a protective effect against preterm delivery. *Family Planning Perspectives, 33*, 355-360.

Brown, J. (1972). Instrumental control of the sucking response in human newborns. *Journal of Experimental Child Psychology 14*, 66-80.

Brown, N.R., Shevell, S.K., & Rips, L.J. (1986). Public memories and their personal context." In D.C. Rubin (Ed.). *Autobiographical Memory.* Cambridge: Cambridge Univ. Press.

Brown, W. (2002). The benefits of physical activity during pregnancy. *Journal of Science and Medicine in Sport, 5* (1) 37-45.

Bruner, J.P. (2003). In their footsteps: A brief history of maternal-fetal surgery. *Clinical Perinatology, 30,* (3), 439-447.

Bruner, J.P., & Tulipan, N. (2005). Intrauterine repair of spina bifida. *Clinical Obstetrics & Gynecology, 48* (4), 942-955.

Bruner, J.P., Tulipan, N., Reed, G., Davis, G.H., Bennett, K., Luker, K.S., & Dabrowiak, M.E. (2004). Intrauterine repair of spina bifida: preoperative predictors of shunt-dependent hydrocephalus. *American Journal of Obstetrics & Gynecology, 190* (5), 1305-1312.

Burch, K.J. & Wells, B.G. (1992). Fluoxetine/Norfluoxetine concentrations in human milk. *Pediatrics, 89,* 676-677.

C

Caffeine & Pregnancy (2001). Organization of Teratology Information Services. Retreived on December 12, 2006 from http://otispregnancy.org/pdf/caffeine.pdf.

Cagnacci, A. (2003). The male disadvantage and the seasonal rhythm of sex ratio at the time of conception. *Human Reproduction, 18* (4), 885-887.

Calguneri, M., Bird, H.A., & Wright, V. (1982). Changes in joint laxity occurring during pregnancy. *Annals of the Rheumatic Diseases, 41,* 126–128.

Cameron, A.D., Swain, S., & Patrick, W.J. (1997). Human parvovirus B19 infection associated with hydrops fetalis. *The Australian & New Zealand Journal of Obstetrics & Gynaecology, 37* (3), 316-319.

Campbell, S. (2002). 4D, or not 4D: that is the question. *Ultrasound in Obstetrics & Gynecology, 19* (1), 1-4.

Campbell, S. (2004). *Watch me grow: A unique 3-dimensional week-by-week look at your baby's behavior and development in the womb.* New York: St. Martins.

Canadian Early and Mid-Trimester Amniocentesis Trial (CEMAT) Group. (1998). Randomized trial to assess safety and fetal outcome of early and midtrimester amniocentesis. *The Lancet, 351,* 242-247.

Canger, R., Battino, D., Canevini, M.P., Fumarola, C., Guidonlin, L., Vignoli, A., Mamoli, D., Palmieri, C., Molteni, F., Granata, T., Hassibi, P., Zamperini, P., Pardi. G., & Avanzini. G. (1999). Malformations in offspring of women with epilepsy: a prospective study. *Epilepsia 40* (9), 1231-1236.

Caplan, F. (1973). *The first twelve months of life.* New York: Grosset & Dunlap.

Caraka. (1982). *The Caraka-samhita of Agnivesa.* (Vol. 1 Sarirasthanam), (P. Sharma, Ed. & Trans.). New Delhi: Chaukhambha Orientalia.

Carbohydrates (2006). Harvard School of Public Health. Retreived on November 7, 2006 from http://www.hsph.harvard.edu/nutritionsource/carbohydrates.html.

Carbon Monoxide & Pregnancy (2006). Organization of Teratology Information Services. Retreived on December 13, 2006 from http://otispregnancy.org/pdf/carbon_monoxide.pdf.

Carlsen, E., Giwereman, A., Keiding, N., & Skakkebaek, N.E. (1992). Evidence for decreasing quality of semen in the past 50 years. *British Medical Journal, 305,* 609-613.

Carlson, B., & La Barba, R.C. (1979). Maternal emotionality during pregnancy and reproductive outcome. *International Journal of Behavior Development 2,* 342-376.

Carlson, B.M. (2004). *Human embryology & developmental biology.* (3rd ed.). Philadelphia: Mosby.

Carnegie Stages 12-23 (2006). The Visible Embryo at ww.viembryo.com. Retreived October 10, 2006 from http://www.visembryo.com/baby/carnegiestages.html.

Carpenter, M.W., Sady, S.P., Hoegsberg, B., Sady, M.A., Haydon, B., Cullinane, E.M. & Thompson, P. (1988). Fetal heart rate response to maternal exertion. *Journal of the American Medical Association, 259,* 3006–3009.

Carter, J., Ernst, A., & Zibrack, J. (1998). Carbon monoxide poisoning. *New England Journal of Medicine, 339,* 1603-1608.

Casper, R.C., Fleisher, B.E., Lee-Ancajas, J.C., Gilles, A., Gaylor, E., DeBattista, A., & Hoyme, H.E. (2003). Follow-up of children of depressed mothers exposed or not exposed to antidepressant drugs during pregnancy. *Journal of Pediatrics, 142,* 402-408.

Cass, D.L. (2005). Fetal surgery for congenital diaphragmatic hernia: the North American experience. Seminars in Perinatology, 29 (2), 104-111.

Casteels, A., Naessens, A., Gordts, F., De Catte, L., Bougatef, A., & Foulon, W. (1999). Neonatal screening for congenital cytomegalovirus infections. *Journal of Perinatal Medicine, 27,* 116-121.

Castilla, E.E., Ashton-Prolla, P., Barreda-Mejia, E., Brunoni, D., Cavalcanti, D.P., Correa-Neto, J., Delgadillo, J.L., Dutra, M.G., Felix, T., Giraldo, A., Juarez, N., Lopez-Camelo, J.S., Nazer, J., Orioli, I.M., Paz, J.E., Pessoto, M.A., Pina-Neto, J.M., Quadrelli, R., Rittler, M., Rueda, S., Saltos, M., Sanchez, O., & Schuler, L. (1996). Thalidomide, a current teratogen in South America. *Teratology, 54* (6), 273-277.

Center for Disease Control and Prevention (CDC) (2004). *2002 Assisted reproductive technology success rates: National summary and fertility reports.* Retrieved on October 4, 2006 from http://www.cdc.gov/ART/ART02/PDF/ART2002.pdf.

Center for Disease Control and Prevention (CDC) (2006). *Pelvic inflammatory disease.* Retrieved on October 3, 2006 from http://www.cdc.gov/std/PID/STDFact-PID.htm.

Center for Disease Control and Prevention (CDC), National Vital Statistics System (NVSS). (2005). *Trend analysis of the sex ratio at birth in the United States.* Retrieved on September 22, 2006 from http://www.cdc.gov/nchs/nvss.htm.

Center for Disease Control and Prevention (CDC), National Vital Statistics System (NVSS). (2005). *Trend analysis of the sex ratio at birth in the United States.* Retrieved on September 22, 2006 from http://www.cdc.gov/nchs/nvss.htm.\

Centers for Disease Control and Prevention (CDC) (2004). Alcohol consumption among women who are pregnant or who might become pregnant--United States, 2002. *Morbidity and Mortality Weekly Report, 53* (50), 1178-1181.

Cernerud, L., Eriksson, M., Jonsson, B., Steneroth, G., & Zetterstrom, R. (1996). Amphetamine addiction during pregnancy. 14 year follow-up in growth and performance. *Acta Paediatrica, 85,* 204-208.

Cernoch, J.M. & Porter, R.H. (1985). Recognition of maternal axillary odours by infants. *Child Development 56,* 1593-98.

Chamberlain, D. (1981). Birth recall in hypnosis. *Birth Psychology Bulletin 2,* 14-18.

Chamberlain, D. (1983). *Consciousness at birth: A review of the empirical evidence.* San Diego: Chamberlain Communications.

Chamberlain, D. (1986). Reliability of birth memories: Evidence from mother and child pairs in hypnosis. *Journal of the American Academy of Medical Hypnoanalysis 1,* 89-98.

Chamberlain, D. (1987a). Consciousness at birth: The range of empirical evidence. In Thomas R. Verny (Ed.). *Pre- and peri-natal psychology: An introduction* (pp. 69-90). New York: Human Sciences Press.

Chamberlain, D. (1987b). The cognitive newborn: A scientific update. *British Journal of Psychotherapy 4,* 30-71.

Chamberlain, D. (1988a). *The mind of a newborn baby: Unexpected thoughts and memories at birth.* Los Angeles: J.P. Tarcher.

Chamberlain, D. (1988b). The mind of the newborn: Increasing evidence of competence." In. P.G. Fedor-Freybergh & M.L.V. Vogel (Eds.). *Prenatal Psychology and Medicine,* (pp. 5-22). Park Ridge NJ: The Parthenon Publishing Group.

Chambers, C.D. (2006). Risks of hyperthermia associated with hot tub or spa use by pregnant women. *Birth Defects Research. Part A, Clinical and Molecular Teratology, 76* (8), 569-573.

Chambers, C.D., Anderson, P.O., Thomas, R.G., Dick, L.M., Felix, R.J., Johnson, K.A., & Jones, K.L. (1999). Weight gain in infants breastfed by mothers who take fluoxetine. *Pediatrics, 104* (5), I1-15.

Chambers, C.D., Hernandez-Diaz, S., Van Marter, L.J., Werler, M.M., Louik, C., Jones, K.L., & Mitchell, A.A. (1998). Spontaneous ecchymoses due to paroxetine administration. *American Journal of Medicine, 104,* 197-198.

Chambers, C.D., Johnson, K.A., Dick, L.M., Felix, R.J., & Jones, K.L. (1996). Outcomes in pregnant women taking fluoxetine. *New England Journal of Medicine, 335* (14), 1010-1015.

Chan, K.L., Tang, M.H., Tse, H.Y., Tang, R.Y., Lam, H.S., Lee, C.P., & Tam, P.K. (2002). Factors affecting outcomes of prenatally-diagnosed tumours. *Prenatal Diagnostics, 22* (5), 437-443.

Chance, P.I. & Smith, D.W. (1978). Hyperthermia and meningomyelocele and anencephaly. *Lancet, 1,* 769.

Chang, L., Smith, L., LoPresti, C., Yonekura, M., Kuo, J., Walot, I., & Ernst, T. (2004). Smaller subcortical volumes and cognitive deficits in children with prenatal methamphetamine exposure. *Psychiatry Research: Neuroimaging, 132* (2), 95-106.

Chasnoff, I.J., Anson, A., Hatcher, R., Stenson, H., Iaukea, K., & Randolph, L. (1998). Prenatal exposure to cocaine and other drugs. Outcome at four to six years. *Annals of the New York Academy of Sciences, 846,* 314-328.

Chasnoff, U., Burns, K.A., & Burns, W.J. (1987). Cocaine use in pregnancy: perinatal morbidity and mortality. *Neurotoxicology and Teratology, 9,* 291-293.

Chavez, G.G., Mulinare, J., & Cordero, J.F. (1989). Maternal cocaine use during early pregnancy as a risk factor for congenital urogenital anomalies. *Journal of the American Medical Association, 262,* 795-798.

Cheek, D.B. & Lecron, L.M. (1968). *Clinical Hypnotherapy.* New York: Grune & Stratton.

Cheek, D.B. (1959). Unconscious perceptions of meaningful sounds during surgical anesthesia as revealed under hypnosis. *American Journal of Clinical Hypnosis 1,* 103-113.

Cheek, D.B. (1974). Sequential head and shoulder movements appearing with age regression in hypnosis to birth. *American Journal of Clinical Hypnosis 16,* 261-266.

Cheek, D.B. (1975). Maladjustment patterns apparently related to imprinting at birth. *American Journal of Clinical Hypnosis 18,* 75-82.

Cheek, D.B. (1986). Prenatal and perinatal imprints: Apparent prenatal consciousness as revealed by hypnosis. *Pre & Peri-Natal Psychology Journal 1,* 97-110.

Chen, K.T., Segu, M., Lumey, L.H., Kuhn, L., Carter, R.J., Bulterys, M., & Abrams, E.J. (2005). Genital herpes simplex virus infection and perinatal transmission of human immunodeficiency virus. *Obstetrics & Gynecology, 106* (6), 1341-1348.

Chernecky, C.C, & Berger, B.J. (Eds). (2004). *Laboratory Tests and Diagnostic Procedures* (4th ed.). Philadelphia: Saunders.

Cherry, D., Lowry, L., Velez, L., Cotrell, C., & Keyes, D.C. (2002). Elemental mercury poisoning in a family of seven. Environmental issues in the health of children. *Family & Community Health, 24* (4):1-8.

Cherry, S.H. (1973). *Understanding Pregnancy and Childbirth.* New York: Bobs-Merrill.

Chiba, T., Albanese, C.T., Farmer, D.L., Dowd, C.F., Filly, R.A., Machin, G.A., & Harrison, M. (2000). Balloon tracheal occlusion for congenital diaphragmatic hernia: experimental studies. *Journal of Pediatric Surgery, 35,* 1566–1570.

Choi, H.S., Shim, Y.K., Kaye, W.E., & Ryan, P.B. (2006). Potential residential exposure to toxics release inventory chemicals during pregnancy and childhood brain cancer. *Environmental Health Perspectives, 114* (7), 1113-1118.

Choi, S.H. (2001). The role of fetal surgery in life threatening anomalies. *Yonsei Medical Journal, 42* (6), 681-685.

Chorionic Villus Sampling (CVS) (2006). March of Dimes at marchofdimes.com. Retrieved October 26, 2006 from http://www.marchofdimes.com/ professionals/ 681_1165.asp.

Christian, M., & Brent R. (2001). Teratogen update: Evaluation of the reproductive and developmental risks of caffeine. *Teratology, 64,* 51-78.

Christo, G.C., Urala, M.S., Duvvi, H.V., & Venkatesh, A. (1987). Maternal hyperthermia as a teratogenic agent. *Indian Pediatrics, 24,* 597-600.

Christoph, J., Kattner, E., Seitz, H.M., & Reiter-Owona, I. (2004). Strategien zur Diagnostik und Behandlung der pränatalen *Toxoplasma*-Infektion - ein aktueller Überblick. *Zeitschrift für Geburtshilfe und Neonatologie, 208,* 10-16.

Churchill, J.A., Berendes, H.W., & Nemore, J. (1969). Neuropsychological deficits in children of diabetic mothers. *American Journal of Obstetrics and Gynecology, 105,* 257-268.

Clapp, J.F. (1985). Fetal heart rate responses to running in midpregnancy and late pregnancy. *American Journal of Obstetrics & Gynecology, 153,* 251–252.

Clapp, J.F. (1990). The course of labor after endurance exercise during pregnancy. *American Journal of Obstetrics and Gynecology, 163* (6 Part 1), 1799-1805.

Clapp, J.F., & Capeless, E.L. (1990). Neonatal morphometrics after endurance exercise during pregnancy. *American Journal of Obstetrics & Gynecology, 163,* 1805-1811.

Clark, T.J., Martin, W.L., Divakaran, T.G., Whittle, M.J., Kilby, M.D., & Khan, K.S. (2003). Prenatal bladder drainage in the management of fetal lower urinary tract obstruction: a systematic review and meta-analysis. *Obstetrics & Gynecology, 102* (2), 367-382.

Clarren, S.K., Smith, D.W., Harvey, M.A., Ward, R.H., & Myrianthopoulos, N.C. (1979). Hyperthermia--a prospective evaluation of a possible teratogenic agent in man. Journal of Pediatrics, 95 (1), 81-83.

Clements, M. (1977). Observations on certain aspects of neonatal behavior in response to auditory stimuli. Paper presented at the 5th International Congress of Psychosomatic Obstetrics and Gynecology, Rome.

Cnattingius, S., Signorello, L.B., Anneren, G., Clausson, B., Ekbom, A., Ljunger, E., Blot, W.J., McLaughlin, J.K., Petersson, G., Rane, A., & Granath, F. (2000) Caffeine intake and the risk of first-trimester spontaneous abortion. *The New England Journal of Medicine, 343,* 1839-1845.

Cocaine & Pregnancy (2001). Organization of Teratology Information Services. Retrieved on December 12, 2006 from http://otispregnancy.org/pdf/cocaine.pdf.

Cocchi, R., Felici, M., Tonni, L., & Venanzi, G. (1984). Behavior troubles in nursery school children and their possible relationship to pregnancy or delivery difficulties. *Acta Psychiatrica Belgica 84,* 173-179.

Cogswell, M.E., Kettel-Khan, L., & Ramakrishnan, U. (2003). Iron supplement use among women in the United States: science, policy and practice. *Journal of Nutrition, 133,* 1974S-1977S.

Cogswell, M.E., Parvanta, I., Ickes, L., Yip, R., & Brittenham, G.M. (2003). Iron supplementation during pregnancy, anemia, and birth weight: a randomized controlled trial. *American Journal of Clinical Nutrition, 78* (4), 773-781.

Cohen, D.J., Doucet, M., Cutlip, D.E., Ho, K.L.K., Popma, J.J., & Kuntz, R.E. (2001). Impact of smoking on clinical and angiographic restenosis after percutaneous coronary intervention. *Circulation, 104,* 773.

Cohen, G. (1989). *Memory in the real world*. London: Lawrence Erlbaum Associates.

Cohen, G., & Faulkner, D. (1986). Memory for proper names: Age differences in retrieval. *British Journal of Developmental Psychology 4*, 187-197.

Cohen, G., & Faulkner, D. (1988). Life span changes in autobiographical memory." In M.M. Gruneberg, P.E. Morris, & R.N. Sykes (Eds.). *Practical Aspects of Memory: Current Research and Issues*. Chichester, John Wiley & Sons.

Cohen, L.B. (1979). Our developing knowledge of infant perception and cognition. *American Psychologist 34*, 894-899.

Cohen, L.S., Friedman, J.M., Jefferson, J.W., Johnson, E.M., & Weiner, M.L.(1994). A reevaluation of risk of in utero exposure to lithium. *Journal of the American Medical Association, 271* (2), 146-150.

Cohn, B. (2002). Can Placenta Factors Explain Race Patterns of Breast Cancer? California Breast Cancer Research Program. Retrieved on October 9, 2006 from http://www.cbcrp.org/research /PageGrant.asp?grant_id=2276

Coley, J.L., Msamanga, G.I., Fawzi, M.C., Kaaya, S., Hertzmark, E., Kapiga, S., Spiegelman, D., Hunter, D., & Fawzi, W.W. (2001). The association between maternal HIV-1 infection and pregnancy outcomes in Dar es Salaam, Tanzania. *British Journal of Gynecology, 108,* 1125-1133.

Collings, C.M.S., Curet, L.B., & Mullin, J.P. (1983). Maternal and fetal responses to a maternal aerobic exercise program. *American Journal of Obstetrics & Gynecology, 145,* 702–707.

Collins, J.H., Collins, C.L., & Collins, C.C. (1990). *Silent Risk: Issues about the Human Umbilical Cord*. The Pregnancy Institute. www.preginst.com. Retrieved on 10/7/06 at http://www.preginst.com/silentrisk.pdf.

Colvin, J., Bower, C., Dickinson, J.E., & Sokol, J. (2005). Outcomes of congenital diaphragmatic hernia: a population-based study in Western Australia. *Pediatrics, 116* (3), 356-363

Comhaire, F.H., & Thiery, M. (1986). Methods for improvement of the success rate of artificial insemination with donor semen. *International Journal of Andrology, 9* (1), 14-20.

Comparetti, A.M. (1981). The neurophysiological and clinical implications of studies on fetal motor behavior. *Seminars in Perinatology 5*, 2.

Comparetti, A.M. (1986). Fetal and neonatal origins of being a person and belonging to the world. *Maturation and Learning*, Supplement 5.

Comparetti, A.M. & Gidoni, E.A. (1967). Pattern analysis of motor development and its disorders. *Developmental Medical and Child Neurology 9*, 5.

Comparetti, A.M. & Gidoni, E.A. (1976). Dalla parte del neonatol proposte per una competenza prognostica. *Neuropsichiatria Infantile*, 175.

Condon, J.T. (1985). The parental-foetal relationship: A comparison of male and female expectant parents. *Journal of Psychosomatic Obstetrics and Gynaecology 4*, 271-284.

Condon, J.T. (1987). Psychological and physical symptoms during pregnancy: A comparison of male and female expectant roles. *Journal of Reproductive and Infant Psychology 5*, 207-219.

Condon, W. (1977). A primary phase in the organization of infant responding. In H.R. Schaffer (Ed.). *Studies in Mother-Infant Interaction*. (pp. 153-176). New York: Academic Press.

Condon, W., & Sander, L. (1974). Neonate movement is synchronized with adult speech: Interactional participation and language acquisition. *Science 183*, 99-101.

Conforti, A., & Losty, P.D. (2006). Perinatal management of congenital diaphragmatic hernia. *Early Human Development, 82* (5), 283-287.

Conner, G.K., & Denson, V. (1990). Expectant fathers' response to pregnancy: review of literature and implications for research in high-risk pregnancy. *The Journal of Perinatal & Neonatal Nursing, 4* (2), 33-42.

Connors, G., Hunse, C., Carmichael, L., Natale, R., Richardson, B. (1987). Control of fetal breathing in the human fetus between 24 and 34 weeks' gestation. *American Journal of Obstetrics and Gynaecology, 160* (4), 932-938.

Connors, G., Hunse, C., Carmichael, L., Natale, R., & Richardson, B. (1989). Control of fetal breathing in the human fetus between 24 and 34 weeks' gestation. *American Journal of Obstetrics and Gynecology, 160* (4), 932-938.

Cook, A.J., Gilbert, R.E., Buffolano, W., Zufferey, J., Petersen, E., Jenum, P.A., Foulon, W., Semprini, A.E., & Dunn, D.T. (2000). Sources of toxoplasmosis in pregnant women. *British Medical Journal, 321,* 142-147.

Cooper, L.Z. (1985). The history and medical consequences of rubella. Review of Infecttious Diseases, 7 (Suppl 1), S2-10.

Copher, D.E., & Huber, C.P. (1967). Heart rate response of the human fetus to induced maternal hypoxia. *American Journal of Obstetrics and Gynecology 98*, 320-335.

Corabian, P., & Hailey, D. (1999). The efficacy and adverse effects of in vitro fertilization and embryo transfer. *International Journal of Technology Assessment in Health Care, 15* (1), 66-85.

Corbett, R.W., Ryan, C., & Weinrich, S.P. (2003). Pica in pregnancy: does it affect pregnancy outcomes? *The American Journal of Maternal Child Nursing, 28* (3), 183-189.

Cortes, R., Keller, R., Townsend, T., Harrison, M, Farmer, D., Lee, H., Piecuch, R., Leonard, C., Hetherton, M., Bisgaard, R., & Nobuhara, K.K. (2005). Survival of severe congenital diaphragmatic hernia has morbid consequences. *Journal of Pediatric Surgery, 40* (1), 36-46.

Cortes, R.A., & Farmer, D.L. (2004). Recent advances in fetal surgery. *Seminars in Perinatology, 28* (3), 199-211.

Cosmi, E.V., La Torre, R., & Cosmi, E. (2001). Response of human fetal pituitary cells to activin, inhibin, hypophysiotropic and factors in vitro. *Early Pregnancy, 5* (1), 51-52.

Costei, A.M., Kozer, E., Ho, T., Ito, S., & Koren, G. (2002). Perinatal outcome following third trimester exposure to paroxetine. *Archives of Pediatrics & Adolescent Medicine, 156*, 1129-1132.

Costeloe, K., Gibson, A.T., Marlow, N., & Wilkinson, A.R.. (2000). The EPICure Study: Outcome to discharge from hospital for babies born at the threshold of viability. *Pediatrics, 106* (4), 659-671.

Coussons-Read, M.E., Okun, M.L., & Nettles, C.D. (2006). Psychosocial stress increases inflammatory markers and alters cytokine production across pregnancy. *Brain, Behavior, and Immunity*, October 5 (E-pub ahead of print).

Couvreur, J., Thulliez, P., Daffos, F., Aufrant, C., Bompard, Y., Gesquiere, A., & Desmonts, G. (1993). In utero treatment of toxoplasmic fetopathy with the combination pyrimethamine-sulfadiazine. *Fetal Diagnosis and Therapy, 8*, 45-50.

Craig, G.J, & Dunn, W.L. (2007). *Understanding Human Development*. Upper Saddle River, NJ: Prentice-Hall.

Crandon, A.J. (1979). Maternal anxiety and obstetric complications. *Journal of Psychosomatic Research 23*, 109-111.

Cunningham, F.G., Gant, N.F., Leveno, K.J., Gilstrap, L.C., Hauth, J.C., & Wenstrom, K.D. (Eds.). (2001). *Williams Obstetrics*. (21st ed.). New York: McGraw-Hill.

Cytomegalovirus & Pregnancy (2001). Organization of Teratology Information Services. Retreived on December 14, 2006 from http://otispregnancy.org/ pdf/cyto megalovirus.pdf.

Czeizel, A.E. (1988). Lack of evidence of teratogenicity of benzodiazepine drugs in Hungary. *Reproductive Toxicology, 1*, 183-188.

D

D'Amato, R.J., Loughnan, E., Flynn, E., & Folkman, J. (1994). Thalidomide is an inhibitor of angiogenesis. *Proceedings of the National Academy of Sciences, 91*, 4082 – 4085.

da Vinci, L. (1945). *The Drawings of Leonard da Vinci*. A.E. Popham (Ed.). New York: Harvest Books.

Dado, G.M., Dobrin, P.B., & Mrkvicka, R.S. (1997). Venous flow through coiled and noncoiled umbilical cords. *Journal of Reproductive Medicine, 42*, 576-580.

Daffos, F., Hohlfeld, P., Costa, J_M., Thulliez, P., Forestier, F., & Vidaud, M. (1988). Prenatal management of 746 pregnancies at risk for congenital toxoplasmosis. *New England Journal of Medicine, 318* (5), 271-275.

Dai, W.S., LaBraico, J.M., & Stern, R.S. (1992). Epidemiology of isotretinoin exposure during pregnancy. *Journal of the American Academy of Dermatology, 26*, 599-606.

Dairo, M.D., & Lawoyin, T.O. (2006). Demographic factors determining compliance to iron supplementation in pregnancy in Oyo State, Nigeria. *Nigerian Journal of Medicine, 15* (3), 241-244.

Danso, K., Parsyan, A., Dompreh, A., Allain, J.P., & Candotti, D. (2006). Maternal-fetal transmission of human parvovirus B19 genotype 3. *Journal of Infectious Diseases, 194* (5), 608-611.

Davenport, M., Warne, S.A., Cacciaguerra, S., Patel, S., Greenough, A., & Nicolaides, K. (2004). Current outcome of antenatally diagnosed cystic lung disease. *Journal of Pediatric Surgery, 39*, 549-556.

Davids, A., Holden, R.H., & Gray, G. (1963). Maternal anxiety during pregnancy and adequacy of mother and child adjustment eight months following childbirth. *Child Development 34*, 993-1002.

Davies, G.A.L., Wolfe, L.A., Mottola, M.F., MacKinnon, C., & Arsenault, M. (2003). Exercise in pregnancy and the postpartum period. *Journal of Obstetrics and Gynaecology Canada, 25* (6), 516-529.

Davies, G.S. (1973). Revolutions and cyclical rhythms in prenatal life: Fetal respiratory movements rediscovered. *Pediatrics, 51*, 965.

Davis, D.L,, Gottlieb, M.G., & Stampnitzky, J.R. (1998). Reduced ratio of male to female births in several industrial countries: A sentinel health indicator? *Journal of the American Medical Association, 279*, 1018-1023.

Davitian, C., Uzan, M., Tigaizin, A., Ducarme, G., Dauphin, H., & Poncelet, C.

(2006). Utilisation maternelle de cannabis et restriction intra-utérine de croissance. *Gynécologie, Obstétrique & Fertilité, 34* (7-8), 632-637.

Day, D.W. (1990). Braxton Hicks vs. preterm labor. *Minnesota Medicine, 73* (8), 21-22.

Day, N.L., Goldschmidt, L., & Thomas, C.A. (2006). Prenatal marijuana exposure contributes to the prediction of marijuana use at age 14. *Addiction, 101* (9), 1313-1322.

Dayton, G.O., Jones, M., Aiu, P., Rawson, P., Steele, B., & Rose. M. (1964). Developmental study of coordinated eye movements in the human infant: I. Visual acuity in the newborn human: A study based on induced optokinetic nystagmus recorded by electro-oculography. *Archives of Opthamology 71*, 865-870.

Dayton, G.O., Jones, M., Steel, B., & Rose, M. (1964). Developmental study of coordinated eye movements in the human infant: II. An electro-oculographic study of the fixation reflex in the newborn. *Archives of Opthamology 71*, 871-875.

de Araujo Burgos, M.G., Bion, F.M., & Campos, F. (2004). Lactation e álcool: efeitos clínicos e nutritivos. *Archivos Latinoamericanos de Nutrición, 54* (1), 25-35.

de Jong, E.P., de Haan, T. Kroes, A., Beersma, M.F., Oepkes, D., & Walther, F.J. (2006). Parvovirus B19 infection in pregnancy. *Journal of Clinical Virology, 36* (1), 1-7.

de Moraes Barros, M.C., Guinsburg, R., de Araujo Peres, C., Mitsuhiro, S., Chalem, E., & Laranjeira, R.R. (2006). Exposure to marijuana during pregnancy alters neurobehavior in the early neonatal period. *Journal of Pediatrics, 149* (6), 781-787.

De Muylder, X. & Wesel, S. (1988). Maternal attitudes and preterm labor. In. P.G. Fedor-Freybergh & M.L.V. Vogel (Eds.). *Prenatal Psychology and Medicine*, (pp. 87-92). Park Ridge NJ: The Parthenon Publishing Group.

De Rocha, A. (1911). Les vies successives: Documents pour l'etude de cette question. Paris: Chacornac Freres.

De Snoo, K. (1937). Das Trinkende Kind im Uterus. *Monatsschrift Geburtsh Gynaekologie*, 105.

De Sousa, A. (1974). Causes of behavior problems in children. *Child Psychiatry Quarterly 7*, 308.

de Vries, J.I.P., Visser, G.H.A., & Prechtl, H.F.R. (1982). The emergence of fetal behaviour. I. Qualitative aspects. *Early Human Development, 7* (4), 301-322.

de Vries, J.I.P., Visser, G.H.A.,& Prechtl, H.F.R. (1985). The emergence of fetal behaviour. II. Quantitative aspects. *Early Human Development, 12* (2), 99-120.

Dean, R.S., & Gray, J.W. (1985). *Maternal Perinatal Scale*. Muncie, Ind.: Ball State University Press.

Debes, F., Budtz-Jorgensen, E., Weihe, P., White, R.F., & Grandjean, P. (2006). Impact of prenatal methylmercury exposure on neurobehavioral function at age 14 years. *Neurotoxicology & Teratology, 28* (3), 363-375.

DeCasper, A.J., & Fefer, W.P. (1980). Of human bonding: Newborn's prefer their mother's voices. *Science 208*, 1174-1176.

DeCasper, A.J., & Prescott, P.A. (1984). Human newborn's perception of male voices: Preference, discrimination and reinforcing value. *Developmental Psychobiology 17*, 481-491.

DeCasper, A.J., & Spence, M.J. (1978). Prenatal maternal speech influences newborn's perception of speech sound. *Infant Behavior and Development 1*, 36-48.

deMause, L. (1982). *Foundations of psychohistory*. New York: Creative Roots.

deMause, L. (1987). The fetal origins of history. In Thomas R. Verny (Ed.). *Pre- and peri-natal psychology: An introduction* (pp. 243-259). New York: Human Sciences Press.

Dempsey, D.A., & Stewart, S.L. (2006). Smoking habits, nicotine use, and congenital malformations. *Obstetrics & Gynecology, 107* (5), 1167-1168.

Denenberg, V.H. (1964). Critical periods, stimulus input and emotional reactivity: A theory of infantile stimulation. *Psychological Review 71*, 335-351.

Deprest, J., Gratacos, E., & Nicolaides, K.H. (2004). Fetoscopic tracheal occlusion (FETO) for severe congenital diaphragmatic hernia: evolution of a technique and preliminary results. *Ultrasound in Obstetrics & Gynecology, 24*, 121–126.

Deprest, J., Jani, J., Gratacos, E., Vandecruys, H., Naulaers, G., Delgado, J., Greenough, A., & Nicolaides, K. (2005). Fetal intervention for congenital diaphragmatic hernia: the European experience. *Seminars in Perinatology, 29* (2), 94-103.

Deprest, J., Jani, J., Van Schoubroeck, D., Cannie, M., Gallot, D., Dymarkowski, S., Fryns, J.P., Naulaers, G., Gratacos, E., & Nicolaides, K. (2006). Current consequences of prenatal diagnosis of congenital diaphragmatic hernia. *Journal of Pediatric Surgery, 41* (2), 423-30.

Deprest, J.A., & Gratacos, E. (1999). Obstetrical endoscopy. *Current Opinions in Obstetrics and Gynecology, 11* (2), 195–203.

Derom, R., & Bryan, E. (2000). Improving the treatment of infertility: Towards avoiding high order multiple gestation. *Twin Research, 3*, 109-112.

Desyrel and Serzone & Pregnancy (2003). Organization of Teratology Information Services. Retreived on December 11, 2006 from http://otispregnancy.org/pdf/zoloft.pdf.

Devoe, L.D., Murray, C., Youssif, A., & Arnaud, M. (1993). Maternal caffeine consumption and fetal behavior in normal third-trimester pregnancy. *American Journal of Obstetrics & Gynecology. 168* (4). 1105-1112.

Dietrich, K.N., Berger, O.G., Succop, P.A., Hammond, P.B., & Bornschein, R.L. (1993). The developmental consequences of low to moderate prenatal and postnatal lead exposure: Intellectual attainment in the Cincinnati lead study cohort following school entry. *Neurotoxicolgy and Teratology, 15,* 37-44.

DiFiore, J.W., & Wilson, J.M. (1994). Lung development. *Seminars in Pediatric Surgery, 3* (4):221-232.

Diguet, A., Patrier, S., Eurin, D., Chouchene, S., Marpeau, L., Laquerriere, A., & Verspyck, E. (2006). Prenatal diagnosis of an exceptional intrauterine herpes simplex type 1 infection. *Prenatal Diagnosis, 26* (2), 154-157.

DiLella, A.G., Kwok, S.C. M., Ledley, F.D., Marvit, J., Woo, S.L.C. (1986). Molecular structure and polymorphic map of the human phenylalanine hydroxylase gene. *Biochemistry, 25,* 743-749.

DiPietro, J.A., Costigan, K.A., & Pressman, E.K. (2002). Fetal state concordance predicts infant state regulation. *Early Human Development, 68* (1), 1-13.

Dobson, V. (1976). Spectral sensitivity of the 2-month infant as measured by the visually evoked cortical potential. *Vision Research 16,* 367-374.

Dodge J.A. (1995). Male fertility in cystic fibrosis. *Lancet, 346* (8975), 587-8.

Dodge. J.A. (1972). Psychosomatic aspects of infantile pyloricstenose. *Journal of Psychosomatic Research 16,* 1-5.

Doering, P.L., Davidson, C.L., LaFauce, L., & Williams, C.A. (1989). Effects of cocaine on the human fetus: a review of clinical studies. *Annals of Pharmacotherapy, 23,* 639-643.

Dolovich, L.R., Addis, A., Vaillancourt, J.M., Power, J.D., Koren, G., & Einarson, T.R. (1998). Benzodiazepine use in pregnancy and major malformations or oral cleft: meta-analysis of cohort and case-control studies. *British Medical Journal, 317* (7162), 839-843.

Donders, G.G., Desmyter, J., De Wet, D.H., & Van Assche, F.A. (1993). The association of gonorrhoea and syphilis with premature birth and low birthweight. *Genitourinary Medicine, 69* (2), 98-101.

Dorner, G. (1967). Tierexperimentelle Untersuchungen zur Frage einer hormonellen Pathogenese der Homosexualitat. *Acta Biologicus Medicus Germanica 19,* 569-584.

Dorner, G. (1968). Hormone induction and prevention of female homosexuality. *Journal of Endocrinology 42,* 163-164.

Dorner, G. (1969). Die Bedeutung der sexualhormonabhangigen Hypothalamusdifferenzierung für die Gonadenfunktion und das Sexualverhalten. *Acta Biologicus Medicus Germanica 23,* 709-712.

Dorner, G. (1970). The influence of sex hormones during the hypothalamic differentiation and maturation phases on gonadal function and sexual behavior during the hypothalamic functional phase. *Endokrinologie 56,* 280-291.

Dorner, G. (1973). Die mogliche Bedeutung der pra- und/oder perinatalen Ernahrung für die Pathogenese der Obesitas. *Acta Biologicus Medicus Germanica 30,* K19-K22.

Dorner, G. (1976). Further evidence of permanent behavioral changes in rats treated neonatally with neurodrugs. *Endokrinologie 68,* 345-348.

Dorner, G. (1978). Über den Einfluss der früpostnatalen Ernahrung auf die Korpergrosse im Adoleszentenalter. *Acta Biologicus Medicus Germanica 37,* 1149-1151.

Dorner, G. (1988). Significance of hormone-dependent brain development and pre-and early postnatal psychophysiology for preventative medicine. In. P.G. Fedor-Freybergh & M.L.V. Vogel (Eds.). *Prenatal Psychology and Medicine,* (pp. 419-430). Park Ridge NJ: The Parthenon Publishing Group.

Dorner, G., & Fatschel, J. (1970). Wirkungen neonatal verabreichter Androgene und Antiandrogene auf Sexualverhalten und Fertilitat von Rattenweibchen. *Endokrinologie 56,* 29-48.

Dorner, G., & Grychtolik, H. (1978). Long-lasting ill-effects of neonatal qualitative and/or quantitative dysnutrition in the human. *Endokrinologie 71,* 81-88.

Dorner, G., & Hinz, G. (1968). Induction and prevention of male homosexuality by androgen. *Journal of Endocrinology 40,* 387-388.

Dorner, G., & Hinz, G. (1971). Mannlicher Hypogonadismus mit sekundarer Hyposexualitat nach hochdosierten Gaben von Ostrogen wahrend der hypothalamischen Differenzierungsphase. *Endokrinologie 58,* 227-33.

Dorner, G., & Hinz, G. (1978). Apparent effects of neurotransmitters on sexual differentiation of the brain without mediation of sex hormones. *Endokrinologie 71,* 104-108.

Dorner, G., & Mohnike, A. (1973). Zur moglichen Bedeutung der pra und/oder frühposnatalen Ernahrung für die Pathogenese des Diabetes mellitus. *Acta Biologicus Medicus Germanica 31,* K7-K10.

Dorner, G., & Mohnike, A. (1976). Further evidence for a predominantly maternal transmission of maturity-onset diabetes. *Endokrinologie 68,* 121-124.

Dorner, G., & Mohnike, A. (1977). Zur Bedeutung der perinatalen Überernahrung für die Pathogenese der Fettsucht under des Diabetes mellitus. *Deutsch Gesundheit Wesen 32,* 2325-2328.

Dorner, G., & Staudt, J. (1968). Structural changes in the preoptic anterior hypothalamic area of the male rat following meonatal castration and androgen treatment. *Neuroendocrinology' 3,* 136-140.

Dorner, G., & Staudt, J. (1969). Structural changes in the hypothalamic ventromedial nucleus of the male rat following neonatal castration and androgen treatment. *Neuroendocrinology 4,* 278-281.

Dorner, G., Bluth, R., & Tonjes, R. (1982). Acetylcholine concentrations in the developing brain appear to affect emotionality and mental capacity in later life. *Acta Biologicus Medicus Germanica 41,* 721-723.

Dorner, G., Docke, F., & Hinz, G. (1968). Entwicklung und Rückbildung neuroendokrin bedingter mannlicher Homosexualitat. *Acta Biologicus Medicus Germanica 21,* 577-580.

Dorner, G., Docke, F., & Hinz, G. (1969). Homo-and hypersexuality in rats with hypothalamic lesions. *Neuroendocrinology 4,* 20-24.

Dorner, G., Docke, F., & Hinz, G. (1971). Paradoxical effects of estrogen on brain differentiation. *Neuroendocrinology 7,* 146-155.

Dorner, G., Docke, F., & Moustafa, S. (1968). Homosexuality in female rats following testosterone implantation in the anterior hypothalamus. *Journal of Reproductive Fertility 17,* 173-175.

Dorner, G., Geier, T., Ahrens, L., Krell, L., Munx, G., Sieler, H., Kittner, E., & Muller, H. (1980). Prenatal stress as possible aetiogenetic factor of homosexuality in human males. *Endokrinologie 75,* 365-368.

Dorner, G., Grychtolik, H., & Julitz, M. (1977). Überernahrung in den ersten drei Lebensmonaten als entscheidender Riskofaktor für die Entwicklung von Fettsucht under ihrer Folgeerkrankungen. *Deutsch Gesundheit Wesen 32,* 6-9.

Dorner, G., Hagen, N., & Witthuhn, W. (1976). Die frühpostnatale Überernahrung als atiopathogenetischer

Faktor der Erwachsenenfettsucht. *Acta Biologicus Medicus Germanica 35*, 799-803.

Dorner, G., Haller, H., & Leonhardt, W. (1973). Zur moglichen Bedeutung der pra- und/oder frühpostnatalen Ernahrung für die Pathogenese der Arteriosklerose. *Acta Biologicus Medicus Germanica 31*, K31-K35.

Dorner, G., Hecht, K., & Hinz, G. (1976). Teratopsychogenetic effects apparently produced by nonphysiological neurotransmitter concentrations during brain differentiation. *Endokrinologie 68*, 1-5.

Dorner, G., Mohnike, A., & Steindel, E. (1975). On possible genetic and epigenetic modes of diabetes transmission. *Endokrinologie 66*, 225-227.

Dorner, G., Mohnike, A., & Thoelke, H. (1984). Further evidence for the dependence of diabetes prevalence on nutrition during perinatal life. *Experimental Clinical Endocrinology 84*, 129-133.

Dorner, G., Mohnike, A., Honigmann, D., Singer, P., & Padelt, H. (1973). Zur moglichen Bedeutung eines pranatalen Hyperinsulinismus für die postnatale Entwicklung Diabetes mellitus. *Endokrinologie 61*, 430-432.

Dorner, G., Schenk, B., Schmiedel, B., & Ahrens, L. (1983). Stressful events in prenatal life of bi- and homosexual men. *Experimental Clinical Endocrinology 81*, 83-87.

Draper, E.S., Manktelow, B., Field, D.J., & James, D. (1999). Prediction of survival for preterm births by weight and gestational age: Retrospective population based study. *British Medical Journal, 319*, 1093–1097.

Dreyfuss, M.L., & Fawzi, W.W. (2002). Micronutrients and vertical transmission of HIV-1. *American Journal of Clinical Nutrition, 75* (6), 959-970.

Drugs and Herbs (2006). The March of Dimes. Retrieved on November 7, 2006 from http://www.marchofdimes.com/pnhec/159_529.asp .

Dubowtiz, L.M.S., Dubowtiz, V., Morante, A., & Verghote, M. (1980). Visual function in the preterm and fullterm newborn infant. *Developmental Medicine and Child Neurology 22*, 465-75.

Dudycha, G.J., & Dudycha, M.M. (1941). Childhood memories: A review of the literature. *Psychological Bulletin 4*, 668-682.

Duin, L.K., Willckes, C., Baldewijns, M.M., Robben, S.G., Offermans. J., & Vles, J. (2007). Major brain lesions by intrauterine herpes simplex virus infection: MRI contribution. *Prenatal Diagnosis, 27* (1), 81-84.

Duley, L., Henderson-Smart, D.J., Knight, M., & King, J.F. (2004). Antiplatelet agents for preventing pre-eclampsia and its complications. *Cochrane Database of Systematic Reviews, 1*, CD004659.

Dunn, P. (1999). John Braxton Hicks & painless uterine contractions *Arch. of Disease in Childhood. Fetal & Neonatal Ed., 81*, F157-158.

Dustman, R.E., & Callner, D.A. (1979). Cortical evoked response and response decrement in non-retarded and Down's syndrome individuals. *American Journal of Mental Deficiency 83*, 391-397.

E

Edison, R, & Muenke, M. (2003). The interplay of genetic and environmental factors in craniofacial morphogenesis: holoprosencephaly and the role of cholesterol. *Congenital anomalies, 43* (1), 1-21.

Edwards, M.J. (1968). Congenital malformation in the rats following induced hyperthermia during gestation. *Teratology, 1*, 173-178.

Edwards, M.J., Shiota, K., Smith, M.S.R. & Walsh, D.A. (1995). Hyperthermia and birth defects. *Reproductive Toxicoogy, 9*, 411-425.

Eggersten, S.C., & Benedetti, T.J. (1984). Fetal well-being assessed by maternal daily fetal-movement counting. *Journal of Family Practice 18*, 771-781.

Ehrhardt, A.A., & Meyer-Bahlburg, H.F.L. (1981). Effects of prenatal sex hormones on gender-related behavior. *Science, 211* (7), 1312.

Eisele, C.J. (1993). Rubella susceptibility in women of childbearing age. *Journal of Obstetric, Gynecologic, and Neonatal Nursing, 22* (3), 260-263.

Eisenberg, R.B. & Marmarou, A. (1981). Behavioral reactions of newborns to speech-like sounds and their implications for developmental studies. *Infant Mental Health Journal 2*, 129-138.

Eisenberg, R.B. (1965). Auditory behavior in the human neonate: Methodologic problems and the logical design of research procedures. *Journal of Auditory Research 5*, 159-177.

Eisenberg, R.B. (1969). Auditory behavior in the human neonate: Functional properties of sound and their ontogenetic implications. *International Audiology 8*, 34-45.

Ekwo, E.E., Gosselink, C.A., Woolson, R., Moawad, A., & Long, C.R. (1993). Coitus late in pregnancy: risk of preterm rupture of amniotic sac membranes. *American Journal of Obstetrics & Gynecology, 168* (1 Pt 1), 22-31.

Ellinger, T.U.H. (1922). *Hippocrates on intercourse and pregnancy*. New York: Schuman.

Elliott, B., Brunham, R.C., Laga, M., Piot, P., Ndinya-Achola, J.O., Maitha, G., Cheang, M., & Plummer, F.A. (1990). Maternal gonococcal infection as a preventable risk factor for low birth weight. *Journal of Infectious Disease, 161* (3), 531-536.

Ellis, D.L., Nanney, L.B., & King, L.E., Jr. (1990). Increased epidermal growth factor receptors in seborrheic keratoses and acrochordons of patients with the dysplastic nevus syndrome. *Journal of the American Academy of Dermatology, 23* (6 Pt 1), 1070-1077.

Endometriosis (2005). IVF.com. Retrieved October 2, 2006 from http://www.ivf.com/ch17mb.html.

Engen T. & Lipsitt, L.P. (1965). Decrement and recovery of responses to olfactory stimuli in the human neonate. *Journal of Comparative & Physiological Psychology 59*, 312-316.

Engen, T., Lipsitt, L.P., & Kaye, H. (1963). Olfactory responses and adaptation in the human neonate. *Journal of Comparative & Physiological Psychology 56*, 73.

England, M.A. (1996). *Life Before Birth* (2nd ed.). London: Mosby-Wolfe.

Enquobahrie, D., Williams, M., Butler, C., Frederick, I. & Luthy, D. (2003). Plasma lipid concentrations in early pregnancy and risk of preecmalpsia. *American Journal of Obstetrics & Gynecology, 189* (6) Supplement 1, S106.

Ergaz, Z., & Ornoy, A. (2006). Parvovirus B19 in pregnancy. *Reproductive Toxicology, 21* (4), 421-435.

Ernhart, C. (1992). A critical review of low-level prenatal lead exposure in the human: Effects on the fetus and newborn. *Reproductive Toxicology, 6*, 9-19.

Eros, E., Czeizel, A.E., Rockenbauer, M., Sorensen, H.T., & Olsen, J. (2002). A population-based case control teratologic study of nitrazepam, medazepam, tofisopam, alprazolam, and clonazepam treatment during pregnancy. *European Journal of Obstetrics, Gynecology, and Reproductive Biology, 101*, 147-54.

Eskenazi, B., Harley, K., Bradman, A., Weltzien, E., Jewell, N.P., Barr, D.B., Furlong, C.E., & Holland, N.T. (2004). Association of in utero organophosphate pesticide exposure and fetal growth and length of gestation in an agricultural population. *Environmental Health Perspectives, 112*, 1116-1124.

Eskes, T.K.A.B. (1985). Verloskundige consequenties van niet vermerke rouw over een perinataal gestorven kind. *Nederlands Tijdschrift voor Geneeskunde 129*, 433-436.

Esteve, E., Saudeau, L., Pierre, F., Barruet, K., Vaillant, L., & Lorette, G. (1994). Signes cutanés physiologiques au cours de la grossesse normale: étude de 60 femmes enceintes. *Annales de Dermatologie et de Vénéréologie, 121* (3), 227-231.

F

F.D.A. (2001). Food and Drug Administration Consumer Advisory. An important message for pregnant woman and women of childbearing age who may become pregnant about the risks of mercury in fish. Center for Food Safety and Applied Nutrition, U.S. Food and Drug Administration, March.

Fabricius, H. (1942). *The embryological Treatises of Hieronymus Fabricius.* H.B. Adelmann (Ed. & Trans.). Ithaca, N.Y.: Cornell Univ. Press.

Fagen, C. (1995). Nutrition management in women with gestational diabetes mellitus: a review by ADA's diabetes care and education dietetic practice group. *Journal of the American Dietetic Association, 95* (4), 460-467.

Fairley, C.K., Smoleniec, J.S., Caul, O.E., & Miller, E. (1995). Observational study of effect of intrauterine transfusions on outcome of fetal hydrops after parvovirus B19 infection. *Lancet, 346* (8986), 1335-1337.

Fairweather, D.V.I., Ward, R.H.T. & Modell, B. (1980). Obstetrics aspects of midtrimester fetal blood sampling by needling or fetoscopy. *British Journal of Obstetrics and Gynaecology, 87,* 87.

Faldella, G. (2006). Prenatal Syphilis Infection Is A Possible Cause Of Preterm Delivery Among Immigrant Women From Eastern Europe. *Sexually Transmitted Infections,* November 10. [Epub ahead of print]

Fall, C.H.D., Yajnik, C.S., Rao, S., Davies, A.A., Brown, N., & Farrant, H.J.W. (2003). Micronutrients and fetal growth. *Journal of Nutrition, 133,* 1747-1756.

Fantz, R.L. (1961). The origin of form perception. *Scientific American 204,* 66-72.

Fantz, R.L. (1963). Pattern vision in newborn infants. *Science 140,* 296-297.

Fantz, R.L. (1964). Visual experience in infants: Decreased attention to familiar patterns relative to normal ones. *Science 146,* 668-670.

Fantz, R.L. (1965). Visual perception from birth as shown by pattern selectivity. *Annals of the New York Academy of Sciences 118,* 793-814.

Farber, E.A., Vaughn, B., & Egeland, B. (1981). The relationship of prenatal maternal anxiety to infant behavior and mother-infant interactions during the first 6 months of life. *Early Human Development 5,* 267-277.

Farrell, S.A., Summers, A.M., Dallaire, L., Singer, J., Johnson, J.M., & Wilson, R.D., (1999). Club foot, an adverse outcome of early amniocentesis: disruption or deformation? *Journal of Medical Genetics, 36,* 843-846.

Fats & Cholesterol, 2006). Harvard School of Public Health. Retreived on November 7, 2006 from http://www.hsph.harvard.edu/nutritionso urce/fats.html.

Fedor-Freybergh, P.G. & Vogel, M.L.V. (1988). Encounter with the unborn: Philosophical impetus behind prenatal and perinatal psychology and medicine. In. P.G. Fedor-Freybergh & M.L.V. Vogel (Eds.). *Prenatal Psychology and Medicine,* (pp. xviii-xxxii). Park Ridge NJ: The Parthenon Publishing Group.

Fedor-Freybergh, P.G. (1983). Psychophysische Gegebenheiten der Perinatalzeit als Umwelt des Kindes. In S. Schindler and H. Zimprich (Eds.). *Okologie der Perinatalzeit.* Stuttgart: Hippokrates Verlag.

Feher, L. (1980). *The psychology of birth: The foundation of the human personality.* London: Souvenir Press.

Feijoo, J. (1975). Ut Conscientia Noscatue. *Cahier de Sophrologie 13,* 14-20.

Feijoo, J. (1981). Le Foetus Pierre et le loup: Ou une approache originale de l'audition prénatale humaine. In H. Herbinet and M.C. Busnel (Eds.). *L'Aube des Sens.* Paris: Stock.

Fensom, A.H., Benson, P.F., Rodeck, C.H., Campbell, S., & Gould, J.D. (1979). Prenatal diagnosis of a galactosaemia heterozygote by fetal blood enzyme assay. *British Medical Journal, 1* (6155), 21–22.

Ferreira, A.J. (1960). The pregnant woman's emotional attitude and its reflection on the newborn. *American Journal of Orthopsychiatry 30,* 553-561.

Ferreira, A.J. (1965). Emotional factors in prenatal environment. *The Journal of Nervous and Mental Disease 141,* 108-118.

Fetoscopy. (2006). Encyclopedia of Surgery. Retrieved October 28, 2006 from http://www.surgeryencyclopedia.com/Ce -Fi/Fetoscopy.html.

Field, D. (1981). Retrospective reports by healthy intelligent elderly people of personal events of their adult lives. *International Journal of Behavioral Development 4,* 77-97.

Field, T. (1985). Stroking dramatically speeds up preemies' growth. *Brain/Mind Bulletin* (Dec 9).

Field, T.M., Woodson, R., Greenberg, R., & Cohen, D. (1982). Discrimination and imitation of facial expressions by neonates. *Science 218,* 179-181.

Finnegan, J. & Quarrington, B. (1979). Pre-, peri- and neonatal factors and infantile autism. *Journal of Child Psychology and Psychiatry 20,* 119-128.

Firth, H.V., Boyd, P., Chamberlain, P.F., & Mackenzie, I.Z. (1994). Analysis of limb reduction defects in babies exposed to chorionic villus sampling. *Lancet, 342,* 1069-1071.

Fisch, H., Hyun, G., Golden, R., Hensle, T. W., Olsson, C.A., Liberson, G.L. (2003). The influence of paternal age on down syndrome. *Journal of Urology, 169* (6), 2275-2278.

Fischbach, F.T., & Dunning, M.B. (Eds). (2004). *Manual of Laboratory and Diagnostic Tests* (7th ed.). Philadelphia: Lippincott Williams and Wilkins.

Fischer-Rasmussen, W., Kjaer, S.K., Dahl, C., & Asping, U. (1991). Ginger treatment of hyperemesis gravidarum. *European Journal of Obstetrics, Gynecology, and Reproductive Biology, 38* (1), 19-24

Fisher, N.L. & Smith, D.W. (1981). Occipital encephalocele and early gestational hyperthermia. *Pediatrics, 68,* 480-483.

Flake, A.W., & Harrison, M.R. (1995). Fetal surgery. *Annual Review of Medicine, 46,* 67-78.

Flanagan, G.L. (1996). *Beginning life.* New York: DK Publishing.

Flaxman, S. & Sherman, P.(2000). Morning sick-ness: a mechanism for protecting mother and embryo. *Quarterly Review of Biology, 75,* 113-148.

Fodor, N. (1949). *The search for the beloved: A clinical investigation of the trauma of birth and pre-natal conditioning.* New York: Hermitage Press.

Fodor, N. (1971). *Freud, Jung and Occultism.* New York: University Books.

Forrester, M.B., & Merz, R.D. (2007). Risk of selected birth defects with prenatal illicit drug use, Hawaii, 1986-2002. *Journal of Toxicology and Environmental Health, 70* (1), 7-18.

Foulatier, F. (1987). L'enfant autiste et la metacommunication. *Evolution Psychiatrique 52,* 471-481.

Foulk, R.A. (2001). From fertilization to implantation. *Early Pregnancy, 5* (1), 61-62.

Foulon, W., Naessens, A., de Catte, L., Amy, J.J., (1990). Detection of congenital toxoplasmosis by chorionic villus sampling and early amniocentesis. *American Journal of Obstetrics & Gynecology, 163,* 1511-1513.

Foulon, W., Pinon, J.M., Stray-Pedersen, B., Pollak, A., Lappalainen, M., Decoster, A., Villena, I., Jenum, P.A., Hayde, M., & Naessens, A. (1990). Prenatal diagnosis of congenital toxoplasmosis. *Obstetrics & Gynecology, 76* (5), 769-772.

Fraser, F.C. & Skelton, J. (1978). Possible teratogenicity of maternal fever. *Lancet, 2,* 634.

Freedman, A.L., Johnson, M.P., Smith, C.A., Gonzalez, R., Evans, M.I. (1999). Long-term outcome in children after antenatal intervention for obstructive uropathies. *Lancet, 354* (9176), 374-377.

Freeland, W.J., & Janzen, D.H. (1974) Strategies in herbivory by mammals: the role of plant secondary compounds. *The American Naturalist, 108* (961), 269-285.

Freud, S. (1933). Lecture #32. *New Introductory Lectures on Psychoanalysis*. New York: W.W. Norton.

Freud, S. (1936). *Inhibitions, symptoms and anxiety*. London: Hogarth Press.

Freud, S. (1951). *Psychopathology of everydaylLife*. New York: Mentor Books.

Fried, P.A., Wtakinson, B., & Gray, R. (1998). Differential effects on cognitive functioning in 9-12 year-olds prenatlly exposed to cigarettes and marijuana, *Neurotoxicology and Teratology, 20*, 293-306.

Friedman, S., Nagy, A.N., & Carpenter, G.C. (1970). Newborn attention: Differential response decrement to visual stimuli. *Journal of Experimental Child Psychology 10*, 44-51.

Friedman, S.L., Zahn-Waxler, C., & Radke-Yarrow, M. Perceptions of cries of full-term and preterm infants. *Infant Behavior and Development 5*, 161-173.

Fuchs, F., & Riis, P. (1956). Antenatal sex determination. *Nature, 177*, 330.

Fulford, J., Vadeyar, S.H., Dodampahala, S.H., Moore, R.J., Young, P., Baker, P.N., James, D.K., & Gowland, P.A. (2003). Fetal brain activity in response to a visual stimulus. *Human Brain Mapping, 20*, 239-245.

G

Gaffney, K.F. (1986). Maternal-fetal attachment in relation to self-concept and anxiety. *Maternal Child Nursing Journal 15*, 91-101.

Gaither, K., Ardite, A., & Mason, T.C. (2005). Pregnancy complicated by emphysematous pyonephrosis. *Journal of the National Medical Association, 97* (10), 1411-1413.

Galen. (1968). *On the usefulness of the parts of the body* (Vol. 2). M.T. May (Ed.). Ithaca, N.Y.: Cornell Univ. Press.

Gardner, R., & Sutherland, G.R. (2004). *Chromosome Abnormalities and Genetic Counseling* (3rd ed.). Oxford: Oxford University Press.

Gaytant, M.A., Rours, G., Steegers, E., Galama, J., & Semmekrot, B.A. (2003). Congenital cytomegalovirus infection after recurrent infection: Case reports and review of the literature. *European Journal of Pediatrics, 162* (4), 248-253.

Genbacev, O. (2001). To proliferate or to divide - To be or not to be. *Early Pregnancy, 5* (1), 40-41.

George, A.O., Shittu, O.B., Enwerem, E., Wachtel, M., & Kuti, O. (2005). The incidence of lower mid-trunk hyperpigmentation (linea nigra) is affected by sex hormone levels. *Journal of the National Medical Association, 97* (5), 685-688.

George, L., Granath, F., Johansson, A.L., Anneren, G., & Cnattingius, S. (2006). Environmental tobacco smoke and risk of spontaneous abortion. *Epidemiology, 17* (5), 500-505.

Gerhardt, K.J. (1990). Prenatal and perinatal risks of hearing loss. *Seminars in Perinatolog, 14* (4), 299-304.

Germain, M.A., Webster, M.S., & Edwards, M.J. (1985). Hyperthermia as a teratogen: Parameters determining hyperthermia-induced head defects in the rat. *Teratology, 31*, 265-272.

Gesell, A. (1945). *The Embryology of Behavior*. New York: Harper and Brothers.

Giannakoulopoulos, X., Sepulveda, W., Kourtis, P., Glover, V., & Fisk, N.M. (1994). Fetal plasma cortisol and β-endorphin response to intrauterine needling. *Lancet, 344* (8915), 77-81.

Giannakoulopoulos, X., Teixeira, J., Fisk, N., & Glover, V. (1999). Human fetal and maternal noradrenaline responses to invasive procedures. *Pediatric Research, 45* (4 Part 1), 494-499.

Giaquinto, C., Rampon, O., & De Rossi, A. (2006). Antiretroviral therapy for prevention of mother-to-child HIV transmission : focus on single-dose nevirapine. *Clinical Drug Investigations, 26* (11), 611-627.

Gidoni, E.A., Casonato, M., & Landi, N. (1988). A further contribution to a functional interpretation of fetal movements. In. P.G. Fedor-Freybergh & M.L.V. Vogel (Eds.). *Prenatal Psychology and Medicine*, (pp. 347-353). Park Ridge NJ: The Parthenon Publishing Group.

Gilbert, S.G. (1989). *Pictorial human embryology*. Seattle: University of Washington Press.

Gillberg, C. & Gillberg, C.I. (1983). Infantile autism: A total population study of reduced optimality in the pre-, peri-, and neonatal period. *Journal of Autism and Developmental Disorders 13*, 153-166.

Gilljam M., Antoniou, M., Shin, J., Dupuis, A., Corey, M., & Tullis, D.E. (2000). Pregnancy in cystic fibrosis. Fetal and maternal outcome. *Chest, 118* (1), 85-91.

Gladstone, D.J., Bologa, M., Maguire, C., Pastuszak, A., & Koren, G. (1992) Course of pregnancy and fetal outcome following maternal exposure to carbamazepine and phenytoin: a prospective study. *Reproductive Toxicology, 6*, 257-261.

Glavin, G.B. (1984). Prenatal maternal stress: Differential effects upon male and female offspring responses to restraint stress as an adult. *Pavlovian Journal of Biological Science 19*, 157-159.

Glover, V., & Fisk, N. (1999). Fetal pain: implications for research and practice. *British Journal of Obstetrics and Gynaecology, 106* (9), 881-886.

Godfrey, K., Robinson, S., Barker, D.J., & Osmond, C. (1996). Maternal nutrition in early and late pregnancy in relation to placental and fetal growth. *British Medical Journal, 312*, 410.

Golanska, Z. & Bacz, A. (1988). The psychological effects of maternal attitudes in cases of repeated unfavorable pregnancy outcome. In. P.G. Fedor-Freybergh & M.L.V. Vogel (Eds.). *Prenatal Psychology and Medicine*, (pp. 93-97). Park Ridge NJ: The Parthenon Publishing Group.

Golbus, M.S., Sagebiel, R.W., Filly, R.A., Gindhart, T.D. & Hall, J.G. (1979a). Prenatal diagnosis of congenital bulllous ichthyosiform erythroderma epidemolytic hyperkeratosis by fetal skin biopsy. *New England Journal of Medicine, 302*, 93.

Golbus, M.S., Stephens, J.D., Mahoney, M.J., Hobbins, J.C., Haseltine, F.P., Caskey, C.T. & Banker, B.Q. (1979b). Failure of fetal creatinine phospokinase as a diagnostic indicator of Duchenne muscular dystrophy. *New England Journal of Medicine, 300*, 860.

Goldenberg, R.L., Andrews, W.W., Yuan, A.C., MacKay, H.T., & St Louis, M,E. (1997). Sexually transmitted diseases and adverse outcomes of pregnancy. *Clinics in Perinatology: Infections in Perinatology, 24* (1), 23-41.

Goldenberg, R.L., Culhane, J.F., & Johnson, D.C. (2005). Maternal infection and adverse fetal and neonatal outcomes. *Clinical Perinatology, 32* (3), 523-559.

Goldenring, J. (1982) Development of the fetal brain. *New England Journal of Medicine., 307*, 564.

Goldschmidt, L., Richardson, G.A., Cornelius, M.D., & Day, N.L. (2004). Prenatal marijuana and alcohol exposure and academic achievement at age 10. *Neurotoxicology and Teratology, 26* (4), 521-532.

Goldstein, D.J., Corbin, L.A., & Sundell, K.L. (1997). Effects of first-trimester fluoxetine exposure on the newborn. *Obstetrics & Gynecology, 89*, 713-718.

Gona, P., Van Dyke, R.B., Williams, P.L., Dankner, W.M., Chernoff, M.C., Nachman, S.A, & Seage, G.R., 3rd. (2006). Incidence of opportunistic and other infections in HIV-infected children in the HAART era. *Journal of the American Medical Association, 296* (3), 292-300.

Goodlin, R.C. (1979). *Care of the fetus*. New York: Masson Publishing Co.

Goodlin, R.C., & Lowe, E.W. (1974). Multiphasic fetal monitoring, a preliminary evaluation. *American Journal of Obstetrics and Gynecology, 119* (3), 341-357.

Goodman, W.S., Appleby, S.V., Scott, J.W., & Ireland, P.E. (1964). Audiometry in newborn children by electro-encephalography. *Laryngoscope 74*, 1316-1328.

Goodwin, A., Astbury, J., & McMeeken, J. (2000). Body image and psychological well-being in pregnancy. A comparison of exercisers and non-exercisers. *The Australian & New Zealand Journal of Obstetrics & Gynaecology, 40*, 442-447.

Goralski, M. (2006). Why Exercise During Pregnancy? University of Tennese at Knoxville. Retrieved on November 13, 2006 from http://web.utk.edu/~cpah/1-Design/index.html.

Goransson, M., Magnusson, A., Bergman, H., Rydberg, U., & Heilig, M. (2003). Fetus at risk: prevalence of alcohol consumption during pregnancy estimated with a simple screening method in Swedish antenatal clinics. *Addiction, 98* (11), 1513-1520.

Goshen-Gottstein, E. (1969). *Marriage and first pregnancy.* London: Tavistock Publications.

Gotz, F., & Dorner, G. (1980). Homosexual behavior in prenatally stressed male rats after castration and estrogen treatment in adulthood. *Endokrinologie 76*, 115-117.

Graber, G.H. (1924). *Die Ambivalenz des Kindes.* Vienna: International Psychoanalytic Books.

Grace, J.T. (1989). Development of maternal-fetal attachment during pregnancy. *Nursing Research 38*, 228-232.

Grand, R.J., Watkins. J.B., & Torti, F.M. (1976). Development of the human gastrointestinal tract. A review. *Gastroenterology, 70* (5 Part 1), 790-810.

Granier-Deferre, C., Lecanuet, J.P., Cohen, H., & Busnel, M.C. (1985). Feasibility of a prenatal hearing test. *Acta Oto Laryngologica, Supplement 421*, 93-101.

Grassi, L., & Caracciolo, S. (1983). Rischio psicobiologico in gravidanza e parto. *Medicina Psicosomatica 28*, 301-320.

Gratacos, E., & Deprest, J.A. (2000). Current experience with fetoscopy and the Eurofoetus registry for fetoscopic procedures. *European Journal of Obstetrics, Gynecology, and Reproductive Biology, 92* (1), 151–159.

Gray, K.A., Day, N.L., Leech, S., & Richardson, G.A. (2005). Prenatal marijuana exposure: effect on child depressive symptoms at ten years of age. *Neurotoxicology & Teratology, 27* (3), 439-448.

Greenacre, P. (1945). The biological economy of birth. *Psychoanalytic Study of the Child,* 1.

Greenacre. P. (1952). *Trauma, growth, and personality.* New York: International Universities Press.

Greenberg, M., Vuorenkoski, V., Partanen, T., & Lind, J. (1967). Behavior and cry patterns in the first two hours of life in early and late clamped newborns. *Finnish Annals of Pediatrics 13.*

Greer, I. (2003). Prevention of venous thromboembolism in pregnancy. *Best Practice & Research in Clin. Haematology, 16* (2), 261-278.

Gregg, V.H. (1986). *Introduction to human memory.* London: Routledge & Kegan Paul.

Grethel, E.J., & Nobuhara, K.K. (2006). Fetal surgery for congenital diaphragmatic hernia. *Journal of Paediatrics and Child Health, 42* (3), 79-85.

Grillner, L., Forsgren, M., Barr, B., Bottiger, M., Danielsson, L., & De Verdier, C. (1983). Outcome of rubella during pregnancy with special reference to the 17th-24th weeks of gestation. *Scandanavian Journal of Infectious Disease, 15* (4), 321-325.

Grof, S. (1975). *Realms of the human unconscious: Observations from LSD research.* New York: Viking Press.

Grof, S., & Halifax, J. (1977). *The human encounter with death.* New York: E.P. Dutton.

Grotegut, C.A., Dandolu, V., Katari, S., Whiteman, V.E., Geifman-Holtzman, O., & Teitelman, M. (2006). Baking soda pica: a case of hypokalemic metabolic alkalosis and rhabdomyolysis in pregnancy. *Obstetrics & Gynecology, 107* (2 Pt 2), 484-486.

Grudzinskas, G. (2001). Mechanisms in implantation: Oestrogen revisited lessons from ovarian hyperstimulation syndrome. *Early Pregnancy, 5* (1), 12-13.

Gruzelier, J.H., & Venebles, P.H. (1972). Skin conductance orienting activity in a heterogenous sample of schizophrenics. *Journal of Nervous and Mental Disorders 155*, 277-287.

Guldberg, P., Henriksen, K.F., Sipila, I., Guttler, F., de la Chapelle, A. (1995). Phenylketonuria in a low incidence population: molecular characterization of mutations in Finland. *Journal of Medical Genetics 32*, 976-978.

Gunter, L. (1963). Psychopathology and stress in the life experience of mothers of premature infants. A comparative study. *American Journal of Obstetrics and Gynecology 86*, 333-340.

Guntrip, H.S. (1952). A study of Fairbairn's theory of schizoid reactions. *British Journal of Medical Psychology, 23* (2 & 3), 86-103.

Guntrip, H.S. (1957). *Psychotherapy and Religion.* New York: Harper Books.

Guntrip, H.S. (1961). *Personality Structure and Human Interaction.* New York: International Universities Press.

Guntrip, H.S. (1968). *Schizoid Phenomena, Object Relations and the Self.* London: Hogarth Press.

Gupta, D., & Datta, B. (1988). The cultural and historical evolution of medicine and psychological ideas concerning conception and embryo development. In .G. Fedor-Freybergh & M.L.V. Vogel (Eds.), *Prenatal and Perinatal Psychology and Medicine,* (pp. 507-534). Park Ridge, NJ: The Parthenon Publishing Group.

H

Hachey, D. (1994). Benefits and risks of modifying maternal fat intake in pregnancy and lactation. *American Journal of Clinical Nutrition, 59*, 454S-464S.

Hale, T.W. (2002). *Medications and Mothers' Milk.* Amarillo, Tx.: Pharmasoft Publishing.

Hamilton, W.J., Boyd, J.D., & Mossman, H.W. (1962). *Human Embryology: Prenatal Development of Form and Function.* Baltimore: The Williams & Wilkins Co.

Hamlin, H. (1964). Life or death by EEG. *Journal of the American Medical Association, AMA, 190*, 112-114.

Hamosh, A., Fitz-Simmons, S.C., Macek, M. Jr., Knowles, M.R., Rosenstein, B.J., & Cutting, G.R. (1998). Comparison of the clinical manifestations of cystic fibrosis in black and white patients. *Journal of Pediatrics, 132* (2), 255-9.

Hansen, C., Neller, A., Williams, G., & Simpson, R. (2006). Maternal exposure to low levels of ambient air pollution and preterm birth in Brisbane, Australia. *BJOG : An International Journal of Obstetrics and Gynaecology, 113* (8), 935-941.

Harding, A.J., & Edwards, M.J. (1993). Micrencephaly in rats caused by maternal hyperthermia on days 13 and 14 of pregnancy. *Congenital Anomalies, 33*, 203-209.

Harrison, M.R., Adzick, N.S., Bullard, K.M., Farrell, J.A., Howell, L.J., Rosen, M.A., Sola, A., Goldberg, J.D., & Filly, R.A. (1997). Correction of congenital diaphragmatic hernia in utero VII: a prospective trial. *Journal of Pediatric Surgery, 32*, 1637–1642.

Harrison, M., Golbus, M., & Filly, R.. (1981). Management of the fetus with a correctable congenital defect. *Journal of the American Medical Association, 246* (7), 774-777.

Harrison, M.R., Golbus, M.S., Filly, R.A., Callen, P.W., Katz, M., de Lorimier, A.A., Rosen, M., & Jonsen, A.R. (1982).

Fetal surgery for congenital hydronephrosis. *New England Journal of Medicine, 306* (10), 591-593.

Harrison, M.R., Keller, R.L., Hawgood, S.B., Kitterman, J.A., Sandberg, P.L., Farmer, D.L., Lee, H., Filly, R.A., Farrell, J.A., & Albanese, C.T. (2003). A randomized trial of fetal endoscopic tracheal occlusion for severe fetal congenital diaphragmatic hernia. *New England Journal of Medicine, 349*, 1916–1924

Hartley, W.J., Alexander, G., & Edwards, M.J. (1974). Brain cavitation and micrencephaly in lambs exposed to prenatal hyperthermia. *Teratology, 9,* 299-303.

Hartmann, S., & Bung, P. (1999). Physical exercise during pregnancy-physiological. *Journal of Perinatal Medicine, 27* (3), 204-215.

Harvey, M.A.S., McRorie, M.M., & Smith, D.W. (1981). Suggested limits to the use of the hot tub and sauna by pregnant women. *Canadian Medical Association Journal, 125,* 50-53.

Haselton, M.G. (2006, April 29). Love special: How to pick a perfect mate. NewScientist.com. Retrieved September 22, 2006 from http://www.newscientist.com/article/mg19025491.300.

Hass, U. (2006). The need for developmental neurotoxicity studies in risk assessment for developmental toxicity. Reproductive Toxicology, 22 (2), 148-156.

Hasse, C. (2001). Hemorrhoids während der Schwangerschaft. *Deutsche Medizinische Wochenschrift, 126* (28-29), 832.

Hasselmeyer, E.C.T. (1964). The premature neonate's response to handling. *Journal of the American Nurses Association, 11,* 14-15.

Hatch, M.C., Shu, X.O., McLean, D.E., Levin, B., Begg, M., Reuss, L., & Susser, M. (1993). Maternal exercise during pregnancy, physical fitness and fetal growth. *American Journal of Epidemiology, 137,* 1105–1114.

Hauzman E., Fedorcsák. P., Halmos, A., Vass, Z., Dévényi, N., Papp, Z. & Urbancsek, J. (2001). Role of serum hCG measurements in predicting pregnancy outcome and multiple gestation after in vitro fertilization. *Early Pregnancy, 5* (1), 26-27.

Hazard Database, (2006) I.M.Sechenov Institute of Evolutionary Physiology and Biochemistry, Russian Academy of Sciences, St.Petersburg, Russia. Retrieved on December 9, 2006 from http://www.iephb.nw.ru/~spirov/hazard/teratogen.html#etiology.

Hecht, K., Poppei, M., Schlegel, T., Hinz, G., Tonjes, R., Gotz, R., & Dorner, G. (1978). Long-term behavioral effects of psychotropic drugs administered during brain development in rats. In G. Dorner

& M. Kawakami (Eds.). *Hormones and Brain Development, vol. 3.* (pp. 277-283). Amsterdam: Elsevier/North Holland Biomedical Press.

Hedrick, H.L., Flake, A.W., Crombleholme, T.M., Howell, L.J., Johnson, M.P., Wilson, R.D., & Adzick, N.S. (2004). Sacrococcygeal teratoma: prenatal assessment, fetal intervention, and outcome. Journal of Pediatric Surgery, 39 (3), 430-438.

Heger, S. (2002). Pica--der Wunsch nach ungenießbaren Substanzen. Rückstände, Haar und Lehm als Gaumen Teasers? *Fortschritte der medizin und Münchener medizinische Wochenschrift, 144* (6), 12-13.

Heger, S., Teyssen, S., & Lieberz, K. (2001). Pica--Ursachen und Komplikationen einer wenig bekannten Essenstörung. *Deutsche medizinische Wochenschrift, 126* (50), 1435-1439.

Heidrich, S.M., & Cranley, M.S. (1989). The effect of fetal movement, ultrasound scans and amniocentesis on maternal-fetal attachment. *Nursing Research 38,* 81-84.

Hendrick, V., Fukuchi, A., Altshuler, L., Widawski, M., Wertheimer, A., Brunhuber, M.V. (2001). Use of sertraline, paroxetine and fluvoxamine by nursing women. *The British Journal of Psychiatry, 179,* 163-166.

Hepper, P.G. (1988). Foetal "Soap Addiction". *Lancet 1,* 1347-1348.

Hepper, P.G. (1989). Foetal learning: Implications for psychiatry? *British Journal of Psychiatry 155,* 289-293.

Hepper, P.G., & Shahidullah, B.S. (1994). Development of fetal hearing. *Archives of Disease in Childhood, 71* (2), F81-F87.

Hepper, P.G., Shahidullah, S., & White, R. (1991). Handedness in the human fetus. *Neuropsychologia, 29* (11), 1107-1111.

Hepper, P.G., Shannon, E.A., & Dornan, J.C. (1997). Sex differences in fetal mouth movements. *Lancet, 350* (9094), 1820-1821.

Herraiz, M.A., Hernandez, A., Asenjo, E., & Herraiz, I. (2005). Infeccion del tracto urinario en la embarazada. *Enfermedades Infecciosas y Microbiología Clínica, 23,* (Suppl 4), 40-46.

Hesseldahl, H., & Larsen, J.F. (2005). Ultrastructure of human yolk sac: Endoderm, mesenchyme, tubules and mesothelium. *American Journal of Anatomy, 126* (3), 315 – 335.

Hilgard, E.R. (1977). *Divided consciousness: Multiple controls in human thought and action.* New York: John Wiley.

Hilgard, E.R. (1980). Consciousness in contemporary psychology. *Annual Review of Psychology 31,* 1-26.

Hill, J.A. (2001) Maternal-embryonic

cross-talk. *Annals of the New York Academy of Sciences, 943,* 17–25.

Hinde, R.E. (1970). *Behavioral habituation.* New York: Cambridge Univ. Press.

Hinz, G., Docke, F., & Dorner, G. (1978). Long-term changes of sexual functions in rats treated neonatally with psychotropic drugs. In G. Dorner & M. Kawakami (Eds.). *Hormones and Brain Development, vol. 3.* (pp. 121-127). Amsterdam: Elsevier/North Holland Biomedical Press.

Hinz, G., Hecht, K., Rhode, W., & Dorner, G. (1983). Long-term effects of early postnatal nutrition on subsequent body weight gain, emotionality and learning behavior in male rats. *Experimental Clinical Endocrinology 82,* 73-77.

Hirose, S., & Farmer, D.L. (2003). Fetal surgery for sacrococcygeal teratoma. *Clinical Perinatology, 30* (3), 493-506.

Hobbins, J.C. & Mahoney, M.J. (1974). In utero diagnosis of haemoglobinopathies. Technique of obtaining fetal blood. *New England. Journal of Medicine, 290,* 1065.

Hobbins, J.C. & Mahoney, M.J. (1977). Fetoscopy in continuing pregnancies. *American Journal of Obstetrics and Gynecology, 129,* 440.

Holding, D.H., Noonan, T.K., Pfau, H.D., & Holding, C. (1986). Date attribution, age, and the distribution of lifetime memories. *Journal of Gerontology 41,* 481-485.

Holmes, L.B., Harvey, E.A., Coull, B.A., Huntington, K.B., Khoshbin, S., Hayes, A.M. & Ryan, L.M. (2001). The teratogenicity of anticonvulsant drugs. *New England Journal of Medicine, 344,* 1132-1138.

Holmes, N., Harrison, M.R., & Baskin, L.S. (2001). Fetal surgery for posterior urethral valves: long-term postnatal outcomes. *Pediatrics, 108* (1), E7.

Hook, E.B. (1981). Rates of chromosomal abnormalities at different maternal ages. *Obstetrics & Gynecology, 58,* 282.

Hook, E.B., Cross, P.K., & Schreinemachers, D.M. (1983). Chromosomal abnormality rates at amniocentesis and in live-born infants. *Journal of the American Medical Association, 249* (15), 2034-2038.

Hooker, D. (1952). *The prenatal origin of behavior.* Lawrence, Kansas: The University of Kansas Press.

Horns, P.N., Ratcliffe, L.P., Leggett, J.C., & Swanson, M.S. (2000). Pregnancy outcomes among active and sedentary primiparous women. *Journal of Obstetrics and Gynecologic Neonatal Nurses, 25,* 49-54.

Howard, D.L., Marshall, S.S., Kaufman, J.S., & Savitz, D.A. (2006). Variations in low birth weight and preterm delivery among blacks in relation to ancestry and nativity: New York City, 1998-2002. *Pediatrics, 118* (5) 1399-1405.

Hoyme, H.E., Jones, K.L., Dixon, S.D., Jewett, T., Hanson, J.W., Robinson, L.K., Msall, M.E., & Allanson, J.E. (1990). Prenatal cocaine exposure and fetal vascular disruption. *Pediatrics, 85,* 743-747.

Huizink, A.C., & Mulder, E.J. (2005). Maternal smoking, drinking or cannabis use during pregnancy and neurobehavioral and cognitive functioning in human offspring. *Neuroscience and Biobehavioral Reviews, 30* (1), 24-41.

Hulse G.K., Milne, E., English, D.R., & Holman, C.D.. (1998). Assessing the relationship between maternal opiate use and neonatal mortality. *Addiction, 93* (7), 1033-1042.

Hulse G.K., Milne, E., English, D.R., & Holman, C.D., (1998). The relationship between maternal use of heroin and methadone and infant birth weight. *Addiction, 92* (11), 312-317.

Hulse, G.K., & O'Neill, G. (2001). Methadone and the pregnant user: a matter for careful clinical consideration. *Australian and New Zealand Journal of Obstetrics and Gynaecology, 41,* (3), 329-332.

Hulse, G.K., O'Neill, G., Pereira, C., & Brewer, C. (2001). Obstetric and neonatal outcomes associated with maternal naltrexone exposure. *Australian and New Zealand Journal of Obstetrics and Gynaecology, 41,* (4), 424-428.

Humphrey, T. (1964). Growth and maturation of the brain - some correlations between the appearance of human fetal reflexes and the development of the nervous system. In P. Dominick P, D.P. Purpura, & J.P. Schadé JP. (Eds.). *Progress in brain research,* Vol 4. (pp. 93-135). Amsterdam: Elsevier.

Humphrey, T. (1970). The development of human fetal activity and its relation to postnatal behavior. In H.W. Reese & L.P. Lipsitt. (Eds.). *Advances in child development and behavior,* Vol 5. New York: Academic.

Humphrey, T. (1978). Function of the newborn systems during prenatal life. In U. Stave (Ed.). *Physiology of the Perinatal Period, vol. 2.* (pp. 751-796). New York: Plenum Medical Books.

Hunter, A.G.W. (1984). Neural tube defects in eastern Ontario and western Quebec: Demography and family data. *Americsan Journal of Medical Genetics, 19,* 45-63.

Hurd, Y.L., Wang, X., Anderson, V., Beck, O., Minkoff, H., & Dow-Edwards, D. (2004). Marijuana impairs growth in mid-gestation fetuses. *Neurotoxicology & Teratology, 27* (2), 221-229.

Hutt, S.J., & Hutt, C. (1964). Hyperactivity in a group of epileptic (and some non-epileptic) brain damaged children. *Epilepsia 5,* 334-351.

Huttunen, M.O., & Niskanen, P. (1978). Prenatal loss of father and psychiatric disorders. *Archives of General Psychiatry 4,* 429-431.

Huxley, R. (2000). Nausea and vomiting in early pregnancy: Its role in placental development. *Obstetrics & Gynecology, 95,* 779-782.

Hyperemesis Gravidarum (2006). The Cleveland Clinic at www.cleveland clinic.org. Retrieved on November 4, 2006 from http://www.clevelandclinic.org/health/health-info/docs/3800/3816.asp.

Hyperthermia & Pregnancy (2006). Organization of Teratology Information Services. Retreived on December 12, 2006 from http://otispregnancy.org/pdf/hyperthemia.pdf.

I

Iatrakis, G.M., Sakellaropoulos, G.G., Kourkoubas, A.H., & Kabounia, S,.E. (1988). Vomiting and nausea in the first 12 weeks of pregnancy. *Psychotherapy and Psychosomatics 49,* 22-24.

Isenberg, K.E. (1990). Excretion of fluoxetine in human breast milk. *Journal of Clinical Psychiatry, 51,* 169.

Ishikawa, A., & Minamide, E. (1984). Correlation between fetal activity and neonatal behavioral assessment scale. *Early Child Development and Care 17,* 155-165.

Istvan, J. (1986). Stress, anxiety, and birth outcome: A critical review of the evidence. *Psychological Bulletin 100,* 331-348.

Ivarsson, S-A, Lernmark, B., & Svanberg, L. (1997). Ten-year clinical, developmental, and intellectual follow-up of children with congenital cytomegalovirus infection without neurologic symptoms on one year of age. *Pediatrics, 99* (6), 800-803.

Izard, C.E. & Read, P. (1986). Measuring emotions. In C.E. Izard & P. Read (Eds.). *Infants and Children, vol. 2.* New York: Cambridge Univ. Press.

J

Jackson, R. (1988). *Doctors and diseases in the Roman empire.* Norman, Okla: Univ of Oklahoma Press.

Jacobs, P.A., Brunton, M., Melville, M.M., Brittain, R.P. & McClermont, W.F. (1965). Aggressive behaviour, mental subnormality and the XYY male. *Nature, 208,* 1351-1352.

Jacobs, P.A., Price, W.H., Richmond, S. & Ratcliff, B.A. W. (1971). Chromosome surveys in penal institutions and approved schools. *Journal of Medical Genetics, 8,* 49-58.

Jaffe, R. (2001). Development of early uteroplacental circulation. *Early Pregnancy, 5* (1), 34-35.

Jakobovits, A. (1983). The effect of maternal physical activity on fetal breathing movements *Archives of Gynecology and Obstetrics, 234* (1), 47-48

James, W.D., & Odom, R.B. (1979). Hyperpigmentation occurring in vascular spiders. *Archives of Dermatology, 115* (8), 929.

Jancin, B. (2000, October 1). STD chemoprophylaxis reduces preterm birth. *Family Practice News,* pp. 24-25.

Jenkins, D.J., Kendall, C.W., Augustin, L.S., Franceschi, S., Hamidi, M., & Marchie, A. (2002). Glycemic index: overview of implications in health and disease. *American Journal of Clinical Nutrition, 76,* 266S-273S.

Jenkins, T., & Wapner, R. (1999). First trimester prenatal diagnosis: chorionic villus sampling. *Seminars in Perinatology, 23* (5), 403-413.

Jensen, O.H., & Flottorp, G. (1982). A method for controlled sound stimulation of the human fetus. *Scandinavian Audiology 11,* 145-150.

Jernerg, M. (1988). Promoting prenatal and perinatal mother-child bonding: A psychotherapeutic assessment of parental attitudes. In. P.G. Fedor-Freybergh & M.L.V. Vogel (Eds.). *Prenatal Psychology and Medicine,* (pp. 253-266). Park Ridge NJ: The Parthenon Publishing Group.

Jimenez Ruiz, C.A. (2006). Terapia del reemplazo de la nicotina durante embarazo. *Archivos de Bronconeumología, 42,* (8), 404-409.

John, E.M., Savitz, D.A., & Shy, C.M. (1994). Spontaneous Abortions among Cosmetologists. *Epidemiology, 5,* 147-155.

Johnson, J.M., Wilson, R.D., Singer, J., Winsor, E., Harman, C., Armson, B.A., Benzie, R., Dansereau, J., Ho, M.F., Mohide, P., Natale, R., & Okun, N. (1999). Technical factors in early amniocentesis predict adverse outcome. Results of the Canadian early (EA) versus mid-trimester (MA) amniocentesis trial. *Prenatal Diagnosis, 19* (8), 732-738.

Johnson, W.F., Emde, R.N., Pannabecker, B.J., Stenborg, C., & Davis, M.H. (1982). Maternal perception of infant emotion from birth to 18 months. *Infant Behavior & Development 5,* 313-322.

Jona, J.Z. (1998). Advances in fetal surgery. *Pediatric Clinic of North America, 45* (3), 599-604.

Jones, K.L., Lacro, R.V., Johnson, K.A., & Adams, J. (1989). Patterns of malformation s in the children of women treated with carbamazepine during pregnancy. *New England Journal of Medicine, 320* (25), 1661-1666.

Jones, R.E. (1991). Human Reproductive Biology. San Diego: Harcourt Brace Jovanovich.

Jukkola, T.M., Makivaara, L.A., Luukkaala, T., Hakama, M., & Laurikka, J. (2006). The effects of parity, oral contraceptive use and hormone replacement therapy on the incidence of varicose veins. *Journal of Obstetrics & Gynaecology, 26* (5), 448-451.

Juntunen, K., Sirvio, P., & Michelsson, K. (1978). Cry analysis of infants with severe malnutrition. *European Journal of Pediatrics 128,* 241-246.

K

Kagan, J. (1978). On emotion and its development: A working paper." In M. Lewis & L.A. Rosenblum (Eds.). *The Development of Affect.* (p. 37). New York: Plenum Press.

Kallen, A.J.B. (1994). Maternal carbamazepine and infant spina bifida. *Reproductive Toxicology, 8* (3), 203-205.

Kamath, S.A. (2006). Hypertension in pregnancy. *The Journal of the Association of Physicians of India, 54,* 269-270.

Kandall, S.R., Albin, S., Lowinson, J., Berle, B., Eidelman, A.I., & Gartner, L.M. (1976). Differential effects of maternal heroin and methadone use on birthweight. *Pediatrics, 58* (5), 681-685.

Kaplan, M. (1983). Fetal breathing movements. An update for the pediatrician. *American Journal of the Disturbed Child, 137,* 177 - 181.

Kapperud, G., Jenum, P.A., Stray-Pedersen, B., Melby, K.K., Eskild, A., Eng, J. (1997). Risk Factors for Toxoplasma gondii Infection in Pregnancy: Results of a Prospective Case-Control Study in Norway. *Obstetrical & Gynecological Survey, 52* (3), 158-159.

Kargas, G.A., Kargas, S.A., Bruyere, H.J. Jr, Gilbert, E.F., & Opitz, J.M. (1985). Perinatal mortality due to interaction of diphenhydramine and temazepam. New England Journal of Medicine, 313, 1417-1418.

Karila, L., Cazas, O., Danel, T., & Reynaud, M. (2006). Conséquences court-et à long terme d'exposition prénatale au cannabis. *Journal de Gynécologie, Obstétrique et Biologie de la Reproduction, 35* (1), 62-70.

Karzel, R.P., & Friedman, M.J. (1991). Orthopedic injuries in pregnancy. In R. Artal, R.A. Wiswell, & B.L. Drinkwater. (Eds.). *Exercise in pregnancy* (2nd ed.). Baltimore: Williams & Wilkins.

Keenan-Lindsay, L., & Yudin, M.H. (2006). HIV Screening in Pregnancy. *Journal of Obstetrics and Gynaecology Canada, 28* (12), 1103-1112.

Kelly, S.J., Day, N., & Streissguth, A.P. (2000). Effects of prenatal alcohol exposure on social behavior in humans and other species. *Neurotoxicology and Teratology, 22,* 143-149.

Kelsey, D.E.R. (1953). Phantasies of birth and prenatal experience recovered from patients undergoing hypnoanalysis. *Journal of Mental Science 99,* 216-223.

Kempley, S. (1995). Methadone maintenance treatment. Pregnant women taking methadone should be warned about withdrawal symptoms in babies. *British Medical Journal, 310* (6977), 464.

Kennell, J.H., & Klaus, M. (1983). Early events: Later effects on the infant." In J. Call, E. Galenson & R. Tyson (Eds.). *Frontiers of Infant Psychiatry.* (pp. 7-16). New York: Basic Books.

Kerem, B., Chiba-Falek, O., & Kerem, E. (1997). Cystic fibrosis in Jews: frequency and mutation distribution. *Genetics Testing, 1* (1), 35-39.

Kessen, W., Haith, M.M., & Salapatek, P. (1970). Human infancy: A bibliography and guide. In P. Mussen (Ed.). *Carmichael's Manual of Child Development.* (pp. 287-444). New York: Wiley.

Khandelwal, M. (2006). Genital herpes complicating pregnancy. *Obstetrics & Gynecology, 107* (3), 740-741.

Khanobdee, C., Sukratanachaiyakul, V., & Gay, J.T. (1993). Couvade syndrome in expectant Thai fathers. *International Journal of Nursing Studies, 30* (2), 125-131.

Kieler, H., Cnattingius, S., Haglund, B., Palmgren, J., & Axelsson, O. (2001) Sinistrality-a side effect of prenatal sonography: A comparative study of young men. *Epidemiology, 12* (6), 618-623.

Kieler, H., Cnattingius, S., Palmgren, J., Haglund, B., & Axelsson, O. (2002). First trimester ultrasound scans and left-handedness. *Epidemiology, 13* (3), 370.

Kieler, H., Haglund, B., Cnattingius, S., Palmgren, J., Axelsson, O. (2005) Does prenatal sonography affect intellectual performance? *Epidemiology, 16* (3), 304-310.

Kimberlin, D.W. (2005). Herpes simplex virus infections in neonates and early childhood. *Seminars in Pediatric Infectious Diseases, 16* (4), 271-281.

Kimmel, C.A., Cuff, J.M., Kimmel, G.L., Heredia, D.J., Tudor, N., Silverman, P.M., & Chen, J. (1993). Skeletal development following heat exposure in the rat. *Teratology, 47,* 229-242.

Kitano, Y., & Adzick, N.S. (1999). New developments in fetal lung surgery. Current Opinions in Pediatrics, 11 (3), 193-199.

Kitano, Y., Flake, A.W., Crombleholme, T.M., Johnson, M.P., & Adzick, N.S. (1999). Open fetal surgery for life-threatening fetal malformations. *Seminars in Perinatology, 23* (6), 448-461.

Klebanoff, M.A., Carey, J.C., Hauth, J.C., Hillier, S.L., Nugent, R.P., Thom, E.A., Ernest, J.M., Heine, R.P., Wapner, R.J., Trout, W., Moawad. A., Leveno, K.J., Miodovnik. M., Sibai, B.M., Van Dorsten, J.P., Dombrowski, M.P., O'Sullivan, M.J., Varner, M., Langer, O., McNellis, D., & Roberts, J.M. (2001). Failure of metronidazole to prevent preterm delivery among pregnant women with asymptomatic Trichomonas vaginalis infection. *New England Journal of Medicine, 345* (7), 487-493.

Klebanoff, M.A., Koslowe, P.A., Kaslow, R., & Rhoads, G.C. (1985). Epidemiology of vomiting in early pregnancy. *Obstetrics and Gynecology, 66,* 612-616.

Klebanoff, M.A., Levine, R.J., DerSimonian, R., Clemens, J.D., & Wilkins, D.G. (1999) Maternal serum paraxanthine, a caffeine metabolite, and the risk of spontaneous abortion. *The New England Journal of Medicine, 341,* 1639-1644.

Klein, H. (1991). Couvade syndrome: male counterpart to pregnancy. International *Journal of Psychiatry in Medicine, 21* (1), 57-69

Klein, M. (1975a). *Love, guilt and reparation and other works* (vol. 3). New York: Delacourt Press.

Klein, M. (1975b). *Envy and gratitude and other works* (vol. 4). New York: Delacourt Press.

Kleinebrecht, J., Michaelis, H., Michaelis, J., & Koller, S. (1979). Fever in pregnancy and congenital anomalies. *Lancet, 1* (8131), 1403.

Klimek, R. (2001). Oxytocinase as the most important marker of fetal development. *Early Pregnancy, 5* (1), 63-64.

Kline, J., Stein, Z., Susser, M., & Warburton, D. (1985). Fever during pregnancy and spontaneous abortion. *American Journal of Epidemiology, 121,* 832-842.

Knopp, R.H., Magee, M.S., & Raisys, V. (1991). Hypocaloric diets and ketogenesis in the management of obese gestational diabetic women. *Journal of the American College of Nutrition, 10* (6), 649-667.

Kobre, K.R., & Lipsitt, L.P. (1972). A negative contrast effect in newborns. *Journal of Experimental Child Psychology 14,* 81-91.

Kocun, C.C., Harrigan, J.T., Canterino, J.C, & Feld, S.M. (2000). Changing trends in patient decisions concerning genetic amniocentesis. *American Journal of Obstetrics and Gynecology, 185* (5), 1018-1020.

Koga, M. (2001). Human parvovirus B19 in cord blood of premature infants. *American Journal of Perinatology, 18* (5), 237-240.

Kohl, T., Hering, R., Heep, A., Schaller, C., Meyer, B., Greive, C., Bizjak, G., Buller, T., Van de Vondel, P., Gogarten, W., Bartmann, P., Knopfle, G., &

Gembruch, U. (2006). Percutaneous fetoscopic patch coverage of spina bifida aperta in the human--early clinical experience and potential. *Fetal Diagnosis & Therapy, 21* (2), 185-193.

Kolata, G. (1984). Studying learning in the womb. *Science 225*, 302-303.

Koldovský, O., Heringová, A., Jirsová, V., Jirásek, J.E., & Uher, J. (1965). Transport of glucose against a concentration gradient in everted sacs of jejunum and ileum of human fetuses. *Gastroenterology, 48* (2), 185-187.

Konotey-Ahulu F. (1973). Effect of environment on sickle cell disease in West Africa: epidemiologic and clinical considerations. In H. Abramson, J. F. Bertles, D. L. Wethers. (Eds.). *Sickle Cell Disease, Diagnosis, Management, Education and Research.* (p. 20). St. Louis: C.V. Mosby.

Koos, B.J., & Longo, L.D. (1976). Mercury toxicity in the pregnant woman, fetus, and newborn infant. *American Journal of Obstetrics & Gynecology, 390* (5), 390-409.

Koppe, J.G., Loewer-Sieger, D.H., & de Roever-Bonnet, H. (1986). Results of 20-year follow-up of congenital toxoplasmosis. *Lancet, 1*, 254-255.

Kramer, L.I., & Pierpoint, M. E. (1976). Rocking waterbeds and auditory stimuli to enhance growth of preterm infants. *Journal of Pediatrics 88*, 297-299.

Krasinski, Z., Sajdak, S., Staniszewski, R., Dzieciuchowicz, L., Szpurek, D., Krasinska, B., Pawlaczyk, K., Oszkinis, G., & Majewski, W. (2006). Brzemienność jak (ponieważ) czynnik rozwoju (opracowywanie) "varicose veins" w kobietach. *Ginekologia Polska, 77* (6), 441-449.

Kristensen, J.H., Ilett, K.F., Hackett, L.P., Yapp, P., Paech, M., & Begg, E.J. (1999). Distribution and excretion of fluoxetine and norfluoxetine in human milk. *British Journal of Clinical Pharmacology, 48* (4), 521-527.

Kruse, F. (1978). Nos souvenirs du corps maternel. *Psychologie Heute* (June), 56.

Kulin, N.A., Pastuszak, A., Sage, S.R., Schick-Boschetto, B., Spivey, G., Feldkamp, M., Ormond, K., Matsui, D., Stein-Schechman, A.K., Cook, L., Brochu, J., Rieder, M., & Koren, G. (1998). Pregnancy outcome following maternal use of the new selective serotonin reuptake inhibitors: a prospective controlled multicenter study. *Journal of the American Medical Association, 279* (8), 609-610.

Kupesic, S. & Kurjak, A. (2001). Volume and vascularity of the yolk sac assessed by three-dimensional and power Doppler ultrasound. *Early Pregnancy, 5* (1), 40-41.

Kurki, T., & Ylikorkala, O. (1993). Coitus during pregnancy is not related to bacterial vaginosis or preterm birth. *American Journal of Obstetrics & Gynecology, 169* (5), 1130-1134.

L

Laegreid, L. (1990). Clinical observations in children after prenatal benzodiazepine exposure. *Developmental Pharmacology and Therapeutics, 15* (3-4), 186-188.

Lagercrantz, H., & Slotkin, T.A. (1986). The 'stress' of being born. *Scientific American 254*, 100-107.

Lagiou, P., Tamimi, R., Mucci, L.A., Trichopoulos, D., Adami, H.O., & Hsieh, C.C. (2003). Nausea and vomiting in pregnancy in relation to prolactin, estrogens and pregesterone: A prospective study. *Obstetrics & Gynecology, 101*, 639-644.

Laibow, R.E (1988). Prenatal and perinatal experience and developmental impairment. . In P.G. Fedor-Freybergh & M.L.V. Vogel (Eds.). Prenatal Psychology and Medicine, (pp. 295-308). Park Ridge NJ: The Parthenon Publishing Group.

Laibow, R.E. (1986). Birth recall: A clinical report." *Pre- and Peri-Natal Psychology Journal 1*, 78-81.

Lain, K.Y., Powers, R.W., Krohn, M.A., Ness, R.B., Crombleholme, W.R., & Roberts, J.M. (1991). Urinary cotinine concentration confirms the reduced risk of preeclampsia with tobacco exposure. *American Journal of Obstetrics and Gynecology, 181* (5), 908-914.

Laing, R.D. (1978). *The facts of life.* New York: Pantheon Books.

Laing, R.D. (1982). *The voice of experience.* New York: Pantheon Books.

Lake, F. (1964). *Clinical theology.* London: Darton, Longman & Todd.

Lake, F. (1967). The bearing of our knowledge of the unconscious on the theology of evangelism and pastoral care. Transcript of speech made at New College Theological Society, Nottingham: CTA.

Lake, F. (1976a). Perinatal events and origins of religious symbols, of symptoms and character problems: The possibility of reliving birth and its effects. Nottingham: CTA.

Lake, F. (1976b). The significance of birth and prenatal events in individual, family and social life. Nottingham: CTA.

Lake, F. (1977a). The internal consistency of the maternal-fetal distress syndrome. Nottingham: CTA.

Lake, F. (1977b). The maternal-fetal distress syndrome/negative umbilical affect: Defenses against invasive pain by symbolic displacement and containment. Nottingham: CTA.

Lake, F. (1978a). Report from the research department #1. Nottingham: CTA.

Lake, F. (1978b). The significance of perinatal experience. *Self & Society, 6,* 35-45.

Lake, F. (1978c) Theological issues in mental health in India. Nottingham: CTA.

Lake, F. (1978d). Transactional Analysis. *Contac, 58,* 14-20.

Lake, F. (1978e). Treating psychosomatic disorders relating to birth trauma. *Journal of Psychosomatic Research, 22,* 227-238.

Lake, F. (1980a). Conception-to-Womb Talkdown. Nottingham: CTA.

Lake, F. (1980b). Report from the Research Department #2. Nottingham: CTA.

Lake, F. (1980c). The theology of pastoral counselling," *Contact, 68,* 1-48.

Lake, F. (1981a). *Clinical Theology Newsletter* #38. Nottingham: CTA.

Lake, F. (1981c). Research into the pre-natal aetiology of mental illness, personality, and psychosomatic disorders. Nottingham: CTA.

Lake, F. (1981d). Studies in constricted confusion: Exploration of a pre- and peri-natal paradigm. Nottingham: CTA.

Lake, F. (1981e). Supplement to Newsletter No. 39. *Clinical Theology Newsletter* #39. Nottingham: CTA, December.

Lake, F. (1981f). Theology and Personality. *Epworth Review, 8,* 61-68.

Lake, F. (1981g). *Tight Corners in Pastoral Counselling.* London: Darton, Longman & Todd.

Lake, F. (1982b). Mutual caring. Oxford: CTA.

Lake, F. (1982c). *With Respect: A Doctor's Response to a Healing Pope.* London: Darton, Longman & Todd.

Lake, F. (1986). The Dynamic Cycle: An Introduction to the Model. *Lingdale Papers #2.* Oxford: CTA.

Lake, F. (1987). Primal integration work. *Self & Society, 15,* 167-173.

Lake, F. (1991b). The origin and development of personal identity. In C. Christian (Ed.) *In the Spirit of Truth.* London: Darton, Longman & Todd.

Lambert, D., Bramwell, M., & Lawther, G. (Eds). (1982). *The brain.* New York: G.P. Putnam Books. 1982.

Lammer, E.J., Chen, D.T., Hoar, R.M., Agnish, S.O., Benke, P.J., Brown, J.T., Curry, C.J., Fernhoff, P.M., Grix, A.W., Loft, I.T., Richard, J.M., & Sun, S.C. (1985). Retinoic acid embryopathy. *New England Journal of Medicine, 313*, 837-841.

Lammer, E.J., Hayes, E.M., Schunior, A., & Holmes, L.B. (1987). Risk for major malformation among human fetuses exposed to isotretinoin (13-cis-retinoic acid). *Teratology, 35*, 68A.

Langeworthy, U.R. (1933). Development of behavior patterns and myelinization of the nervous system in the human fetus and infant. *Contributions to Embryology*, XXIV, No. 139.

Lanzetta, M.(1992) Fetal microsurgery. The past and present of a frontier of surgery. *Minerva Chirurgica, 47* (21-22), 1687-1689.

Larroque, B., Kaminski, M., Lelong, N., Subti,l D., & Dehaene, P. (1993). Effects on birthweight of alcohol and caffeine consumption during pregnancy. *American Journal of Epidemiology, 137,* 941-950.

Larrouche, J.C. (1962). Quelques apects anatomiques du developpment cerebral. *Biologie Neonatal 4,* 126-153.

Larrouche, J.C (1966). "The Development of the Central Nervous System During Intrauterine Life." In Human Development, ed. Frank Falkner, 257-276. Philadelphia: W. B. Saunders Co.

Laukaran, V., & Van den Berg, B. (1980). The relationship of maternal attitude to pregnancy outcomes and obstetrical complications. A cohort study of unwanted pregnancy. *American Journal of Obstetrics and Gynecology 136,* 374-379.

Launer, L.H., Villar, J., Kestler, E., & DeOnis, M. (1990). The effect of maternal work on fetal growth and duration of pregnancy: a prospective study. *British Journal of Obstetrics & Gynaecology, 97,* 62–70.

Lauria, M.R., Gonik, B., & Romero, R. (1995). Pulmonary hypoplasia: pathogenesis, diagnosis and antenatal prediction. *Obsterics & Gynecology, 86* (3), 467-475.

Lawson, A.H., (1987). Perinatal imagery in UFO abduction reports. *Pre- and perinatal psychology: An introduction.* (T. R. Verny Ed.), 260-291. NY: Human Sciences Press.

Layde, P.M., Edmonds, L.D., & Erickson, J.D. (1980). Maternal fever and neural tube defects. *Teratology, 21,* 105-108.

Lead & Pregnancy (2005). Organization of Teratology Information Services. Retrieved on December 18, 2006 from http://otispregnancy.org/pdf/lead.pdf.

Leader, L.R. (1995). Studies in fetal behaviour. *British Journal of Obstetrics and Gynaecology, 102* (8), 595-597.

Leader, L.R., Baille, P., & Martin, B. (1982). Foetal habituation in high-risk pregnancies. *British Journal of Obstetrics and Gynaecology 89,* 441-446.

Leader, L.R., Baille, P., & Martin, B. (1984). Foetal responses to vibrotactile stimulation: A possible predictor of foetal and neonatal outcome. *Australian and New Zealand Journal of Obstetrics and Gynaecology 24,* 251-256

Leboyer, F. (1975). *Birth without violence.* NY: Knopf.

Lecanuet, J.P., Granier-Deferre, C., Cohen, H., & le Houezec, R. (1986). Fetal responses to acoustic stimulation depend on heart variability pattern, stimulus intensity and repetition. *Early Human Development 13 ,* 269-283.

Lecanuet, J.P., & Schaal, B. (1996). Fetal sensory competencies. *European Journal of Obstetrics, Gynecology, and Reproductive Biology, 68* (1-2), 1-23.

Lecron, L. (1954). A hypnotic technique for uncovering unconscious material. *International Journal of Clinical & Experimental Hypnosis 2,* 1-3.

Lecron, L. (1963). Uncovering early memories by ideomotor responses to questions. *International Journal of Clinical & Experimental Hypnosis 11,* 137-142.

Lecyk, M. (1966) The effect of hyperthermia applied in the given stages of pregnancy on the number and form of vertebrae in the offspring of white mice. *Experientia, 22,* 254-255.

Lee, G.M., Gortmaker, S.L., McIntosh, K., Hughes, M.D., & Oleske, J.M. (2006). Quality of life for children and adolescents: impact of HIV infection and antiretroviral treatment. *Pediatrics, 117* (2), 273-283.

Lee, H.S., Kim, M.S., Kim, M.H., Kim, Y.J., & Kim, W.Y. (2006). Iron status and its association with pregnancy outcome in Korean pregnant women. *European Journal of Clinical Nutrition, 60* (9), 1130-1135.

Lee, P.J., Ridout, D., Walker, J.H., & Cockburn, F. (2005). Maternal phenylketonuria: report from the United Kingdom Registry 1978–97. *Archives of Disease in Childhood, 90,* 143-146.

Leem, J.H., Kaplan, B.M., Shim, Y.K., Pohl, H.R., Gotway, C.A., Bullard, S.M., Rogers, J.F., Smith, M.M., & Tylenda, C.A. (2006). Exposures to air pollutants during pregnancy and preterm delivery. *Environmental Health Perspectives, 114* (6), 905-910.

Leen-Mitchell, M., Carey, J., Allen, J., Manchester, D., Quinn, D., Hoyme, G., & Feldkamp, M. (1995). Teratogen update. *Genetic Drift, 12.* Retrieved on December 9, 2006 from http://mostgene.org/gd/gdvol12a.htm.

Leet, T., & Flick, L. (2003). Effect of exercise on birthweight. *Clinical Obstetrics and Gynecology, 46* (2), 423-431.

Leith, E.N., & Upatnicks, J. (1965). Photography by laser. *Scientific American 212,* 24-35.

Lenz, W. (1962). Kindliche Mißbildungen nach Medikament-Einnahme während der Gravidat. *Deutsche Medizinische Wochenschrift, 86,* 2555–2556.

Lester, B. (1976). Spectrum analysis of the cry sounds of well-nourished and malnourished infants. *Child Development 47,* 237-241.

Lester, B.M., & C.F.Z. Boukydis (1985). *Infant crying: Theoretical and research perspectives.* NY: Plenum.

Lester, B.M., Cucca, J., Andreozzi, L., Flanagan, P., & Oh, W. (1993). Possible association between fluoxetine hydrochloride and colic in an infant. *Journal of the American Academy of Child and Adolescent Psychiatry, 6,* 1253-1255.

Leung, W-C. (2000). Parvovirus B19 infection: association with third-trimester intrauterine fetal death. BJOG: An International Journal of Obstetrics and Gynaecology, *107 (10), 1324 October 2000*

Levinson-Castiel, R., Merlob, P., Linder, N., Sirota, L., & Klinger, G. (2006). Neonatal abstinence syndrome after in utero exposure to selective serotonin reuptake inhibitors in term infants. *Archives of Pediatrics & Adolescent Medicine, 160,* 173-176.

Lewis, B.A., Singer, L.T., Short, E.J., Minnes, S., Arendt, R., Weishampel, P., Klein, N., & Min M.O. (2004). .Four year language outcomes of children exposed to cocaine in utero. *Neurotoxicology and Teratology, 26* (5), 617-627.

Lewis, R.J. (2005). *Sax's Dangerous Properties of Industrial Materials* (11th ed). Indianapolis: Wiley-Interscience.

Liley, A.W. (1972). The foetus as a personality. *The Australian and New Zealand Journal of Psychiatry, 6* (2), 99-105.

Liley, A.W. (1991). The fetus as personality. *Pre- and Peri-Natal Psychology Journal, 5,* 191-202.

Linton, M. (1982). Transformations of memory in everyday life. In *Memory observed: Remembering in naturalcContexts* (U. Neisser, Ed.). San Francisco: W.H. Freeman & Co.

Lipkin, M. Jr, & Lamb, G.S. (1982). The couvade syndrome: an epidemiologic study. Annals of internal medicine. Annals of Internal Medicine, 96 (4), 509-511.

Lipsitt, L.P. (1969). Learning capacities of the human infant. In *Brain and Early Behavior Development in the Fetus and Infant.* (R.J. Robinson, Ed.). 227-249. London: Academic Press.

Lipsitt, L.P., & Kaye, H. (1977). The study of sensory and learning processes of the newborn. *Clinics in Perinatology 4,* 163-186.

Lipsitt, L.P., & Werner, J.S. (1981). The infancy of human learning processes. In *Developmental plasticity.* (E.S. Gollin, Ed.). 101-133. NY: Academic Press.

Lipson, A., Webster, W., & Edwards, M. (1985) Sauna and birth defects. *Teratology, 32,*147-148.

List, J.A. (1986). Age and schematic differences in thc reliability of eyewitness testimony. *Developmental Psychology 22,* 50-57.

Listeriosis (2005). Centers for Disease Control. Retreived on November 7, 2006 from http://www.cdc.gov/ncidod/dbmd/diseaseinfo/listeriosis_g.htm.

Lithium & Pregnancy (2004). Organization of Teratology Information Services. Retrieved on December 11, 2006 from http://otispregnancy.org/pdf/lithium.pdf.

Little, B.B., Ghali, F.E., Snell, L.M., Knoll, K.A., Johnston, W., & Gilstrap, L.C. (1991). Is hyperthermia teratogenic in humans? *American Journal of Perinatology, 8,* 185-189.

Little, B.B., Snell, L.M., Klein, V.R., & Gilstrap, L.C., 3rd. (1989). Cocaine abuse during pregnancy: maternal and fetal implications. *Obstetrics & Gynecology, 73,* 157-160.

Little, B.B., Snell, L.M., Van Beveren, T.T., Crowell, R.B., Trayler, S., & Johnston, W.L. (2003). Treatment of substance abuse during pregnancy and infant outcome. *American Journal of Perinatology, 20* (5), 255-262.

Little, R.E., & Hook, E.B. (1979). Maternal alcohol and tobacco consumption and their association with nausea and vomiting during pregnancy. *Acta Obstetrics & Gynecology Scandinavia, 58,* 15-17.

Liu, S., & Willett, W.C. (2002) Dietary glycemic load and atherothrombotic risk. *Current Atherosclerosis Reports, 4,* 454-461.

Locke, J. (1956). *Essay concerning human understanding.* Chicago: Henry Regnery.

Loftus, E.F. (1979). *Eyewitness testimony.* Cambridge, Mass.: Harvard Univ. Press.

Loftus, E.F. (1980). *Memory.* Reading, Mass.: Addison-Wesley.

Loftus, E.F. (1975). Leading questions and the eyewitness report. *Cognitive Psychology 7,* 560-572.

Loftus, E.F. (1979). Reactions to blatantly contradictory information. *Memory and Cognition 7,* 368-374.

Loftus, E.F., & Greene, G.R. (1980). Warning: Even memory for faces may be contagious. *Law and Human Behavior 4,* 323-334.

Loftus, E.F., & Loftus, G.R. (1980). On the permanence of stored information in the human brain. *American Psychologist 35,* 409-420.

Loftus, E.F., & Palmer, J.C. (1974). Reconstruction of automobile destruction: An example of the interaction between language and memory. *Journal of Verbal Learning and Verbal Behavior 13,* 585-589.

Loftus, E.F., & Marburger, W. (1983). Since the eruption of Mount St. Helens has anyone beat you up? Improving the accuracy of retrospective reports with landmark events. *Memory and Cognition 11,* 114-120.

Loftus, E.F., Miller, D.G., & Burns, H. (1978). Semantic integration of verbal information into a visual memory. *Journal of Experimental Psychology, Human Learning and Memory 4,* 19-31.

Logan, B. (1987). Teaching the unborn: Precept and practice. *Pre-and Peri-Natal Psychology Journal 2,* 14-17.

Logan, B. (1988). The ultimate preventive: Prenatal stimulation. In *Prenatal and Perinatal Psychology and Medicine.* (P. Fedor-Freybergh & M.L.V. Vogel, eds.). 559-562. Park Ridge, NJ: The Parthenon Publishing Group.

Logan, B. (1991). Infant outcomes of a prenatal stimulation pilot study. *Pre-and Peri-Natal Psychology Journal 6,* 7-31.

London, R. (1988). Saccharin and aspartame. Are they safe to consume during pregnancy? *Journal of Reproductive Medicine, 33* (1), 17-21.

Longaker, M.T., Golbus, M.S., Filly, R.A., Rosen, M.A., Chang, S.W., & Harrison, M.R. (1991). Maternal outcomes after open fetal surgery: A review of the first 17 cases. *Journal of the American Medical Association, 265,* (6), 737–741.

Longo, L. (1977). The biological effects of carbon monoxide on the pregnant woman, fetus, and newborn infant. *American Journal of Obstetrics & Gynecology, 129,* 69-103.

Longo, L.D. (1975). Classic pages in obstetrics and gynecology. On the contractions of the uterus throughout pregnancy: their physiological effects and their value in the diagnosis of pregnancy. John Braxton Hicks Transactions of the Obstetrical Society of London, vol. 13, pp. 216-231, 1871. *American Journal of Obstetrics and Gynecology, 123* (4), 442.

Lopez, L.B., Ortega Soler, C.R., & de Portela, M.L. (2004). Cuadratín durante embarazo: un problema con frecuencia subestimado. *Archivos Latinoamericanos de Nutrición, 54* (1), 17-24.

Loureiro, K.D., Kao, K.K., Jones, K.L., Alvarado, S., Chavez, C., Dick, L., Felix, R., Johnson, D., & Chambers, C.D. (2005). Minor malformations characteristic of the retinoic acid embryopathy and other birth outcomes in children of women exposed to topical tretinoin during early pregnancy. *American Journal of Medical Genetics, Part A, 136* (2), 117-121.

Low, N., Egger, M., Sterne, J.A.C., Harbord, R.M., Ibrahim, F., Lindblom, B., & Herrmann, B. (2006). Incidence of severe reproductive tract complications associated with diagnosed genital chlamydial infection: the Uppsala Women's Cohort Study. *Sexually Transmitted Infections, 82,* 212-218.

Lowen, A. (1958). *Physical dynamics of character structure.* New York: Grune & Stratton.

Lowen,.A. (1967). *The betrayal of the body.* NY: Macmillan.

Lowen, A. (1970). *Pleasure.* NY: Coward-McCann.

Lowen, A. (1975). *Bioenergetics and the language of the body.* NY: Coward, McCann & Geoghegan.

Lower, A. (2006). Uterine fibroids. The London Fibroid Clinic. Retrieved on October 2, 2006 from http://www.fibroidsspecialist.co.uk/fibroids.htm.

Lukesch, M. (1975). Psychologie Faktoren der Schwangerschaft. Ph.D. diss., University of Salzburg.

Lumey, L.H. (1998). Compensatory placental growth after restricted maternal nutrition in early pregnancy. *Placenta, 19,* 105-111.

Lundington-Hoe, S., & Galant, S.K. (1985). *How to have a smarter baby.* NY: Collier-Macmillan.

Luoba, A.I., Geissler, P.W., Estambale, B., Ouma, J.H., Magnussen, P., Alusala, D., Ayah, R., Mwaniki, D., & Friis, H. (2004). Geophagy among pregnant and lactating women in Bondo District, western Kenya. *Transactions of the Royal Society of Tropical Medicine and Hygiene, 98* (12), 734-741.

Luoba, A.I., Wenzel-Geissler, P., Estambale, B., Ouma, J.H., Alusala, D., Ayah, R., Mwaniki, D., Magnussen, P., & Friis, H. (2005). Earth-eating and reinfection with intestinal helminths among pregnant and lactating women in western Kenya. *Tropical Medicine & International Health, 10* (3), 220-227.

Luria, S., & Shoham, Z. (1995). Induced midtrimester abortions and future fertility – where are you today? *International Journal of Fertility and Menopausal Studies, 40* (6), 311-315.

M

Ma, X., Buffler, P.A., Gunier, R.B., Dahl, G., Smith, M.T., Reinier, K., & Reynolds, P. (2002). Critical windows of exposure to household pesticides and risk of childhood leukemia. *Environmental Health Perspectives, 110* (9), 955-960.

Macdonald, T. (Director). (2005). *In the Womb* [DVD]. Washington, D.C.: National Geographic.

Macfarlane, A. 91975). Olfaction in the development of social preferences in the human neonate. *Parent-Child Interaction, CIBA Symposium 33.*

MacKinnon, K., & McIntyre, M. (2006). From Braxton Hicks to preterm labour: the constitution of risk in pregnancy. *The Canadian Journal of Nursing Research, 38* (2), 56-72.

Madison, L.S. (1986). Fetal response decrement: True habituation? *Journal of Developmental and Behavioral Pediatrics 7*, 14-20.

Madison, L.S., Adubato, S.A., & Madison, J.K. (1986). Foetal response decrement: True habituation. *Developmental and Behavioral Pediatrics 7*, 14-20.

Madison, L.S., Madison, J.K., & Adubato, S.A. (1986). Infant behavior and development in relation to fetal movement and habituation. *Child Development 57*, 1475-1482.

Maier, S.E., & West, J.R. (2001). Drinking patterns and alcohol-related birth defects. *Alcohol Research & Health, 25* (3), 168-174.

Makin, E.C., Hyett, J., Ade-Ajayi, N., Patel, S., Nicolaides, K., & Davenport, M. (1993). Outcome of antenatally diagnosed sacrococcygeal teratomas: single-center experience (1993-2004). *Journal of Pediatric Surgery, 41* (2), 388-393.

Mancia, M. (1981). On the beginning of mental life in the foetus. *The International Journal of Psycho-Analysis, 62*, 351-357.

Mancuso, S., & Palla, G. (1996). Intrauterine nutrition and development. *Advances in Contraception, 12* (4), 285-291.

Mansfield, C., Hopfer, S., & Marteau, T. (1999). Termination rates after prenatal diagnosis of Down syndrome, spina bifida, anencephaly, and Turner and Klinefelter syndromes: a systematic literature review. *Prenatal Diagnosis, 19* (9), 808-812.

Marlow, N., Wolke, D., Bracewell, M., & Samara, M. (2005). Neurologic and developmental disability at six years of age after extremely preterm birth. *New England Journal of Medicine, 352*, 9-19.

Marques, R.C., Garrofe Dorea, J., Rodrigues Bastos, W., de Freitas, R.M., de Freitas, F.M., & Malm, O. (2006). Maternal mercury exposure and neuromotor development in breastfed infants from Porto Velho (Amazon), Brazil. *International Journal of Hygiene and Environmental Health*, Sep 28 [Epub ahead of print].

Martin, G. (1981, October). Newborns pacified by tapes of their own crying. *Brain/Mind Bulletin, 2*.

Martin, J.C. (1982). An overview: Maternal nicotine and caffeine consumption and offspring outcome. *Neurobehavioral Toxicology and Teratology 4*, 421-427.

Martin, J.C. (1986). Irreversible changes in mature and aging animals following intrauterine drug exposure. *Neurobehavioral Toxicology and Teratology 8*, 335-343.

Maslow, A. (1968). Toward a psychology of being. NY: Van Nostrand Reinhold.

Mason-Brothers, A., Ritvo, E.R. & Guze, B. (1987). Pre-, peri- and postnatal factors in 181 autistic patients from single and multiple incidence families. *Journal of the American Academy of Child and Adolescent Psychiatry 26*, 39-42.

Masoni, S., Maio, A., Trimarchi, G., de Punzio, C., & Fioretti, P. (1994). The couvade syndrome. *Journal of Psychosomatic Obstetrics and Gynaecology, 15* (3), 125-131.

Masson, G.M., Anthony, F., & Chau, E. (1985). Serum chorionic gonadotropin (hCG), schwangerschaftprotein 1 (SP1), progesterone and estradiol levels in patients with nausea and vomiting in early pregnancy. *Brtisih Journal of Obstetrics & Gynecology, 92*, 211-215.

Mastukova, E.M. (1986). Role of parental alcoholism in origin of nervous-mental disorders in children. *Defektologiya 2*, 77-83.

Mathai, S., Fernandez, A., Mondkar, J., & Kanbur, W. (2001). Effect of tactile-kinesthetic stimulation in preterms: A controlled trial. *Indian Pediatrics, 38*, 1091-1098

Mathison, L.A. (1981). Does your child remember? *Mothering 21*,103-107.

Matijasevich, A., Santos, I.S., & Barros, F.C. (2005). Does caffeine consumption during pregnancy increase the risk of fetal mortality? A literature review. *Cadernos de Saúde Pública, 21* (6), 1676-1684.

Matt, U., LeRoux, M.G., Benichou, B., Moisan, J.P., & Giugliani, R. (1996). Study on possible increase in twinning rate at a small village in South Brazil. *Acta Genetic Medical Gemellol (Roma), 45*, 431-437.

Mattson, S.N., & Riley, E.P. (1998). A review of the neurobehavioral deficits in children with fetal alcohol syndrome or prenatal exposure to alcohol. *Alcoholism: Clinical and Experimental Research, 22*, 279-294.

May, P.A., & Gossage, J.P. (2001). Estimating the prevalence of fetal alcohol syndrome. A summary. *Alcohol Research & Health, 25* (3), 59-67.

May, P.A., Gossage, J.P., White-Country, M., Goodhart, K., Decoteau, S., Trujillo, P.M., Kalberg, W.O., Viljoen, D.L., & Hoyme, H.E. (2004). Alcohol consumption and other maternal risk factors for fetal alcohol syndrome among three distinct samples of women before, during, and after pregnancy: the risk is relative. *American Journal of Medical Genetics. Part C, Seminars in Medical Genetics, 127* (1), 10-20.

Mayer, C., & Kapfhammer, H.P. (1993). Couvade Syndrom, eine psychogenic Krankheit im übergang zur Vaterschaft. *Fortschritte der Neurologie-Psychiatrie 61* (10), 354-360.

Maynard, S.E., Min, J.Y., Merchan, J., Lim, K.H., Li, J., Mondal, S., Libermann, T.A., Morgan, J.P., Sellke, F.W., Stillman, I.E., Epstein, F.H., Sukhatme, V.P., & Karumanchi S.A. (2003). Excess placental soluble fms-like tyrosine kinase 1 (sFlt1) may contribute to endothelial dysfunction, hypertension, and proteinuria in preeclampsia. *Journal of Clinical Investigation, 111* (5), 600-602.

McAnulty, R. & Burnette, M.M. (2001) Exploring Human Sexuality. Boston: Allyn & Bacon.

McBride, W.G. (1962). Thalidomide and congenital abnormalities. *Lancet, 2*, 1358.

McClosky, M., & Zaragoza, M. (1985). Misleading postevent information and memory for events: Arguments and evidence against memory impairment hypotheses. *Journal of Experimental Psychology: General 114*, 1-16.

McCool, W.F., & Simeone, S.A. (2002). Birth in the United States: an overview of trends past and present. *The Nursing Clinics of North America, 37* (4), 735-746.

McDonald, A.D. (1958). Maternal health and congenital defect. *New England Journal of Medicine, 258*, 767-773.

McDonald, A.D. (1961). Maternal health in early pregnancy and congenital defect: Final report on a prospective inquiry. *British Journal of Preventive and Social Medicine, 15*, 154-166.

McDonald, A.D., McDonald, J.C., Armstrong, B., Cherry, N.M., Nolin, A.D., & Robert, D. (1988). Prematurity and work in pregnancy. *British Journal of Industrial Medicine, 45*, 56–62.

McDonald, R.L. (1968). The role of emotional factors in obstetric complications. *Psychosomatic Medicine 30*, 222-237.

McElhatton, P.R. (1994). The effects of benzodiazepine use during pregnancy and lactation. *Reproductive Toxicology, 8* (6), 461-475.

McLaren, A. (1985). The pleasures of procreation: Traditional and biomedical theories of conception. In W.F. Bynum & R. Porter (Eds.). *William Hunter and the Eighteenth-Century Medical World*. (pp. 330-360). New York: Cambridge Univ. Press.

Means, B., Mingay, D.J., Nigam, A., & Zarrow, M. (1988). A cognitive approach to enhancing health survey reports of medical visits. In *Practical Aspects of Memory: Current Research and Issues*. M.M. Gruneberg, P.E. Morris, & R.N. Sykes. (Eds.). Chichester: John Wiley & Sons.

Medical Genetics (2006). Lucille Packard Children's Hospital at Stanford. Retrieved on December 9, 2006 from http://www.lpch.org/DiseaseHealthInfo/HealthLibrary/ genetics/identify.html.

Medick, S.A., Machon, R.A., & Huttunen, M.O. (1988). Adult schizophrenia following prenatal exposure to an influenza epidemic. *Archives of General Psychiatry 45*, 189-192.

Medick, S.A., Parnas, J. & Schulsinger, F. (1987). The Copenhagan high risk project, 1962-86. *Schizophrenia Bulletin,* 485-495.

Meher, S., & Duley, L. (2006a). Exercise or other physical activity for preventing pre-eclampsia and its complications. *Cochrane Database of Systematic Reviews, 2,* CD005942.

Meher, S., & Duley, L. (2006b). Rest during pregnancy for preventing pre-eclampsia and its complications in women with normal blood pressure. *Cochrane Database of Systematic Reviews, 2,* CD005939.

Meltzoff, A., & Moore, M.K. (1977). Imitation of facial and manual gestures by human neonates. *Science 195,* 75-78.

Meltzoff, A., & Moore, M.K. (1983). The origins of imitation in infancy: Paradigm, phenomena, and theories. In *Advances in Infancy Research,* vol. 2. L.P. Lipsitt & C. Rovee-Collier (Eds.). 265-301. Norwood, NJ: Ablex.

Menees, T.O., Millar, J.D. & Holly, L.E. (1930). Amniography. Preliminary report. *American Journal of Roentgenology, 24,* 353-366.

Mennella, J.A. (2001). Alcohol's effect on lactation. *Alcohol Research & Health, 25* (3), 230-234.

Mennella, J.A., & Garcia-Gomez, P.L. (2001). Sleep disturbances after acute exposure to alcohol in mothers' milk. *Alcohol, 25* (3), 153-158

Mennella, J.A., Jagnow, C.P., & Beauchamp, G.K. (2001). Prenatal and postnatal flavor learning by human infants. *Pediatrics, 107* (6), 88.

Mennella, J.A., Johnson, A., & Beauchamp, G.K. (1995). Garlic ingestion by pregnant women alters the odor of amniotic fluid. *Chemical Senses 20,* 207-209,

Mercer, M.E., & Holder, M.D. (1997). Food cravings, endogenous opioid peptides, and food intake: a review. *Appetite, 29* (3), 325-352.

Mercer, R.T., Ferketich, S., May, K., & DeJospeh, J. (1988). Further exploration of maternal and paternal fetal attachment. *Research in Nursing and Health 11,* 83-95.

Meredith, H.V. (1978). *Human body growth in the first ten years of life.* Columbia, S.C.: The State Printing Company.

Methamphetamines & Pregnancy (2005). Organization of Teratology Information Services. Retrieved on December 11, 2006 from http://otispregnancy.org/pdf/methamph etamines.pdf.

Meuli, M., Meuli-Simmen, C., Hutchins, G.M., Seller, M.J., Harrison, M.R., & Adzick, N.S. (1997). The spinal cord lesion in human fetuses with myelomeningocele: implications for fetal surgery. *Journal of Pediatric Surgery, 32* (3), 448-452.

Meylan, P. (2005). Recommandations suisses pour la gestion des herpers gential et l'infection recto de virus d'herpès du nouveau-né. *Revue Médicale Suisse, 1* (36), 2315-2316, 2318-2322, 2324-2326.

Michel, C. and H. Fritz-Niggli. "Induction of Developmental Anomalies in Mice by Maternal Stress." Experientia 34 (1978): 105-106.

Mikkelsen, T.B., Andersen, A.M., & Olsen, S.F. (2006). Pica in pregnancy in a privileged population: myth or reality. *Acta Obstetricia et Gynecologica Scandinavica, 85* (10), 1265-1266.

Millar, L., & Cox, S.. (1997). Urinary tract infections complicating pregnancy. *Infectious Disease Clinics of North America, 11* (1), 13-26.

Miller, A.J. (1982). Deglutition. *Physiological Reviews, 62* (1), 129-181.

Miller, E., Cradock-Watson, J.E., & Pollock, T.M. (1982). Consequences of confirmed maternal rubella at successive stages of pregnancy. *Lancet, 2* (8302), 781-784.

Miller, E., Fairley, C.K., Cohen, B.J., & Seng, C. (1998). Immediate and long term outcome of human parvovirus B19 infection in pregnancy. *BJOG: An International Journal of Obstetrics & Gynaecology, 105* (2), 174.

Miller, G.A., Galanter, E., & Pribram, K.H. (1960). *Plans and the structure of behavior.* NY: Holt, Rinehart & Winston.

Mills, J.L. (1999). Cocaine, smoking and spontaneous adortion. *New England Journal of Medicine, 340,* 380-381.

Mills, J.L., Holmes, L.B., Aarons, J.H., Simpson, J.L., Brown, Z.A., Jovanovic-Peterson, L.G., Conley, M.R., Graubard, B.I., Knopp, R.H., & Metzger, B.E. (1993). Moderate caffeine use and the risk of spontaneous abortion and intrauterine growth. *The Journal of the American Medical Association, 269,* 593-597.

Milunsky, A., Ulcickas, M., Rothman, K.J., Willett, W., Jick, S.S., & Jick, H. (1992). Maternal heat exposure and neural tube defects. *Journal of the American Medical Association, 268,* 882-885.

Milunsky, J.M. (2004). Prenatal Diagnosis of Sex Chromosome Abnormalities. In A. Milunsky. (ed.) *Genetic Disorders and the Fetus: Diagnosis, Prevention, and Treatment* (5th ed.). (pp. 297-340). Baltimore: Johns Hopkins University Press.

Minnes, S., Singer, L.T., Arendt, R., & Satayathum, S. (2005). Effects of prenatal cocaine/polydrug use on maternal-infant feeding interactions during the first year of life. *Journal of Developmental and Behavioral Pediatrics, 26* (3), 194-200.

Mirmiran, M. (1986). The importance of fetal/neonatal REM sleep. *European Journal of Obstetrics and Gynecological Reproductive Biology, 21* (5-6), 283-291.

Misri, S., Kim, J., Riggs, K.W., & Kostaras, X. (2000). Paroxetine levels in postpartum depressed women, breastmik, and infant serum. *The Journal of Clinical Psychiatry, 61* (11), 828-832.

Mistretta, C.M., & Bradley, R.M. (1975). Taste and swallowing in utero. *British Medical Bulletin, 31* (1), 80-84.

Mistretta, C.M., & Bradley, R.M. (1977). Taste in utero: Theoretical considerations. In *Taste and development: The genesis of sweet preference.* J.M. Weiffenbach (Ed.). 51-69. Washington DC: US Government Printing Office.

Mitsuhiro, S.S., Chalem, E., Barros, M.C., Guinsburg, R., & Laranjeira, R. (2006). Prevalence of cocaine and marijuana use in the last trimester of adolescent pregnancy: Socio-demographic, psychosocial and behavioral characteristics. *Addictive Behaviors, 31* (8).

Mocarelli, P., Brambilla, P., Gerthous, P.M., Patterson, D.G., & Needham, L.I. (1996). Change in sex ratio with exposure to dioxin. *Lancet, 348,* 409.

Mocarelli, P., Gerthoux, P.M., Ferrari, E., Patterson, D.G., Kieszak, S.M., Brambilla, P., Vincoli, N., Signorini, S., Tramacere, P., Carreri, V., Sampson, E.J., Turner W.E., & Needham, L.L. (2000). Paternal concentrations of dioxin and sex ratio of offspring. *Lancet, 355,* 1858-1863.

Moise, K.J., Jr. (2003). Maternal-fetal surgery for spina bifida: on the brink of a new era? American Journal of Obstetrics & Gynecology, 189 (2), 311.

Møller, H. (1996). Change in male-female ratio among newborn infants in Denmark. *Lancet, 348,* 828-829.

Møller, H. (1998). Trends in sex-ratio, testicular cancer and male reproductive hazards: Are they connected? *Acta Pathologica, Microbiologica et Immunologica Scandinavica (APMIS), 106,* 232-239.

Molliver, M.E., Kostovic, I. and H. Van der Loos. "The Development of Synapses in the Cerebral Cortex of the Human Fetus." Brain Research 50 (1973): 403-407.

Montagu, A. Prenatal Influences. Springfield, Ill.: Charles Thomas, 1962.

Moore, K.L. (1980). *Clinically oriented anatomy.* Baltimore: Williams & Wilkins.

Moore, K.L., & Persaud, T.V.N. (2003). *The developing human, clinically oriented embryology.* (7th ed.). Philadelphia: W.B. Saunders.

Mori, K., Yoshida, K., Hoshikawa, S., Ito, S., Yoshida, M., Satoh, M., & Watanabe, C. (2006). Effects of perinatal exposure to low doses of cadmium or methylmercury on thyroid hormone metabolism in metallothionein-deficient mouse neonates. *Toxicology, 228* (1), 77-84.

Morishima, H.O., Glaser, B., Biermann, W.H., & James, L.S. (1975). Increased uterine activity and fetal deterioration during maternal hyperthermia. *American Journal of Obstetrics and Gynecology, 121,* 531-538.

Morrell, P., Sutherland, G.R., Buamah, P.K., Oo, M., & Bain, H.H. (1983). Lithium toxicity in the neonate. *Archives of Disease in Childhood, 58,* 539-541.

Morris, S.N. & Johnson, N.R. (2005). Exercise during pregnancy: a critical appraisal of the literature. *Journal of Reproductive Medicine, 50* (3), 181-188.

Moss, R. (1983, December). Frank Lake's maternal-fetal distress syndrome and primal integration workshops. *CTA Occasional Paper #2.*

Moss, R. (1983, May). Primal integration: A first report from the workshops. *CTA Occasional Paper #1.* Oxford: CTA.

Moss, R. (1984). Review of research: Frank Lake's primal integration workshops. Oxford: CTA.

Moss, R. (1986). Frank Lake's maternal-fetal distress syndrome and primal integration workshops. *Pre- and Peri-Natal Psychology Journal,1,* 52-63.

Moss, R. (1987). Frank Lake's maternal-fetal distress syndrome: Clinical and theoretical considerations. In T.R. Verny (Ed.) *Pre- and peri-natal psychology: An introduction* (pp. 201-208). New York: Human Sciences Press.

Moss, R. (1990). *In the beginning: A handbook on primal integration.* Exeter, UK.

Mott, F.J. (1964). *The universal design of creation.* Edenbridge, Kent: Mark Beech Publishers.

Moyer, J.A., Herrenkohl, L.R., & Jacobowitz, D.M. (1978). Stress during pregnancy: Effect on catecholamines in discrete regions of offspring as adults. *Brain Research 144,* 173-178.

Mulder, E.J., & Visser, G.H. (1987). Braxton Hicks' contractions and motor behavior in the near-term human fetus. *American Journal of Obstetrics and Gynecology, 156* (3), 543-549.

Mulder, E.J., Visser, G.H., Bekedam, D.J., & Prechtl, H.F. (1987). Emergence of behavioral states in fetuses of type-1 diabetic women. *Early Human Development 15,* 231-251.

Mulders, L.G., Muijsers, G.J., Jongsma, H.W., & Nijhuis, J.G. (1986). The umbilical artery blood flow velocity waveform in relation to fetal breathing movements, fetal heart rate and fetal behavior states in normal pregnancy at 37 to 39 weeks. *Early Human Development 14,* 283-293.

Murdoch, H. (1984). Maternal rubella: The implications. *AEP Association of Educational Psychologists Journal 6 ,* 3-6.

Murray, M. (1981). The jagged edge: A biographical essay on Simone Weil. In *Simone Weil: Interpretations of a life.* George Abbott White (Ed.). Amherst, Mass.: The University of Massachusetts Press.

Mussen, P.H., Conger, J.J., & Kagan, J. (1980). *Essentials of Child Development and Personality* (5th ed.). NY: Harper & Row.

Mustaph, M. (1988). The importance of early skin contact in emotional care. In *Prenatal psychology and medicine.* P. Fedor-Freybergh & M.L.V. Vogel (Eds.). 249-252. Park Ridge NJ: The Parthenon Publishing Group.

Mwapasa, V., Rogerson, S.J., Kwiek, J.J., Wilson, P.E., Milner, D., Molyneux. M.E., Kamwendo. D.D., Tadesse, E., Chaluluka, E., & Meshnick, S.R. (2006). Maternal syphilis infection is associated with increased risk of mother-to-child transmission of HIV in Malawi. *AIDS, 20* (14), 1869-1877.

Myrianthefs, P., Ladakis, C., Lappas, V., Pactitis, S., Carouzou, A., Fildisis, G., & Baltopoulos, G. (2000). Ovarian hyperstimulation syndrome (OHSS): diagnosis and management. *Intensive Care Medicine, 25* (5), 631-634.

N

Naeye, R.L (1983). Maternal use of dextroamphetamine and growth of the fetus. *Pharmacology 26,* 117-120.

Naeye, R.L. (1981). Influence of maternal cigarette smoking during pregnancy on fetal and childhood growth. *Obstetrics & Gynecology, 57,* 18-21.

Naeye, R.L. (1985). Umbilical cord length: Clinical significance. *Journal of Pediatrics, 107,* 278-281.

Naeye, R.L. (1992). *Disorders of the Placenta, Fetus, and Neonate: Diagnosis and Clinical Significance.* London: Mosby.

Naeye, R.L., & Chez, R.A. (1981). Effects of maternal acetonuira and low pregnancy weight gain on children's psychomotor development. *American Journal of Obstetrics and Gynecology, 139,* 189-193.

Naeye, R.L., & Peters, E. (1982). Working during pregnancy, effects on the fetus. *Pediatrics, 69,* 724–727.

Naimi, T.S., Lipscomb, L.E., Brewer, R.D., & Gilbert, B.C. (2003). Binge drinking in the preconception period and the risk of unintended pregnancy: implications for women and their children. *Pediatrics, 111* (5 Part 2), 1136-1141.

Nanda, N., Michel, R.G., Kurdgelashvili, G., & Wendel, K.A. (2006). Trichomoniasis and its treatment.

Expert Review of Anti-infective Therapy, 4 (1), 125-135.

Napiorkowski, B., Lester, B.M., Freier, M.C., Brunner, S., Dietz, L., Nadra, A., & Oh, W. (1996). Effects of in utero substance exposure on infant neurobehavior. *Pediatrics, 98* (1), 71-75.

Nathaniels, P.W. (1992*). Life before birth.* NY: Freeman.

National Institutes of Health (NIH). (2004). *Clinical features of Turner syndrome.* Retrieved on September 22, 2006 from http://turners.nichd.nih.gov/ClinFrIntro.html.

Nau, H., Kuhnz, W., Egger, H.J., Rating, D., & Helge, H. (1982). Anticonvulsants during pregnancy and lactation. Transplacental, maternal and neonatal pharmacokinetics. *Clinical Pharmacokinetics, 7* (6), 508-543.

Navarrete-Palacios, E., Hudson R., Reyes-Guerrero, G., Guevara-Guzman, R. (2003). Lower olfactory threshold during the ovulatory phase of the menstrual cycle. *Biological Psychology, 63* (3), 269-279.

Nduati, R., Mbori-Ngacha, D., John, G., Richardson, B., & Kreiss, J. (2000). Breastfeeding in women with HIV. *Journal of the American Medical Association, 284* (8), 956-957.

Neerhof, M.G., MacGregor, S.N., Retzky, S.S., & Sullivan, T.P. (1989). Cocaine abuse during pregnancy: peripartum prevalence and perinatal outcome. *American Journal of Obstetrics & Gynecology, 161,* 633-638.

Neighbour, R.N. (1981). Antenatal memories and psychopathology. *The Journal of the Royal College of General Practitioners.*

Nelson, C., & Demmler, G. (1997). Cytomegalovirus infection in the pregnant mother, fetus, and newborn infant. *Clinics in Perinatology, 24,* 151-160.

Nelson, S.M., & Greer, I.A. (2006). Thrombophilia and the risk for venous thromboembolism during pregnancy, delivery, and puerperium. *Obstetrics and Gynecology Clinics of North America, 33* (3), 413-427.

Nelson. W.E. (1964) *Textbook of pediatrics.* Philadelphia: Sanders.

Ness, R.B., Grisso, J.A., Hirschinger, N., Markovic, N., Shaw, L.M., Day, N.L., & Kline, J. (1999). Cocaine and tobacco use and the risk of spontaneous abortion. *New England Journal of Medicine, 340* (5), 333-339.

Newburger, P.E., Kruskall, M.S., Rappeport, J.M., Robinson, S.H., Chovaniec, M.E., & Cohen, H.J. (1980). Chronic granulomatous disease. Expression of the metabolic defect by in vitro culture of bone marrow progenitors. *Journal of Clinical Investigation, 66* (3), 599–602.

Newman, L.F., & Buka, S.L. (1991). Clipped wings: The fullest look yet at how prenatal exposure to drugs, alcohol, and nicotine hobbles children's learning. *American Educator, 42,* 27-33.

Newnham, J.P., Evans, S.F., Michael, C.A., Stanley, F.J., & Landau L.I. (1993). Effects of frequent ultrasound during pregnancy: a randomised controlled trial. *Lancet. 342* (8876), 887-891.

Newton, R.W. (1988). Psychosocial aspects of pregnancy: The scope for intervention. *Journal of Reproductive and Infant Psychology 6,* 23-39.

Ngoc, N.T., Merialdi, M., Abdel-Aleem, H., Carroli, G., Purwar, M., Zavaleta, N., Campodonico, L., Ali, M.M., Hofmeyr, G.J., Mathai, M., Lincetto, O., & Villar, J. (2006). Causes of stillbirths and early neonatal deaths: Data from 7993 pregnancies in six developing countries. *Bulletin of the World Health Organization, 84* (9), 699-705.

Nihoul-Fekete, C. (1990). Role of fetal surgery in the treatment of abnormalities. Apropos of diaphragmatic hernia. *Chirurgie, 116* (6-7), 529-536.

Nilson, L. (Director). (1986). *The Miracle of Life* [VHS]. Boston: WGBH Educational Foundation.

Noback, C.R., Strominger, N.L., & Demarest, R.J. (1996). *The human nervous system.* (5th ed.). Baltimore: Williams & Wilkins.

Noland, J.S., Singer, L.T., Arendt, R.E., Minnes, S., Short, E.J., & Bearer, C.F. (2003). Executive functioning in preschool-age children prenatally exposed to alcohol, cocaine, and marijuana. *Alcoholism, Clinical and Experimental Research, 27* (4), 647-656.

Noland, J.S., Singer, L.T., Short, E.J., Minnes, S., Arendt, R.E., Kirchner, H.L., & Bearer, C. (2005). Prenatal drug exposure and selective attention in preschoolers. *Neurotoxicology and Teratology, 27* (3), 429-438.

Norcia, A.M., & Tyler, C.W. (1985). Spacial frequency weep VEP: Visual acuity during the first year of life. *Vision Research 25,* 1399-1408.

Norwitz, E.R., Schust, D.J., & Fisher, S.J. (2001). Implantation and the survival of early pregnancy. *New England Journal of Medicine, 345,* 1400-1408.

Nugent, J.K., Greene, S., & Mazor, K. (1990). The effects of maternal alcohol and nicotine use during pregnancy in birth outcome. Paper presented at Bebe XXI Simposio Internacional, Lisbon, Portugal.

Nulman, I., Rovet, J., Stewart, D.E., Wolpin, J., Gardner, H.A., Theis, J.G., Kulin, N., & Koren, G. (1997). Neurodevelopment of children exposed in utero to antidepressant drugs. *New England Journal of Medicine, 336* (4), 258-262.

Nulman, I., Scolnik, D., Chitayat, D., Farkas, L.D., & Koren, G. (1997). Findings in children exposed in utero to phenytoin and carbamazepine monotherapy: independent effects of epilepsy and medications. *American Journal of Medical Genetics, 68,* 18-24.

O

O'Brien, C.M., & Jeffrey, H.E. (2002). Sleep deprivatrion, disorganization and fragmentation during opiate withdrawal in newborns. *Pediatric Child Health, 38,* 66-71.

O'Brien, B., & Zhou, Q. (1995). Variables related to nausea and vomiting during pregnancy. *Birth, 22* (2), 93-100.

O'Callaghan, F.V., O'Callaghan, M., Najman, J.M., Williams, G.M., & Bor, W. (2003). Maternal alcohol consumption during pregnancy and physical outcomes up to 5 years of age: a longitudinal study. *Early Human Development, 71* (2), 137-148.

Ockleford, E.M., Vince, M.A., & Layton, C. (1988). Responses of neonates to parent's and other's voices. *Early Human Development 18,* 27-36.

Ohman, R., Hagg, S., Carleborg, L., & Spigset, O. (1999). Excretion of paroxetine into breast milk. *Journal of Clinical Psychiatry, 60* (8), 519-523.

Okai, T., Kozuma, S., Shinozuka. N., Kuwabara. Y., & Mizuno, M. (1992). A study on the development of sleep-wakefulness cycle in the human fetus. *Early Human Development, 29* (1-3), 391-396.

Olds, C. (1986). A sound start in life. *Pre- and Peri-Natal Psychology Journal 1,* 82-85.

Olds, D. (1997). Tobacco exposure and impaired development: A review of the evidence. *Mental Retardation and Developmental Research Reviews, 3,* 257-269.

Oligohydramnios (2006). March of Dimes at marchofdimes.com. Retrieved October 10, 2006 from http://www. marchofdimes.com/pnhec/188_1033.asp.

Olney, R.S., Moore, C.A., Khoury, M.J., Erickson, J.D., Edmonds, L.D., Botto, L.D., & Atrash, H.K. (1995). Chorionic villus sampling and amniocentesis: recommendations for prenatal counseling. *Morbidity and Mortality Weekly Report, 44* (RR-9).

Online Mendelian Inheritance in Man (OMIM). (2004). McKusick-Nathans Institute for Genetic Medicine, Johns Hopkins University (Baltimore) and National Center for Biotechnology Information, National Library of Medicine (Bethesda, MD.). http://www.ncbi.nlm.nih.gov/omim.

O'Rahilly, R,, & Müller, F. (1984). Respiratory and alimentary relations in staged human embryos. New embryological data and congenital anomalies. *The Annals of Otology, Rhinology, and Laryngology, 93* (5 Part 1), 421-429.

O'Rahilly, R. (1977). Prenatal human development. In R.M. Wynn (Ed.). *The biology of the uterus.* (2nd ed.). New York: Plenum.

O'Rahilly, R., & Müller, F. (2001). *Human embryology and teratology.* (3rd ed.). New York: Wiley-Liss.

Orne, M.T (1979). The use and misuse of hypnosis in court. *International Journal of Clinical and Experimental Hypnosis 27,* 311-341.

Orne, M.T. (1962). Hypnotically induced hallucinations. In *Hallucinations.* L.J. West (Ed.). NY: Grune & Stratton.

Ornoy, A., & Cohen, E. (1996). Outcome of children born to epileptic mothers treated with carbamazepine during pregnancy. *Archives of Disease in Childhood, 75,* 517-520.

Ornoy, A., Arnon, J., Shechtman, S., Moerman, L., & Lukashova, I. (1998). Is benzodiazepine use during pregnancy really teratogenic? *Reproductive Toxicology, 12,* 511-515.

Orr, L., & Ray, S. (1977). *Rebirthing in the new age.* Berkeley, Ca.: Celestial Arts.

Paisley, T., Joy, E., & Price, R. (2003). Exercise during pregnancy: a practical approach. *Current Sports Medicine Reports, 2* (6), 325-330.

P

Palinski, W., & Napoli, C. (2002). The fetal origins of atherosclerosis: maternal hypercholesterolemia, and cholesterol-lowering or antioxidant treatment during pregnancy influence in utero programming and postnatal susceptibility to atherogenesis *Federation of American Societies for Experimental Biology Journal, 16,* 1348-1360.

Papousek, H. (1967). Experimental studies of appetitional behavior in human newborns and Infants. In *Early behavior: Comparative and developmental approaches.* H.W. Stevenson, E.H. Hess, & H.L. Rheingold (Eds.)., 249-277. NY: John Wiley.

Papousek, H. (1969). Individual variability in learned responses in human infants. In *Brain and Early Behavior.* R.J. Robinson (Ed.). London: Academic Press.

Papousek, H., & Papousek, M. (1977) Mothering and the cognitive head-start: Psychobiological considerations. In *Studies in mother-infant interaction.* H.R. Schaffer (Ed.). London: Academic Press.

Papousek, H., & Papousek, M. (1982). Integration into the social world: Survey of research. In *Psychobiology of the human newborn.* P.M. Stratton (Ed.). 367-390. NY: John Wiley.

Papousek, H., & Papousek, M. (1987). Intuitive parenting: A didactic counterpart to the infant's precocity in integrative capacities. *Handbook of Infant Development,* (2nd ed.). J. Osofsky (Ed.). NY: John Wiley.

Papousek, H., Papousek, M., & Harris, B.J. (1986). The emergence of play in parent-infant interactions. In *Curiosity,Imagination, & play: On the development of spontaneous cognitive and motivationalpProcesses.* D. Gorlitz & J.F. Wohlwill (Eds.). 214-246. NY: Erlbaum Associates.

Parasara. (1968). *Parasarasmrti.* D.S. Vasudeva (Ed. & Trans.). Benares: Chowkhamba Sanskrit Series Office.

Parasara. Parasarasmrti, ed. Daivajnavacaspati Sri Vasudeva. Benares: Chowkhamba Sanskrit Series Office, 1968.

Parazzini, F., Chiaffarino, F., Chatenoud, L., Tozzi, L., Cipriani, S., Chiantera, V., & Fedele, L. (2004). Maternal coffee drinking in pregnancy and risk of small for gestational age birth. *European Journal of Clinical Nutrition, 59,* 299–301.

Pastuszak, A., Schick-Boschetto, B., Zuber, C., Feldkamp, M., Pinelli, M., Sihn, S., Donnenfeld, A., McCormack, M., Leen-Mitchell, M., & Woodland, C. (1993). Pregnancy outcome following first trimester exposure to fluoxetine (Prozac). *Journal of the American Medical Association, 269* (17), 2246-2248.

Patrick, J., Campbell, K., Carmichael. L., Natale. R., & Richardson, B. (1980). Patterns of human fetal breathing during the last 10 weeks of pregnancy. *Obstetrics & Gynecology, 56* (1), 24-30.

Patten, B.M. (1946). *Human embryology.* Philadelphia: The Blakiston Company.

Paulson, M.J. (1983). The addicted fetus and newborn: Intervention conflicts. *Journal of Clinical Child Psychiatry 12,* 284-287.

Pavlov, I. (1928), *Lectures on Conditioned Reflexes.* (Vols. 1 & 2). W.H. Gantt (Trans.). New York: International Publishers.

Pavlov, I. (1957). *Experimental psychology and other essays.* New York: Philosophical Library.

Pavlov, I. (1960). *Conditioned reflexes: An investigation of the physiological activity of the cerebral cortex.* G.V. Anrep (Ed. & Trans.). New York: Dover Publications.

Paxil & Pregnancy (2006). Organization of Teratology Information Services. Retrieved on December 11, 2006 from http://otispregnancy.org/pdf/paxil.pdf.

Pearson, A,A. (1980). The development of the eyelids. Part I. External features. *Journal of Anatomy, 130* (1), 33-42.

Peckham, C.H., King, R.W. (1963). A study of intercurrent conditions observed during pregnancy. *American Journal of Obstetrics and Gynecology 87,* 609-624.

Peckham, C.S., Coleman, J.C., Hurley, R., Chin, K.S., Henderson, K., & Preece, P.M. (1983). Cytomegalovirus infection in pregnancy: preliminary findings from a prospective study. *Lancet, 1,* 1352-1355.

Peek, H.V.S., & Hertz, M.J. (1973). *Habituation, vols. 1 and 2.* NY: Academic Press.

Peerbolte, M.L. (1951). Psychotherapeutic evaluations of birth-trauma analysis. *Psychiatric Quarterly 25,* 596-600.

Peerbolte, M.L. (1954). *Psychic energy in prenatal dynamics.* Amsterdam: Wassener.

Peiper, A. (1925). Sinnesemp findungen des Kindes vor seiner geburt. *Monatsschrift fur Kinderheilkunde 29,* 237-241.

Peiper, A. (1963). *Cerebral function in infancy and childhood.* NY: Consultants Bureau.

Pelletier, K.R. (1978). *Toward a science of consciousness.* NY: Delta Books.

Penrose, L.S., & Ohara, P.T. (1973). The development of epidermal ridges. *Journal of Medical Genetics, 10* (3), 201-208.

Pepper, G.V., & Roberts, S.C. (2006). Rates of nausea and vomiting in pregnancy and dietary characteristics across populations. *Proceedings of The Royal Society B.* Published on-line by FirstCite e-publishing. Retrieved on November 4, 2006 from http:// www.liv.ac.uk/ evolpsyc/ 2006_NVP_PRSB.pdf.

Perault, M.C., Favreliere, S., Minet, P., & Remblier, C. (2000). Benzodiazépines et grossesse. *Therapie, 55* (5), 587-595.

Pereira, M.A., & Liu, S. (2003). Types of carbohydrates and risk of cardiovascular disease. *Journal of Women's Health, 12,* 115-122.

Pergament, E., Schechtman, A.S., & Rochanayon, A. (1997). Hyperthermia and Pregnancy. *Risk Newsletter, 5* (6), 1-7. Northwestern University Medical school. Retrieved on January 27, 2007 from http://www.fetal-exposure.org/HYPERTH.html.

Perls, F.S. (1969a). *Gestalt therapy verbatim.* Lafayette, Ca.: Real People Press.

Perls, F.S. (1969b) *In and out the garbage pail.* Lafayette, Ca.: Real People Press.

Perry, B.D. (1984). Prenatal exposure to drugs of abuse in humans: Effects on placental neurotransmitter receptors. *Neurobehavioral Toxicology and Teratology 6,* 295-301.

Perry, T.B., Hechtman, P. & Chow, J.C.W. (1979) Diagnosis of Tay Sachs disease on blood obtained at fetoscopy. *Lancet, 1,* 972.

Persinger, M.A. (2001). Shifting gustatory thresholds and food cravings during pregnancy as expanding uterine-induced steady potential shifts within the insula: an hypothesis.*Perceptual & Motor Skills, 92* (1), 50-52.

Peterfreund, E. (1971). *Information, systems and psychoanalysis.* NY: International Universities Press.

Peters, D.A. (1988). Effects of maternal stress during different gestational periods on the serotonergic system in adult rat offspring. *Pharmacology, Biochemistry and Behavior 31,* 839-843.

Petersen, P.E., Stewart, W.B., Greer, C.A., & Shepherd, G.M. (1983). Evidence for olfactory function in utero. *Science 221,* 478-480.

Peterson, G., Mehl, L., & McRae, J. (1988). Relationship of psychiatric diagnoses, anxiety and stress with birth complications. In *Prenatal and Perinatal Psychology and Medicine.* P.G. Fedor-Freybergh & M.L.V. Vogel (Eds.). 399-416. Park Ridge, NJ: The Parthenon Publishing Group.

Petitti, D.B. (1986). Nausea and pregnancy outcome. *Birth, 13* (4), 223-226.

Petrikovsky, B., & Gross, B. (1996). Umbilical cord: Coiled versus noncoiled - Is there a third variant. *Journal of Clinical Ultrasound, 24,* 321-22.

Petrikovsky, B., Schifrin, B., & Diana, L. (1993). Effects of fetal acoustic stimulation on fetal swallowing and amniotic fluid index. *Obstetrics & Gynecology, 81* (4), 548-550.

Petrikovsky, B.M., Kaplan. G.P., & Pestrak, H. (1995). The application of color Doppler technology to the study of fetal swallowing. *Obstetrics & Gynecology, 86* (4 Part 1), 605-608.

Petropoulou, H., Stratigos, A.J., & Katsambas, A.D. (2006). Human immunodeficiency virus infection and pregnancy. *Clinical Dermatology, 24* (6), 536-542

Philip, J., Silver, R.K., Wilson, R.D., Thom, E.A., Zachary, J.M., Mohide, P., Mahoney, M.J., Simpson, J.L., Platt, L.D., Pergament, E., Hershey, D., Filkins, K., Johnson, A., Shulman, L.P., Bang, J., MacGregor, S., Smith, J.R., Shaw, D., Wapner, R.J., & Jackson, L.G. (2004). Late first-trimester invasive prenatal diagnosis: Results of an international randomized trial *Obstetrics & Gynecology, 103,* 1164-1173.

Pichini, S., & Garcia-Algar O. (2006). In utero exposure to smoking and newborn neurobehavior: how to assess neonatal withdrawal syndrome? *Therapeutic Drug Monitoring, 28* (3), 288-290.

Pierson, L.L. (1996). Hazards of noise exposure on fetal hearing. *Seminars in Perinatology, 20* (1), 21-29.

Pijnenborg, R., Robertson, W.B., Brosens, I., & Dixon, G. (1981) Trophoblast invasion and the establishment of haemochorial placentation in man and laboratory animals. *Placenta, 2*, 71-91.

Piper, J., & Wen, T. (1999). Perinatal cytomegalovirus and toxoplasmosis: challenges of antepartum therapy. *Clinical Obstetrics and Gynecology, 42*, 81-96.

Plant, M.L., & Plant, M.A. (1988). Maternal use of alcohol and other drugs during pregnancy and birth abnormalities: Further results of a prospective study. *Alcohol and Alcoholism 23*, 229-233.

Pleet, H., Graham, J,M., Jr., & Smith, D.W. (1981). Central nervous system and facial defects associated with maternal hyperthermia at four to 14 weeks' gestation. *Pediatrics, 67*, 785-789.

Ployé, P.M (1973). Does prenatal mental life exist? *International Journal of Psycho-Analysis 54*, 241-246.

Ployé, P.M. (1976). Existe-t-il un Psychisme Pré-natal? *L'Evolution Psychiatrique 41*, 663-674.

Plutarch. (1603). *Moralis.* P. Holland (Trans.). London: Hatfield.

Poissonnet, C.M., Burdi, A.R., & Bookstein, F.L. (1983). Growth and development of human adipose tissue during early gestation. *Early Human Development, 8* (1), 1-11.

Poissonnet, C.M., Burdi, A.R., & Garn, S.M. (1984). The chronology of adipose tissue appearance and distribution in the human fetus. *Early Human Development, 10* (1-2), 1-11.

Pokrzywnicka, M., Krajewski, P., & Kwiatkowska, M. (2005). Chlamydia infections in the neonatal period. *Medycyna Wieku Rozwojowego, 9* (1), 65-69.

Polikanina, R.I.(1961). The relation between autonomic and somatic components in the development of the conditioned reflex in premature infants. *Pavlov Journal of Higher Nervous Activity 11*, 51.

Polyhydramnios (2006). March of Dimes at marchofdimes.com. Retrieved October 10, 2006 from http://www.marchofdimes.com/pnhec/188_1044.asp.

Ponzetto, A., Cardaropoli, S., Piccoli, E., Rolfo, A., Gennero, L., Kanduc, D., & Todros, T. (2006). Pre-eclampsia is associated with Helicobacter pylori seropositivity in Italy. *Journal of Hypertension, 24* (12), 2445-2449.

Porter, F.L., Miller, R.H. & Marshall, R.E. (1986). Neonatal pain cries: Effect of circumcision on acoustic features of perceived urgency. *Child Development 57*, 790-802.

Prechtl, H.F., & Nijhuis, J.G. (1983). Eye movements in the human fetus and newborn. *Behavioral Brain Research 10*, 119-124.

Prematurity (2005). March of Dimes at march of dimes.com. Retrieved on November 30, 2006 from http://www.marchofdimes.com/prematurity/13454_5810.asp.

Preyer, R.W. (1885). *Spezielle physiologic des embryo.* Leipzig.

Pribram, K.H. (`1971). *Languages of the brain: Experimental paradoxes and principles in neuropsychology.* Englewood Cliffs, NJ: Prentice-Hall.

Pribram, K.H. (1969). The four R's of remembering. In *On the Biology of Learning.* Karl H. Pribram (Ed.). 191-225. New York: Harcourt, Brace & World.

Pribram, K.H., & Broadbent, D.E. (1970). *Biology of memory.* NY: Academic Press.

Price, J.H., Jordan, T.R., & Dake, J.A. (2006). Obstetricians and gynecologists' perceptions and use of nicotine replacement therapy. *Journal of Community Health, 31* (3), 160-175.

Pringle, K.C. (1986). Fetal surgery: it has a past, has it a future? *Fetal Therapy, 1* (1), 23-31.

Pringle, K.C. (1988). A reassessment of pregnancy staging. *Fetal Therapy, 3* (3), 173-184.

Profet, M. (1992). Pregnancy sickness as adaptation: a deterrent to maternal ingestion of teratogens. In *The adapted mind. Evolutionary psychology and the generation of culture.* J.H. Barkow, L. Cosmides, & J. Tooby (Eds). 327-365. NY: Oxford University Press.

Prozas/Serafem & Pregnancy (2006). Organization of Teratology Information Services. Retreived on December 11, 2006 from http://otispregnancy.org/pdf/prozac.pdf.

Purpura, D.P. (1975). Normal and aberrant neuronal development in the cerebral cortex of the human fetus and young infant. In *Basic mechanisms in mental retardation* (UCLA Forum in Medical Sciences, No. 18). M.A.G. Brazier & N.A. Buchwald (Eds.). 141-169. NY: Academic Press.

Purpura, D.P. (1975). Dendrite differentiation in human cerebral cortex; Normal and aberrant developmental patterns. *Advances in Neurology 12*, 91-116.

Purpura, D.P. (1979). Consciousness. Behavior Today 27, 437-448.

Putnam, W.H. (1979). Hypnosis and distortions in eyewitness testimony. *International Journal of Clinical and Experimental Hypnosis 27*, 437-448.

Q

Querleu, D., Renard, X., Boutteville, C., & Crepin, G. (1989). Hearing by the human fetus? *Seminars in Perinatology, 13* (5), 409-420.

R

Rados, C. (2004). FDA Cautions Against Ultrasound 'Keepsake' Images. *FDA ConsumerMagazine, 38* (1). Retrieved on November 3, 2006 from http://www.fda.gov/fdac/features/2004/104_images.html.

Rahbar, F. (1975). Observations on methadone withdrawal in 16 neonates. *Clinical Pediatrics, 14* (4), 369-371.

Raikov, V.L. (1980). Age regression to infancy by adult subjects in deep hypnosis. *American Journal of Clinical Hypnosis 22*, 156-163.

Raikov, V.L. (1982). Hypnotic age-regression to the neonatal period: Comparisons with role playing. *International Journal of Clinical & Experimental Hypnosis 30* , 108-116.

Ramón y Cajal, C.L,, & Martinez, R.O. (2003). Defecation in utero: a physiologic fetal function. *American Journal of Obstetrics and Gynecology, 188* (1), 153-156.

Ramsey, M.E., Miller, E., & Peckham, C.S. (1991). Outcome of confirmed symptomatic congential cytomegalovirus infection. *Archives of Disease in Chldhood, 66*, 1068-1069.

Rank, O. (1952). *The trauma of birth.* New York: Robert Brunner.

Rao, C.V. (2001). Tropic effects of LH and hCG on early pregnancy events in women's reproductive tract. *Early Pregnancy, 5* (1), 18-19.

Rao, R., & Desai, N.S. (2002). OxyContin and neonatal abstinence syndrome. *Journal of Perinatology, 22* (4), 324-325.

Rau, H. (1982). Frühe Kindheit. In R. Oerter & L. Montada (Eds.). *Entwicklungpsychologie.* 131. München: Urban & Schwarzenberg.

Rau, H. (1983). Frühkindliche Entwicklung. In *Entwinklungspsychologie.* R.K Silberseisen & L. Montada (Eds.). 83. München: Urban & Schwarzenberg.

Ravelli, G.P. (1976). Obesity in young men after famine exposure in utero and early infancy. *The New England Journal of Medicine, 349*-353.

Ray, E., & Martinez, H. (1984). *Rational handling of the premature child.* NY: Report to UNICEF.

Ray, W.S. (1932). A preliminary report on the study of foetal conditioning. *Child Development 3*, 175-177.

Reading, A.E. (1983). The influence of maternal anxiety on the course and outcome of pregnancy: A review. *Health Psychology 2*, 187-202.

Reading, A.E., Cox, D.N., Sledmere, C., & Campbell, S. (1984). Psychological changes over the course of pregnancy: A study in attitudes toward the fetus/neonate. *Health Psychology 3*, 211-221.

Reich, W. (1972). *Character analysis* (3rd ed.). V.R. Carfagno (Trans.). NY: Farrer, Straus & Giroux.

Reinis, S., & Goldman, J.M. (1980). Prenatal and early postnatal development of brain function. *The development of the brain: biological and functional perspectives.* Springfield: Charles C. Thomas.

Relton, C.L., Hammal, D.M., Rankin, J., & Parker, L. (2005). Folic acid supplementation and social deprivation. *Journal of Public Health Nutrition, 8* (3), 338-340.

Relton, C.L., Pearce, M.S., & Parker, L. (2005). The influence of erythrocyte folate and serum vitamin B_{12} status on birth weight. *British Journal of Nutrition, 93*, 593-599.

Reppert, S.M., & Schwartz, W.J. (1983). Maternal coordination of fetal biological clock "in utero". *Science 220,* 969-971.

Reppert, S.M., Henshaw, D., Schwartz, W.J., & Weaver, D.R. (1987). The circadian-gated timing of birth in rats: Disruption by maternal SCN lesions or by removal of the fetal brain. *Brain Research 403,* 398-402.

Reppert, S.M., Weaver, D.R., & Rivkees, S.A. (1988). Maternal communication of circadian phase to the developing mammal. *Psychoneuroendocrinology 13*, 63-78.

Resino, S., Resino, R., Maria Bellon, J., Micheloud, D., Gutierrez, M.D., de Jose, M.I., Ramos, J.T., Fontelos, P.M., Ciria. L., & Munoz-Fernandez. M.A. (2006). Clinical outcomes improve with highly active antiretroviral therapy in vertically HIV type-1-infected children. *Clinical Infectious Disease, 43* (2), 243-252.

Rhees, R.W., & Fleming, D.E. (1981). Effects of malnutrition, maternal stress, or ACTH injections during pregnancy on sexual behavior of male offspring. *Physiology and Behavior 27*, 879-882.

Rhodes, J. (1991). Report on research project: Interviews with 2 1/2 to 3 1/2 year old children regarding their memories of birth and the pre-natal period. *Pre- and Peri-Natal Psychology Journal 6*, 97-103.

Rice, R. (1977). Neurophysiological development in premature infants following stimulation. *Developmental Psychology 13*, 69-76.

Richmond, J.B. & Herzog, J.M. (1979). From conception to delivery. In *Basic Handbook of Child Psychiatr.* (vol. 1). J.D. Noshpitz (Ed.). NY: Basic Books.

Rider, R.O., Rosenthal, D., Wender, P. & Blumenthal, H (1975). The offspring of schizophrenics: Fetal and neonatal deaths. *Archives of General Psychiatry 32*, 200-211.

Ridge, B.R., & Budd, G.M. (1990). How long is too long in a spa pool? *New England Journal of Medicine, 323* (12), 835.

Ridgeway, R. (1987). *The unborn child.* London: Karnac Publishers.

Rieser, J., Yonas, A., & Wikner, K. (1976). Radial localization of odors by human newborns. *Child Development 47,* 856-859.

Riley, C.M. (1988). Teaching mother/fetus communication: A workshop on how to teach pregnant mothers to communicate with their unborn Children. *Pre- and Peri-Natal Psychology Journal 3,* 77-86.

Ringler, N.M., Trause, M.A., Klaus, M.H., & Kennell, J.H. (1978). The effects of extra post-partum contact and maternal speech patterns on children's IQs, speech, and language comprehension at five. *Child Development 49*, 862-865.

Ritzman, T.A. (1989). Schizophrenia, it's cause and cure. *Medical Hypnoanalysis Journal 4*, 27-37.

Rizzo, T., Metzger, B.E., Burns, W.J., & Burns K. (1991). Correlation between antepartum maternal metabolism and intelligence of offspring. *New England Journal of Medicine. 325*, 911-916.

Robert-Gangneux, F., Gavinet, M-F., Ancelle, T., Raymond, J., Tourte-Schaefer, C., & Dupouy-Camet, J. (2004). Value of Prenatal Diagnosis and Early Postnatal Diagnosis of Congenital Toxoplasmosis: Retrospective Study of 110 Cases. *Journal of Clinical Microbiology, 37* (9), 2893-2898.

Roberts, A.B., Griffin, D., Mooney, R., & Cooper, D.J. (1980). Fetal activity in 100 normal third trimester pregnancies. *British Journal of Obstetrics and Gynecology 87,* 480-484.

Roberts, S.C., Havlicek, J., Flegr, J., Hruskova, M., Little, A.C., Jones, B.C., Perrett, D.I., Petrie, M. (2003). Female facial attractiveness increases during the fertile phase of the menstrual cycle. *Proceedings of the Royal Biological Society, 271* (Supplement 5), 5270-5272.

Robertson, S.S. (1988). Infants of diabetic mothers: Late normalization of fetal cyclic motility persists after birth. *Developmental Psychobiology 21,* 477-490.

Robertson, S.S., & Dierker, L.J. (1986). The development of cyclic motility in fetuses of diabetic mothers. *Developmental Psychobiology 19,* 223-234.

Robinson, G.E., Stewart, D.E., & Flak, E. (1986). The rational use of psychotropic drugs in pregnancy and postpartum. *Canadian Journal of Psychiatry 31*, 183-190.

Robinson, J.L., Lee, B.E., Preiksaitis, J.K., Plitt, S., & Tipples, G.A. (2006). Prevention of congenital rubella syndrome--what makes sense in 2006? *Epidemiologic Reviews, 28*, 81-87.

Robinson, R.J., & Tizard, J.P.M. (1966). Central nervous system in the new-born. *British Medical Bulletin, 22* (1), 49-55.

Rodeck, C.H. and Campbell, S. (1979). Umbilical cord insertion as source of pure fetal blood for prenatal diagnosis. *Lancet, 1,* 1244

Rodeck, C.H., & Campbell, S. (1978a). Early prenatal diagnosis of neural tube defects by ultrasound guided fetoscopy. *Lancet, 2,* 1128.

Rodeck, C.H., & Campbell, S. (1978b). Sampling pure fetal blood by fetoscopy in second trimester of pregnancy. *British Medical Journal, 2,* 728

Rodeck, C.H., Eadi, R.A.J., & Gosden, C.M. (1980) Prenatal diagnosis of epydermolysis bullosa letalis. *Lancet 1*, 949-952.

Rodeck, C.H., Patrick, A.D., & Pembrey, M.E. (1982). Fetal liver biopsy for prenatal diagnosis of ornithine carbamyltransferace deficiency. *Lancet, 1,* 189-194.

Rodgers, B. (1978). Feeding in infancy and later ability and attainment: A longitudinal study. *Developmental Medical Child Neurology 20,* 421-426.

Rodier, P.M., Aschner, M., & Sager, P.R. (1984). Mitotic arrest in the developing CNS after prenatal exposure to methylmercury. *Neurobehavioral Toxicology and Teratology, 6*, 379-385.

Roedenback, S.D. (1974). Prenatal protein deficiency and the development of the nervous system: II. Neuropsychological aspects. *Revista de Neuro Psiquiatria 37*, 155-168.

Roffwarg, H.P., Muzio, J.N., & Dement, W.C. (1966). Ontogenetic development of the human dream cycle. *Science 152,* 604-619.

Rogers, C. (1961). *On becoming a person.* NY: Houghton Mifflin.

Rogers, J.F., & Dunlop, A.L. (2006). Air pollution and very low birth weight infants: a target population? *Pediatrics, 118* (1), 156-164.

Romanini, C., & Rizzo, G. (1995). Fetal behaviour in normal and compromised fetuses. An overview. *Early Human Development, 43* (2), 117-131.

Rommelspacher, H. (1991). Die Pharmakologie der Drogen (Heroin, L-Methadon, Kokain, Haschisch) und ihrer Effekte auf Schwangerschaft, Fötus und Neugeborenen. *Der Gynäkologe, 24* (6), 315-321.

Rosa, F.W. (1991). Spina bifida in infants of women treated with carbamazepine during pregnancy. *New England Journal of Medicine, 324* (10), 674-677.

Rosa, F.W. (1993). Teratogenicity of isotretinoin. *Lancet, 2,* 513.

Rose, S.A., & Wallace, I.F. (1985). Visual recognition memory: A predictor of later cognitive functioning in preterms. *Child Development 56*, 843-852.

Rose, S.A., Schmidt, K., Riese, M.L., & Bridger, W.H. (1980). Effects of prematurity and early inter-vention on responsivity to tactual stimulation: A comparison of preterm and full-term infants. *Child Development, 51*, 416-425.

Rosecan, J.S., & Gross, B.F. (1986). Newborn victims of cocaine abuse. *Medical Aspects of Human Sexuality 20*, 30-35.

Rosenfeld, M., Davis, R., FitzSimmons, S., Pepe, M., & Ramsey, B. (1997). Gender gap in cystic fibrosis mortality. *American Journal of Epidemiology, 145*, 794-803

Rosenstein, B.J., & Cutting, G.R. (1988). The diagnosis of cystic fibrosis: a consensus statement. Cystic Fibrosis Foundation Consensus Panel. *Journal of Pediatrics, 132* (4), 589-595.

Rosenwasser, A.M. (2001). Alcohol, antidepressants, and circadian rhythms. *Alcohol Research & Health, 25* (2), 126-135.

Rossi, N. (1987). La ricerca psicologica di fronte alla vita fetale. Prospettive e metodi di indagine. *Eta-evolutiva 26*, 65-70.

Rossi, N., Avveduti, P., Rizzo, N., & Lorusso, R. (1989). Maternal stress and fetal motor behavior: A preliminary report. *Pre- and Peri-Natal Psychology Journal 3*, 311-318.

Rosslin, E. (1910). *Der Swangern Frawen und Hebammen Rosegarten*. G. Klein (Ed.). Munich: C. Kuhn.

Rothenberg, S.J., Khan, F., Manalo, M., Jiang, J., Cuellar, R., Reyes, S., Acosta, S., Jauregui, M., Diaz, M., Sanchez, M., Todd, A.C., & Johnson, C. (2000) Maternal bone lead contribution to blood lead during and after pregnancy. *Environmental Research, 82* (1), 81-90.

Rottman, G. (1974). Untersuchungen über Einstellung zur Schwanger schaft und zür fotalen Entwicklung. In *Pranatale Psychologie*. Hans Graber (Ed.). Munchen: Kindler Verlag.

Rouse, B., Azen, B., Koch, R., Matalon, R., Hanley, W., de la Cruz, F., Trefz, F., Friedman, E., Shifrin, H. (1997). Maternal phenylketonuria collaborative study (MPKUCS) offspring: Facial anomalies, malformations, and early neurological sequelae. *American Journal of Medical Genetics, 69* (1), 89–95.

Rovee-Collier, C. (1985, October). Baby's memory. *American Psychological Association Monitor, 25*.

Rubin, D.C., and M. Kozin. "Vivid Memories." Cognition 16 (1984): 81-95.

Rubin, D.C., Wetzler, S.E., & Nebes, R.D. (1986). Autobiographical memory across the life span. In *Autobiographical Memory*. D.C. Rubin (Ed.). Cambridge: Cambridge Univ. Press.

Rubin, D.H., Krasilnikoff, P.A., Leventhal, J.M., & Berget, A. (1988). Cigarette smoking and alcohol consumption during pregnancy by Danish women and their spouses: A potential source of fetal morbidity. *American Journal of Drug and Alcohol Abuse 14*, 405-417.

Rumbold, A., Crowther, C., Haslam, R., Dekker. G., & Robinson, J. (2006). Vitamins C and E and the risks of preeclampsia and perinatal complications. *New England Journal of Medicine, 354* (17), 1796-806.

Rutt, C.N., & Offord, D.R. (1971). Prenatal and perinatal complications in childhood schizophrenics and their siblings. *Journal of Nervous and Mental Disorders 152*, 324-331.

Rutter, M.L. (2003). Genetic influences on fertility: Strengths and limitations of quantitative inferences. In K.W. Wachter & R.A. Bulatao (Eds.) *Offspring: Human Fertility Behavior in Biodemographic Perspective.* (pp. 18-45). Washington, DC.: The National Academies Press.

Ryan, V.S. (1977). Effect of prenatal and postnatal nutrition on development, behavior, and physiology of the rat. Ph.D. diss., Wayne State University.

Ryder, G.H. (1943). Vagitus uterinus. *American Journal of Obstetrics and Gynecology 46*, 867-872.

Rylander, L., Axmon, A., Toren, K., & Albin, M. (2002). Reproductive outcome among female hairdressers. *Occupational & Environmental Medicine, 59*, 517-522.

S

Sadger, J. (1941). Preliminary study of the psychic life of the fetus and the primary germ. *The Psychoanalytic Review, 28*.

Sagi, A., & Hoffman, M.L. (1976). Epathetic distress in the newborn. *Developmental Psychology 12*, 175-176.

Saha, U.K., Gupta, M., & Sengupta, D. (1986). Studies on the 'in vitro' effect of doxepin on cholinesterase and monoamine oxidase activity of human fetal brain. *IRCS Medical Science Psychology and Psychiatry 14*, 597-598.

Saha, U.K., Sengupta, T., Dutta, C., & Chakrabortyl, A. (1986). In vitro effect of haloperidol on cholinesterase activity of human fetal brain. *IRCS Medical Science Psychology and Psychiatry 14*, 461-462.

Salam, M., Millstein, J., Li, Y., Lurmann, F., Margolis, H., & Gilliland, F. (2005). Birth outcomes and prenatal exposure to ozone, carbon monoxide, and particulate matter: results from the Children's Health Study. *Environmental Health Perspectives, 113*, 1638-1644.

Salk, L. (1970). The critical nature of the postpartum period in the human for the establishment of the mother-infant bond: A controlled study. *Diseases of the Nervous System 31*, 110-116.

Salk, L. (1973). The role of the heartbeat in the relations between the mother and infant. *Scientific American,* 24-29.

Sameroff, A.J. (1972). Learning and adaptation in infancy: A comparison of models. *Advances in Child Development 7*, 170-214.

Samren, E.B., van Duijn, C.M., Christiaens, G.C., Hofman, A., & Lindhout, D. (1999). Antiepileptic drug regimens and major congenital abnormalities in the offspring. *Annals of Neurology, 46* (5), 739-746.

Sander, L. (1980). New knowledge about the infant from current research: Implications for psychoanalysis. *Journal of the American Psychoanalytic Association 28*, 181-198.

Sangtawesin, V., Lertsutthiwong, W., Kanjanapattanakul, W., Khorana, M., & Horpaopan, S. (2005). Outcome of maternal syphilis at Rajavithi Hospital on offsprings. *Journal of the Medical Association of Thailand, 88* (11), 1519-1525.

Sanin, L.H., López, S.R., Olivares, E.T., Terrazas, M.C., Silva, M.A.R., & Carrillo, M.L. (2001). Relation between birth weight and placenta weight. *Biology of the Neonate, 80*, 13-117.

Santos, I.S., Victora, C.G., Huttly, S. & Morris, S. (1998). Caffeine intake and pregnancy outcomes: a meta-analytic review. *Cadernos de Saúde Pública, 14* (3), 523-530.

Sanz, E.J., De-las-Cuevas, C., Kiuru, A., Bate, A., & Edwards, R. (2005). Selective serotonin reuptake inhibitors in pregnant women and neonatal withdrawal syndrome: a database analysis. *Lancet, 365*, 482-487.

Sarbin, T.R. (1950). Contributions to role-taking theory: Hypnotic behavior. *Psychological Review 57*, 255-270.

Saurel-Cubizolles, M.J., & Kaminski, M. (1987). Pregnant women's working conditions and their changes during pregnancy: a national study in France. *British Journal of Industrial Medicine, 44*, 236–243.

Saxen, L., Holmberg, P.C., Nurminen, M., & Kuosma, E. (1982). Sauna and congenital defects. *Teratology, 25* (3), 309-313.

Saxon, L., & Rapola, J. (1969*). Congenital defects.* NY: Holt.

Sayle, A.E., Savitz, D.A., & Williams, J.F. (2003). Accuracy of reporting of sexual activity during late pregnancy. *Paediatric and Perinatal Epidemiology, 17* (2), 143-147.

Sayle, A.E., Savitz, D.A., Thorp, J.M. Jr., Hertz-Picciotto, I., & Wilcox, A.J. (2001). Sexual activity during late pregnancy and risk of preterm delivery. *Obstetrics & Gynecology, 97* (2), 283-289.

Scafidi, F.A., Field, T., & Schanberg, S.M. (1993). Factors that predict which preterm infants benefit most from massage therapy. *Journal of Developmental Behavioral Pediatrics, 14*, 146-180.

Scarr-Salapatek, S. & Williams, M.L. (1973). The effects of an early stimulation program for low birth weight infants. *Child Development 44*, 94-100.

Schaal, B. (1988). Olfaction in infants and children: Developmental and functional perspectives. *Chemical Senses 13*, 145-190.

Schaal, B., Marlier, L., & Soussignan, R. (2000). Human foetuses learn odours from their pregnant mother's diet. *Chemical Senses, 25* (6), 729 – 737.

Schaffir, J. (2006). Sexual intercourse at term and onset of labor. *Obstetrics & Gynecology, 107* (6), 1310-1314.

Schindler, S. (1988). A new view of the unborn: Toward a developmental psychology of the prenatal period. In P.G. Fedor-Freybergh & M.L.V. Vogel (Eds.). *Prenatal and Perinatal Psychology and Medicine* (pp. 23-33). Park Ridge, NJ: The Parthenon Publishing Group.

Schmidt, W., Cseh, I., Hara, K., Neusinger, J., & Kubli, F. (1982). Die mütterliche Vorstellung der fötalen Bewegungen während des letzten Trimesters der Schwangerschaft. *Geburtshilfe und Frauenheilkunde, 42* (11), 798-802

Schmitz, M., Denardin, D., Laufer Silva, T., Pianca, T., Hutz, M.H., Faraone, S., & Rohde, L.A. (2006). Smoking during pregnancy and attention-deficit/hyperactivity disorder, predominantly inattentive type: a case-control study. *Journal of the American Academy of Child and Adolescent Psychiatry, 45* (11), 1338-1345.

Schmutz, J.L. (2003). Physiological skin changes during pregnancy. *La Presse Médicale, 32* (38), 1806-1808.

Schneider, M.L., Roughton, E.C., & Lubach, G.R. (1997). Moderate alcohol consumption and psychological stress during pregnancy induce attention & neuoromotor impairments in primate infants. *Child Development, 68*, 747-759.

Schou, M. (1990). Lithium treatment during pregnancy, delivery, and lactation: an update. *Journal of Clinical Psychiatry, 51* (10), 410-413.

Schreinemachers, D.M,, Cross, P.K., & Hook, E.B. (1982) Rates of trisomies 21, 18, 13 and other chromosome abnormalities in about 20,000 prenatal studies compared with estimated rates in live births. *Human Genetics, 61* (4), 318-324.

Schulman-Galambos, C., & Galambos, R. (1979). Assessment of hearing. In *Infants Born at Risk: Behavior and Development.* T.M. Field (Ed.). NY: S.P. Medical & Scientific Books.

Schulze, M.B., Liu, S., Rimm, E.B., Manson, J.E., Willett, W.C., & Hu, F.B. (2004). Glycemic index, glycemic load, and dietary fiber intake and incidence of type 2 diabetes in younger and middle-aged women. *American Journal of Clinical Nutrition, 80*, 348-356.

Scolnik, D., Nulman, I., Rovet, J., Gladstone, D., Czuchta, D., Gardner, A., Gladstone, R., Ashby. P., Weksberg, R., Einarson, T., & Koren, G. (1994). Neurodevelopment of children exposed in utero to phenytoin and carbamazepine monotherapy. *Journal of the American Medical Association, 271* (10), 767-770.

Selinger, D.L. (1973). Effect of prenatal maternal administration of d-amphetamine on rat offspring activity and passive avoidance learning. *Physiological Psychology 1*, 273-280.

Sex trivia (2006). coolnurse.com. Retrieved September 22, 2006, from http://www.coolnurse.com/sex_trivia.htm.

Sexton, M., Fox, N., & Heber, J. (1986). The effect of maternal smoking on the cognitive development of three year old children. *Teratology, 33*, 31c-32c.

Shah, T,, & Sullivan, K. (2006). Sudden infant death syndrome and reported maternal smoking during pregnancy. *American Journal of Public Health, 96* (10), 1757-1759.

Shanmugam, S., Thappa, D.M., & Habeebullah, S. (1998). Pruritus gravidarum: a clinical and laboratory study. *Journal of Dermatology, 25* (9), 582-586.

Shannon, M. (2003). Severe lead poisoning in pregnancy. *Ambulatory Pediatrics, 3* (1), 37-39.

Sheffield, J.S., & Cunningham, F.G. (2005). Urinary tract infection in women. *Obstetrics & Gynecology, 106* (5 Pt 1), 1085-1092.

Sheiner, E., Ohel, I., Levy, A., & Katz, M. (2006). Pregnancy outcome in women with pruritus gravidarum. *Journal of Reproductive Medicine, 51* (5), 394-398

Shepard, T.H. (1982). Detection of human teratogenic agents. *Journal of Pediatrics, 101* (5), 810-815.

Shepard, T.H., Brent, R.L., Friedman, J.M., Jones, K.L., Miller, R.K., Moore, C.A., & Polifka, J.E. (2002). Update on new developments in the study of human teratogens. *Teratology, 66* (6), 273.

Sherman, M.P., & Wheeler-Sherman, J. (2000). Cranky babies: outcomes associated with prenatal amphetamine exposure. *Journal of Perinatology, 20* (7), 478.

Sheskin, J. (1966). Therapie der Lepra-Reaktion mit Thalidomid (Eine Doppelblind-Studie) Vorlaufige Mitteiling. *Der Hautarzt, 17*, 548 –549.

Sheth, S.S. (2006). Missing female births in India. *Lancet, 367* (9506), 185-186.

Shetler, D.J. (1989). The inquiry into prenatal musical experience: A report of the Eastman Projects, 1980-1987. *Pre- and Peri-Natal Psychology Journal 3*, 171-189.

Shimada K., Hosokawa, S., Tohda, A., Matsumoto, F., Suzuki, M., & Morimoto, Y. (1998). Follow-up of children after fetal treatment for obstructive uropathy. *International Journal of Urology, 5* (4), 312-316.

Shiono, P.H., & Mills, J.L. (1984). Oral clefts and diazepam use during pregnancy. *New England Journal of Medicine, 311*, (14), 919-920.

Shiota, K. (1982) Neural tube defects and maternal hyperthermia in early pregnancy: Epidemiology in a human embryo population. *Am. J. Med. Genet.* , 12: 281-288.

Shu, X.O., Hatch, M.C., Mills, J., Clemens, J., & Sussers, M. (1995). Maternal smoking, alcohol drinking, caffeine consumption and fetal growth: Results from a prospective study. *Epidemiology, 6*, 115-120.

Signorello, L.B., Nordmark, A., Granath, F., Blot, W.J., McLaughlin, J.K., Annerén, G., Lundgren, S., Ekbom, A., Rane, A., & Cnattingius, S. (2001). Caffeine metabolism and the risk of spontaneous abortion of normal karyotype fetuses. *Obstetrics & Gynecology, 98*, 1059-1066.

Siklósi, G., Ács, N., Demendi, C., Börzsönyi, B., Gimes, G., Bakos, L., Olajos, F., & Marcsek, Z. (2001). Luteal function as the main determinant of pregnancy outcome: Successful prevention of spontaneous abortion, prematurity and IUGR. *Early Pregnancy, 5* (1), 22-23.

Silverman, W.A. (2002). The schizophrenic career of a "monster drug". *Pediatrics, 110* (2), 404-406.

Simkin, P. (1986). Stress, pain and catecholamines in labor: A review. *Birth issues in Perinatal Care and Education 13*, 227-233.

Simner, M. (1971). Newborns' response to the cry of another infant. *Developmental Psychology 5*, 136-150.

Simoni, G., Brambati, B., Danesino, C., Rossella, F., Terzoli, G.L., Ferrari, M. & Fraccaro, M. (1983). Efficient direct chromosome analysis and enzyme determinations from chorionic villi samples in the first trimester of pregnancy. *Human Genetics, 63*, 349-57

Simpson, J.L. (2000). Invasive diagnostic procedures for prenatal genetic diagnosis. *Journal Watch Women's Health, 5* (6), 47.

Singer, L.T., Arendt, R., Minnes, S., Farkas, K., Salvator, A., Kirchner, H.L., & Kliegman, R. (2002). Cognitive and motor outcomes of cocaine-exposed infants. *Journal of the American Medical Association, 287* (15), 1952-1960.

Singer, L.T., Minnes, S., Short, E., Arendt, R., Farkas, K., Lewis, B., Klein, N., Russ, S., Min, M.O., Lester Kirchner, L. (2004). Cognitive outcomes of preschool children with prenatal cocaine exposure. *Journal of the American Medical Association, 291*, 2448-2456.

Singer, L.T., Salvator, A., Arendt, R., Minnes, S., Farkas, K., & Kliegman, R. (2002). Effects of cocaine/polydrug exposure and maternal psychological distress on infant birth outcomes. *Neurotoxicology and Teratology, 24* (2), 127-135.

Singleton, E.G., Harrell, J.P., & Kelly, M.L (1986). Racial differences in the impact of maternal cigarette smoking during pregnancy on fetal development and mortality: Concerns for black psychologists. *Journal of Black Psychology 12*, 71-83.

Siqueland, E.R., & Lipsitt, L.P. (1966). Conditioned head-turning in human newborns. *Journal of Experimental Child Psychology 3*, 356-376.

Sjogren, B., & Uddenberg, N. (1988). Prenatal diagnosis and maternal attachment to the child-to-be: A prospective study of 211 women undergoing prenatal diagnosis with amniocentesis or chronic villi biopsy. *Journal of Psychosomatic Obstetrics and Gynaecology 9*, 73-87.

Skjöldebrand-Sparre, L., Tolfvenstam, T., Papadogiannakis, N., Wahren, B., Broliden, K., & Nyman, M. (2000). Parvovirus B19 infection: association with third-trimester intrauterine fetal death. *BJOG: An International Journal of Obstetrics & Gynaecology, 107* (4), 476.

Skreb, N., & Frank, Z. (1963). Developmental abnormalities in the rats induced by heat shock. *Journal of Embryology and Experimental Morphology, 11*, 445-457.

Slater, A., Morison, V., & Rose, D. (1982). Visual imagery at birth. *British Journal of Psychology 73 *, 519-525.

Sleep and Early Brain Development and Plasticity. (2006). National Center on Sleep Disorder Research. National Institutes of Health (http://www.ncsdr.nih.gov). Retrieved on November 4, 2006 from http://www.nhlbi.nih.gov/health/prof/sl eep/res_plan/section6/section6.html.

Slupik, R.I., & Allison, K.C. (1996). *The American Medical Association Complete Guide to Women's Health.* New York: Random House.

Smidt-Jensen, S., Hahnemann, N., Jensen, P.K.A., & Therkelsen, A.J. (1984) Experience with find needle biopsy in the first trimester-an alternative to amniocentesis. *Clinical Genetics, 26*, 272.

Smith, A.M., Fried, P.A., Hogan, M.J., & Cameron, I. (2006). Effects of prenatal marijuana on visuospatial working memory: an fMRI study in young adults. *Neurotoxicology & Teratology, 28* (2), 286-295.

Methylmercury & Pregnancy (2004). Organization of Teratology Information Services. Retreived on December 18, 2006 from http://otispregnancy.org/pdf/methylmercury.pdf.

Smith, L., Yonekura, M.L., Wallace, T., Berman, N., Kuo, J., & Berkowitz, C.M. (2003). Effects of prenatal methamphetamine exposure on fetal growth and drug withdrawal symptoms in infants born at term. *Journal of Developmental & Behavioral Pediatrics, 24* (1), 17-23.

Smith, M.S., Edwards, M.J., & Upfold, J.B. (1986). The effects of hyperthermia on the fetus. *Developmental Medicine and Child Neurology 28,* 806-809.

Smith, R.P., Gitau, R., Glover. V., & Fisk, N.M. (2000). Pain and stress in the human fetus. *European Journal of Obstetrics, Gynecology, and Reproductive Biology, 92* (1), 161-165.

Smithells, R., & Newman, C.G. (1992). Recognition of thalidomide defects. *Journal of Medical Genetics, 29*, 716-723.

Smotherman, W.P. (1982). Odor aversion learning by the rat fetus. *Physiology and Behavior 29*, 769-771.

Smythe, C.N. (1965). Experimental methods for testing the integrity of the foetus and neonate. *Journal of Obstetrics and Gynecology of the British Commonwealth 72*, 920.

Sodhi, V.K., & Sausker, W.F. (1988). Dermatoses of pregnancy. *American Family Physician, 37* (1), 131-138.

Sontag, L.W. (1941) The significance of fetal environmental differences. *American Journal of Obstetrics and Gynecology 42*, 996-1003.

Sontag, L.W. (1944). War and the maternal-fetal relationship. *Marriage and Family Living 6*, 1-5.

Sontag, L.W. (1966). Implications of fetal behavior and environment for adult personalities. *Annals of the New York Academy of Sciences 134*, 782-786.

Sontag, L.W., & Wallace, R.F. (1934). Preliminary report of the Fels fund: Study of foetal reactivity. *American Journal of Diseases of Children 48,* 1050-1057.

Sontag, L.W., & Wallace, R.F. (1935). The effect of cigarette smoking during pregnancy upon the fetal heart rate. *American Journal of Obstetrics and Gynecology 29*, 77-83.

Soranus of Ephesus. (1894). *Die Gynakologie der Soranus von Ephesus.* H. Luneberg (Trans.). Munich: C. Kuhn.

Sornes, T. (1989). Short umbilical cord as a cause of fetal distress. *Acta Obstetrics Gynecology Scandinavia, 68*, 609-611.

Sorokin, Y., & Dierker, L.J. (1982). Fetal movement. *Clinical Obstetrics and Gynecology, 25* (4), 719-734.

Soulie, J.C. (1995). Cardiac involvement in fetal parvovirus B19 infection. *Pathologie-biologie Paris, 43* (5), 416-419.

Spehr, M., Gisselmann, G., Poplawski, A., Riffell, J.A., Wetzel, C.H., Zimmer, R.K., & Hatt, H. (2003). Identification of a testicular odorant receptor mediating human sperm chemotaxis. *Science, 299* (5615), 2054 – 2058.

Spelt, D.K. (1948). The conditioning of a human fetus "in utero". *Journal of Experimental Psychology 38*, 338-346.

Spielberger, C. & Jacobs, G. (1979). Emotional reactions to the stress of pregnancy and obstetrics complications. In *Emotion and Reproduction.* L. Carenza & L. Zichella (Eds.). 13. London: Academic Press.

Spragget, K. & Fraser, F.C. (1982a) Teratogenicity of maternal fever in women - A retrospective study. *Teratology, 25,* 78.

Spragget, K. & Fraser, F.C. (1982b). Sauna-induced hyperthermia in women. *Teratology, 25,* 77.

Spraycar, M. (Ed.). (1995). *Stedman's medical dictionary.* (26th ed.). Baltimore: Williams & Wilkins.

Stahl, F., Gotz, F., Poppe, I., Amendt, P., & Dorner, G. (1978). Pre- and early postnatal testosterone levels in rat and human. In *Hormones and Brain Development. Developments in Endocrinology (* vol. 3). G. Dorner & M. Kawakami (Eds.). 99-109. Amsterdam: Elsevier/North-Holland Biomedical Press.

Stainton, C.M. (1985). The fetus: A growing member of the family. *Family Relations Journal of Applied Family and Child Studies 34*, 321-326.

Star, R.B. (1986). *The healing power of birth.* Austin, Texas: Star Publishing.

Stark, C.R., Orleans, M., Haverkamp, A.D., & Murphy, J. (1984). Short- and long-term risks after exposure to diagnostic ultrasound in utero *Obstetrics & Gynecology, 63*, 194-200.

Staun-Ram, E., & Shalev, E. (2005). Human trophoblast function during the implantation process. *Reproductive Biology and Endocrinology, 3*, 56.

Stechler, G., & Halton, A. (1982). Prenatal influences on human development. *In Handbook of Developmental Psychology.* B.B. Wolman (Ed.). 175-189. Englewood Cliffs, NJ.

Steen, R.G. (1996). *DNA and destiny,nature & nurture in human behavior.* New York: Plenum Press.

Steiner, J.E. (1977). Facial expressions of the neonate infant indicating hedonics of food-related chemical stimuli. In *Tastes and development: The genesis of sweet preference.* J.M. Weiffenbach (Ed.). Washington DC: US Govt Printing Office.

Steiner, J.E. (1979). Human facial expressions in response to taste and smell stimulation. *Advances in Child Development and Behavior 13,* 257-295.

Steinhausen, H.C., & Spohr, H.L. (1998). Long-term outcomes of children with fetal alcohol syndrome: Psychopathology, behavior and intelligence. *Alcoholism: Clinical and Experimental Research, 22,* 334-338.

Stephens, T., & Brynner, R. (2001). *Dark Remedy. The Impact of Thalidomide and Its Revival as a Vital Medicine.* Cambridge, MA: Perseus Publishing.

Sternfeld, B. (1997). Physical activity and pregnancy outcome. Review and recommendations. *Sports Medicine, 23* (1), 33-47.

Sternfeld, B., Quesenberry, C.P., Jr, Eskenazi, B., & Newman, L. (1995). Exercise during pregnancy and pregnancy outcome. *Medicine & Science in Sports & Exercise, 27,* 634–640.

Stewart, J.L., & Meeker, J.E. (1997). Fetal and infant deaths associated with maternal methamphetamine abuse. Journal of Analytical Toxicology, 21, 515-517.

Stone, L.J., Smith, H.T., & Murphy, L. (1973). The competence of infants. In L.J. Stone, H.T. Smith & L. Murphy (Eds.). *The competent infant: Research and commentary.* NY: Basic Books.

Storey, A.E., Walsh, C.J., Quinton, R. & Wynne-Edwards, E. (2000). Hormonal correlates of paternal responsiveness in men. *Evolution and Human Behavior, 21,* 79-95.

Stott, D. (1973). Follow-up study from birth of the effects of prenatal stresses. *Developmental Medicine and Child Neurology 15,* 770-787.

Stott, D. (1977 May). Children in the womb: The effects of stress. *New Society,* 329-331.

Stott, D. & Latchford, S. (1976). Prenatal antecedents of child health, development, and behavior: An epidemiological report of incidence and association. *Journal of the American Academy of Child Psychiatry 15,* 161-191.

Stowe, Z.N., Cohen, L.S., Hostetter, A., Ritchie, J.C., Owens, M.J., & Nemeroff, C.B. (2000). Paroxetine in human breastmilk and nursing infants. *The American Journal of Psychiatry, 157* (2), 185-189.

Stratton. P. (1982). *Psychobiology of the Human Newborn.* London, J. Wiley.

Streissguth, A.P. (1997). *Fetal alcohol syndrome: a Guide for families and communities.* Baltimore: Brookes.

Streissguth, A.P., Barr, H.M., Bookstein, F.L., Sampson, P.D., & Olsen, H.C. (1999). The long-term neurocognitive consequences of prenatal alcohol exposure. *Psychological Science, 10,* 186-190.

Streissguth, A.P., Martin, D.C., & Barr, H.M. (1984). Intrauterine alcohol and nicotine exposure: Attention and reaction time in 4-year-old children. *Developmental Psychology 20,* 533-541.

Streissguth, A.P., Sampson, P.D., Barr, H.M., Darbym B.L., & Martin, D.C. (1989). IQ at age 4 in relation to maternal alcohol use and smoking during pregnancy. *Developmental Psychology, 25,* 3-11.

Strong, T.H., Elliot, J.P., & Radin, T. (1993). Non-coiled umbilical blood vessels: a new marker for the fetus at risk. *Obstetrics & Gynecology, 81,* 409-411.

Stuart, D. & Solis, J. (2001) *Advocacy in Genetics: A Teaching Guide and Workbook.* The Mountain States Genetics Regional Collaborative Center. Retrieved on September 23, 2006 from http://www.mostgene.org/advocacy/section15.htm.

Sturtevant, F.M. (1985). Use of aspartame in pregnancy. *International Journal of Fertility, 30* (1), 85-87.

Susruta, S. Sarirasthanam and Cikitsasthanam, ed. Ambikadatta Sastri. Benares: Chowkhanba Sanskrit Series Office, 1954..

Susruta. (1954). *Sarirasthanam and Cikitsasthanam* . (A. Sastri Ed. & Trans.). Benares: Chowkhanba Sanskrit Series Office.

Svare, J., Schmidt, H., Hansen, B., & Lose, G. (2006). Bacterial vaginosis in a cohort of Danish pregnant women: prevalence and relationship with preterm delivery, low birthweight and perinatal infections. *BJOG : An International Journal of Obstetrics and Gynaecology, 113* (12), 1419.

Sydorak, R.M., Hirose, S., Sandberg, P.L., Filly, R.A., Harrison, M.R., Farmer, D.L., & Albanese, C.T. (2002). Chorioamniotic membrane separation following fetal surgery. *Journal of Perinatology, 22,* 407-410.

T

Tachibana, T. (1986). Effects of prenatal X-irradiation on open-field behavior in rats: Application of randomized fostering technique and mapping results. *The Journal of General Psychology 113,* 379-392.

Taddio, A., Ito, S., & Koren, G. (1996). Excretion of fluoxetine and its metabolite, norfluoxetine, in human breastmilk. *Journal of Clinical Pharmacology, 36* (1), 42-47.

Taft, J. (1958). *Otto Rank: A biographical study based on notebooks, letters, collected writings, therapeutic achievements and personal associations.* NY: Julian Press.

Takeuchi, I.K., & Takeuchi, Y.K. (1986). Congenital hydrencephalus following X-irradiation of pregnant rats on an early gestational day. *Neurobehavioral Toxicology and Teratology 8,* 143-150.

Tan, J.Y. (2002). Thrombophilia in pregnancy. *Annals of the Academy of Medicine, Singapore, 31* (3), 328-334.

Tan, P.C., Andi, A., Azmi, N., & Noraihan, M.N. (2006). Effect of coitus at term on length of gestation, induction of labor, and mode of delivery. *Obstetrics & Gynecology, 108* (1), 134-140.

Tannahill, R. (1980*). Sex in history.* New York: Scarborough Books.

Tanner, J.M., & Taylor, G.R. (1965). *Growth.* New York: Time/Life Books.

Tegretol & Pregnancy (2003). Organization of Teratology Information Services. Retrieved on December 11, 2006 from http://otispregnancy.org/pdf/tegretol.pdf .

Tennes, K. (1984). Effects of marijuana on pregnancy and fetal development in the human. *National Institute on Drug Abuse Research Monograph Series, Monograph # 44,* 115-123.

Teratogens (2006). University of South Dakota Medical School. Retrieved on December 9, 2006 from http://www.usd.edu/med/som/genetics/curriculum/2DTERAT4.htm.

Thadhani, R., Stampfer, M.J., Hunter, D.J., Manson, J.E., Solomon, C.G., & Curhan, G.C. (1999). High body mass index and hypercholesterolemia: Risk of hypertensive disorders of pregnancy. *Obstetrics & Gynecology, 94,* 543-550.

Thalidomide & Pregnancy (2003). Organization of Teratology Information Services. Retrieved on December 12, 2006 from http://otispregnancy.org/pdf/thalidomide.pdf.

Thangappah, R.B. (2000). Maternal and perinatal outcome with drug abuse in pregnancy. *Journal of Obstetrics & Gynaecology, 20* (6), 597-600.

Thiery, M., Le Sian Yo, A., Vrijens, M. & Janssens, D. (1973). Vagitus uterinus. *Journal of Obstetrics and Gynaecology of the British Commonwealth 80,* 183-185.

Thompson, R.F., & Spenser, W.A. (1966). Habituation: A model for the study of neuronal substrates of behavior. *Psychological Review 73,* 16-43.

Thurman, L. (1986). Parental singing during pregnancy and infancy can assist in cultivating bonding and later development. In *Prenatal Psychology and Medicine*. P. Fedor-Freybergh & M.L.V. Vogel (Eds.). 273-282. Park Ridge NJ: The Parthenon Publishing Group.

Tierson, F.D., Olsen, C.L., & Hook, E.B. (1986). Nausea and vomiting of pregnancy and association with pregnancy outcome. *American Journal of Obstetrics and Gynecology, 155*, 1017-1022.

Tikkanen, J. & Heinonen, O.P. (1991). Maternal hyperthermia during pregnancy and cardiovascular malformations in the offspring. *European Journal of Epidemiology, 7*, 628-635.

Timor-Tritsch, I.E., Peisner, D.B., & Raju, S. (1990). Sonoembryology: an organ-oriented approach using a high-frequency vaginal probe. *Journal of Clinical Ultrasound, 18* (4), 286-298.

Timor-Tritsch, I.E., Zador. I., Hertz. R.H., & Rosen, M,G. (1976). Classification of human fetal movement. *American Journal of Obstetrics and Gynecology, 126* (1), 70-77.

Tomatis, A.A. (1987). Ontogenesis of the faculty of hearing. In *Pre- and Peri-Natal Psychology: An Introduction*. T.R. Verny (Ed.). 23-35. NY: Human Sciences Press.

Tong, S., Baghurst, P., McMichael, A., Sawyer, M., & Mudge, J. (1996). Lifetime exposure to environmental lead and children's intelligence at 11-13 years: The Port Pirie cohort study. *British Medical Journal, 312*, 1569-1575.

Torry, E.F., Hersh, S.P., & McCabe, K.D. Early childhood psychosis and bleeding during pregnancy: A prospective study of gravid women and their offspring. *Journal of Autism and Childhood Schizophrenia 5*, 289-297.

Toxoplasmosis & Pregnancy (2002). Organization of Teratology Information Services. Retreived on December 15, 2006 from http://otispregnancy.org/pdf/toxoplasmosis.pdf

Tridapalli, E.,.Capretti, M.G., Sambri, V., Marangoni, A., Moroni, A., D'Antuono. A., Bacchi, M.L., & Trotula. (1981). *Medieval woman's guide to health*. Beryl Rowland (Ed. & Trans.) Kent, Ohio: Kent State Univ. Press.

Trowell, J. (1982). Effects of obstetric management on the mother-child relationship. In *The Place of Attachment in Human Behavior*. C.M. Parks & J. Stevenson-Hinde (Eds.). 79-94. NY: Basic Books.

Truax, C.B. & R.R. Carkhuff. (1967). *Towards effective counseling and psychotherapy*. Chicago: Aldine.

Truby, H.M. (1975). Prenatal and neonatal speech, pre-speech, and an infantile speech lexicon. *Child Language/Word 27*, parts 1-3.

Truby, H.M., & Lind, J. (1965). Cry sounds of the newborn infant. In *Newborn Infant Cry*. J. Lind (Ed.). Acta Paediatrica Scandinavica (1965): Supplement 163.

Tuchmann-Duplessis, G.D. & Haegel, P. (1971). *Illustrated human embryology*. vols. 1, 2, & 3. (L.S. Hurdley, Trans.). NY: Springer Verlag.

Tuchsen, F., Hannerz, H., Burr, H., & Krause, N. (2005). Prolonged standing at work and hospitalisation due to varicose veins: a 12 year prospective study of the Danish population. *Occupational and Environmental Medicine, 62* (12), 847-850.

Tulving, E. (1972). Episodic and semantic memory. In *Organization of Memory*. E. Tulving & W. Donaldson (Eds.). London: Wiley.

Tulving, E. (1983). *Elements of episodic memory*. Oxford: Oxford Univ. Press.

Tulving, E. (1985). How many memory systems are there?" *American Psychologist 40*, 385-398.

Tuomisto, J. (2006). Protecting our unborn children: how to measure exposure to thousands of chemicals? *Archives of Disease in Childhood, 91* (8), 627-628.

Turner, E.K. (1956). The syndrome in the infant resulting from maternal emotional tension during pregnancy. *The Medical Journal of Australia 4*, 221-222.

Turner, J.R. (1988). Birth, life and more life: Reactive patterning based on prebirth events. In *Prenatal Psychology and Medicine*. P. Fedor-Freybergh & M.L.V. Vogel (Eds.). 309-316. Park Ridge NJ: The Parthenon Publishing Group.

Turners Syndrome. (2006). Wikipedia.com. Retreived on October 5, 2006 from http://en.wikipedia.org/wiki/Turner_syndrome.

Turnpenny, P. & Ellard, S. (2004). *Emery's Elements of Medical Genetics* (12th ed.). London: Churchill Livingstone.

U

Ukaonu, C., Hill, D.A.,& Christensen, F. (2003). Hypokalemic myopathy in pregnancy caused by clay ingestion. *Obstetrics & Gynecology, 102* (5 Pt 2), 1169-1171.

Ungerer, J.A., Brody, L.R., & Zelazo, P.R. (1978). Long-term memory for speech in 2-4 week-old infants. *Infant Behavior & Development 1*, 177-186.

Urban, G., Marinoni, E., Di Iorio, R., Lucchini, C., Alò, P., & Di Tondo, U. (2001). New placental factors: Between implantation and inflammatory reaction. *Early Pregnancy, 5* (1), 70-71.

V

Valentin, L. & Marsal, K. (1986). Fetal movement in the third trimester of normal pregnancy. *Early Human Development 14*, 295-306.

Valman, H.B., & Pearson. J.F. (1980). What the fetus feels. *British Medical Journal, 280* (6209), 233-234.

Van Bogaert, L.J. (2006). Anaemia and pregnancy outcomes in a South African rural population. *Journal of Obstetrics & Gynaecology, 26* (7), 617-619.

van de Carr, K., & Lehrer, M. (1986). Enhancing early speech, parental bonding, and infant physical development using prenatal intervention in standard obstetrical practice. *Pre-and Per-Natal Psychology Journal 1*, 20-30.

van de Carr, K., van de Carr, R., & Lehrer, M. (1988). Effects of a prenatal intervention program. In *Prenatal and Perinatal Psychology and Medicine*. P. Fedor-Freybergh & M.L.V. Vogel (Eds.). 489-496. Park Ridge, NJ: The Parthenon Publishing Group.

van de Carr, R., & Lehrer, M. (1988). Prenatal university: Commitment to fetal-family bonding and the strengthening of the family unit as an educational institution. *Pre- and Peri-Natal Psychology Journal 3*, 87-102.

Van den Bergh, B.R.H. (1983). Der Psychische Toestand van de zwangere en de Prenatale Ontwikkeling: Literatuurstudie en schets van een heuristische Model. *Tijdschrift vor Orthopedagogie, Kinderpsychiatrie en Kliinische Kinderpsychologie 8* , 18-37.

Van den Bergh, B.R.H. (1988). The relationship between maternal emotionality during pregnancy and the behavioral development of the fetus and neonatus. In *Prenatal Psychology and Medicine*. P. Fedor-Freybergh & M.L.V. Vogel (Eds.). 131-142. Park Ridge NJ: The Parthenon Publishing Group.

Van den Bergh, B.R.H. (1990). The influence of maternal emotions during pregnancy on fetal and neonatal behavior. *Pre- and Peri-Natal Psychology Journal 5*, 119-130.

Van den Bergh, B.R.H., Mulder, E.J., Visser, G.H., & Poelmann-Wessjes, G. (1989). The effect of (induced) maternal emotions on fetal behavior: A controlled study. *Early Human Development 19*, 9-19.

Van Dongen, L.G.R., & Goudie, E.G. (1980). Fetal movements in the first trimester of pregnancy. *British Journal of Obstetrics and Gynecology 87*, 191-193.

van Wijngaarden, E., Beck, C., Shamlaye, C.F., Cernichiari, E., Davidson, P.W., Myers, G.J., & Clarkson, T.W. (2006). Benchmark concentrations for methyl mercury obtained from the 9-year follow-up of the Seychelles Child

Development Study. *Neurotoxicology, 27* (5), 702-709.

Van Woerden, E.E., Van Geijn, H.P., Caron, F.J., & Swartjes, J.M. (1989). Automated assignment of behavioral states in the human near term fetus. *Early Human Development 19*, 137-146.

Varley, C.K. (1984). Attention deficit disorder (the hyperactivity syndrome): A review of selected issues. *Journal of Developmental and Behavioral Pediatrics 5*, 254-258.

Vaughn, B.E., Bradley, C.F., Joffe, L.S., Seifer, R., & Barglow, C. (1987). Maternal characteristics measured prenatally are predictive of ratings of temperament "difficulty" on the caret temperament questionnaire. *Developmental Psychology 23*, 152-161.

Vaughn, H.G., Jr. (1975). Electrophysiological analysis of regional cortical maturation. *Biological Psychiatry 10*, 513-526.

Venkatesha, S., Toporsian, M., Lam, C., Hanai, J., Mammoto, T., Kim, Y.M., Bdolah, Y., Lim, K.H., Yuan, H.T., Libermann, T.A., Stillman, I.E., Roberts, D., D'Amore, P.A., Epstein, F.H., Sellke, F.W., Romero, R., Sukhatme, V.P., Letarte, M., & Karumanchi, S.A. (2006). Soluble endoglin contributes to the pathogenesis of preeclampsia. *Nature Medicine, 12* (6), 642-649.

Verma, A., Dhawan, A., Zuckerman, M., Hadzic, N., Baker, A.J., & Mieli-Vergani, G. (2006). Neonatal herpes simplex virus infection presenting as acute liver failure: prevalent role of herpes simplex virus type I. *Journal of Pediatric Gastroenterology and Nutrition, 42* (3), 282-286.

Verny, T. (1981). *The secret life of the unborn child.* NY: Summit Books.

Vertinsky P. (1988). "Of no use without health": late nineteenth century medical prescriptions for female exercise through the life span. *Women's Health, 14* (1), 89-115

Vertinsky, P. (1994). *The Eternally Wounded Woman.* Urbana, Il.: The University of Illinois Press.

Ververs, T., Kaasenbrood, H., Visser, G., Schobben, F., de Jong-van den Berg, L., & Egberts, T. (2006). Prevalence and patterns of antidepressant drug use during pregnancy. *European Journal of Clinical Pharmacology, 62* (10), 863-870.

Vigano, P., Mangioni, S., Pompei, F., & Chiodo, I (2003). Maternal-conceptus cross talk – A review. *Placenta, 24*, S56-S61.

Villamor, E., & Cnattingius, S. (2006). Interpregnancy weight change and risk of adverse pregnancy outcomes: a population-based study. *Lancet, 368* (9542), 1164-1170.

Villar, J., Abdel-Aleem, H., Merialdi, M., Mathai, M., Ali, M., Zavaleta, N., Purwar, M., Hofmeyr, J., Nguyen, T., Campodonico, L., Landoulsi, S., Carroli, G., Lindheimer, M. (2006). World Health Organization randomized trial of calcium supplementation among low calcium intake pregnant women. *American Journal of Obstetrics & Gynecology, 194* (3), 639-649.

Visser, G.H., Bekedam, D.J., Mulder, E.J., & Van-Ballegooie, E. (1985). Delayed emergence of fetal behavior in type-1 diabetic women. *Early Human Development 12*, 167-172.

Visser, G.H.A., Mulder, H.H., Wit, H.P., Mulder, E.J.H., & Prechtl, H,F,R. (1989). Vibro-acoustic stimulation of the human fetus: effect on behavioral state organization. *Early Human Development, 19* (4), 285-296.

Volpe, A., Correnti, E., Grasso, A., Di Renzo, G.C., Pini, A., Sternieri, E. (1983). Drug addiction during pregnancy. *Biological Research in Pregnancy and Perinatology, 4* (3), 137-138.

von Hofsten, C. (1983). Foundations of perceptual development. In *Advances in Infancy Research* (vol. 2), L.P. Lipsitt & C.K. Rovee-Collier (Eds.). 241-264. Norwood, NJ: Ablex Books.

von Kaisenberg, C.S., Bender, G., Scheewe, J., Hirt, S.W., Lange, M., Stieh, J., Kramer, H.H., & Jonat, W. (2001). A case of fetal parvovirus B19 myocarditis, terminal cardiac heart failure, and perinatal heart transplantation. *Fetal Diagnosis and Therapy, 16* (6), 427-432.

Vuorenkoski, V., Lind, J., Partanen, T., Lejeune, J., & Wasz-Hockert, O. Spectrographic analysis of cries from children with "maladie du cri du chat". *Annales Paediatricias Fenniae 12*, 174-180.

W

W.H.O. (2005). HIV/AIDS. World Health Organization. Retrieved on December 19, 2006 from http://www.who.int/hiv/FS_SubSaharan Africa_Nov05_en.pdf.

W.H.O. (2006). Paediatric HIV and treatment of children living with HIV World Health Organization. Retrieved on December 19, 2006 from http://www.who.int/hiv/paediatric/en/i ndex.html.

Wagenaar, W. (1986). My memory: A study of autobiographical memory over six years. *Cognitive Psychology 18*, 225-252.

Wald, A. (2003). Constipation, diarrhea, and symptomatic hemorrhoids during pregnancy. *Gastroenterology Clinics of North America, 32* (1), 309-322.

Walker, A.R., Walker, B.F., Jones, J., Verardi, M., & Walker, C. (1985). Nausea and vomiting and dietary cravings and aversions during pregnancy in South African women. *British Journal of Obstetrics & Gynaecology, 92* (5), 484-489.

Walker, L., Levine, H., & Jucker, M. (2006). Koch's postulates and infectious proteins. *Acta Neuropathologica, 112,* (1), 1-4.

Walsh, D.S., & Adzick, N.S. (2003). Fetal surgery for spina bifida. *Seminars in Neonatology, 8,* 197-205.

Wang, A., Holladay, S.D., Wolf, D.C., Ahmed, S.A., & Robertson, J.L. (2006). Reproductive and developmental toxicity of arsenic in rodents: a review. *International Journal of Toxicology, 25* (5), 319-331.

Ward, R.H.T., Modell, B., Petrou, M., Karagozlu, F., & Douratsos, E. (1983). A method of sampling chorionic villi in first trimester of pregnancy under guidance of realtime ultrasound. *British Medical Journal, 286*, 1542-1544,

Wasz, O., Lind, J., Vuorenkoski, V., Partanen, T. & Valanne, E. (1968). *The infant cry: A spectrographic & auditory analysis.* London: Spestics International Medical Publications/William Heinnemann Medical Books.

Wasz-Hockert, O., Koivisto, M., Vuorenkoski, M., Partanen, T., & Lind, J. (1971). Spectrographic analysis of the pain cry in hyperbilirubinemia. *Biology of the Neonate 17*, 260-271.

Weaver, D.R., & Reppert, S.M. (1989). Direct in utero perception of light by the mammalian fetus. *Developmental Brain Research 47*, 151-155.

Webster, W.S., Lipson, A.H., & Brown-Woodman, P.D.C. (1987). Uterine trauma and limb defects. *Teratology, 35*, 253-260.

Wedenberg, E. & Johansson, B. (1970 April). When the fetus isn't listening. *Medical World News*, 28-29.

Weigel, M.M., & Weigel, R,M, (1989a). Nausea and vomiting of early pregnancy and pregnancy outcome. An epidemiological study. *British Journal of Obstetrics and Gynaecology, 96*, 1304-1311.

Weigel, M.M., & Weigel, R,M, (1989b) Nausea and vomiting of early pregnancy and pregnancy outcome. A meta-analytical review. *British Journal of Obstetrics and Gynaecology, 96*, 1312-1318.

Weisshaar, E., Witteler, R., Diepgen, T.L., Luger, T.A., & Stander, S. (2005). Pruritus in der Schwangerschaft – Eine haufige diagnostische und therapeutische Herausforderung. *Der Hautarzt: Zeitschrift für Dermatologie, Venerologie, und verwandte Gebiete, 56* (1), 48-57.

Weitzman, E.D., Fishbein, W., & Graziani, L (1965). Auditory evoked responses obtained from the scalp electroencephalogram of the full ferm neonate during sleep. *Pediatrics 35* , 458-462.

Werner, J.S., & Siqueland, E.R. (1978). Visual recognition memory in the preterm infant. *Infant Behavior and Development 1*, 79-94.

Werner, J.S., & Lipsitt, J.B. (1981). The infancy of human sensory systems. In *Developmental Plasticity*. E.S. Gollin (Ed.). 35-38. NY: Academic Press.

Wertheimer, M. (1961). Psychomotor coordination of auditory and visual space at birth. *Science 134*, 1692.

Wertheimer, N., & Leeper, E. (1986). Possible effects of electric blankets and heated waterbeds on fetal development. *Bioelectromagnetics, 7*, 13.

West, R.W., Sheldon, W.G., Gaylor, D.W., Haskin, M.G., Delongchamp, R.R., & Kadlubar, F.F. (1986). The effects of saccharin on the development of neoplastic lesions initiated with n-methyl-n-nitrosourea in the rat urothelium *Toxicological Sciences, 7* (4), 585-600.

Westfall, R., Janssen, P., Lucas, P., & Capler, R. (2006). Survey of medicinal cannabis use among childbearing women: patterns of its use in pregnancy and retroactive self-assessment of its efficacy against "morning sickness". *Complementary Therapies in Clin. Prac., 12* (1), 27-33.

Westin, B. (1954). Hysteroscopy in early pregnancy. *Lancet, 11*, 872.

Westrom, L.V. (1994). Sexually transmitted diseases and infertility. Sexually Transmitted Diseases, 21 (2), S32-S37.

White-Traut, R.C., Nelson, M.N., Silvestri, J.M., Patel, M.K., & Kilgallona, D. (1993). Responses of preterm infants to unimodal and multimodal sensory intervention. *Pediatric Nursing, 19*, 625-629.

Wide, K., Winbladh, B., Tomson, T., Sars-Zimmer, K., & Berggren, E. (2000). Psychomotor development and minor anomalies in children exposed to antiepileptic drugs in utero: a prospectivepopulation-based study. *Developmental Medicine & Child Neurology, 42*, 87-92.

Wijewardene, K., Fonseka, P., & Goonaratne, C. (1994). Dietary cravings and aversions during pregnancy. *Indian Journal of Public Health, 38* (3), 95-98.

Wilcox, A.J., Weinberg, C.R., O'Connor, J.F., Baird, D.D., & Schlatterer, J.P. (1988). Incidence of early loss of pregnancy. *The New England Journal of Medicine*, 319 (4), 189.

Wilkinson, C., & Robinson, J. (1982). Braxton-Hicks contractions and fetal breathing movements. *The Australian & New Zealand Journal of Obstetrics & Gynaecology, 22* (4), 212-214.

Willen, E.J. (2006). Neurocognitive outcomes in pediatric HIV. *Mental Retardation and Developmental Disabilities Research Reviews, 12* (3), 223-228.

Willett, W., Manson, J., & Liu, S. (2002). Glycemic index, glycemic load, and risk of type 2 diabetes. *American Journal of Clinical Nutrition, 76*, 274S-80S.

Williams, P.L., Wendell-Smith, C.P. & Treadgold, S. (1966). *Basic human embryology*. Philadelphia: J.B. Lippincott Co.

Williams, R.L., Creasy, R.K., Cunningham, G.C., Hawes, W.E., Norris, F.D., & Tashiro, M. (1982). Fetal growth and perinatal viability. *Obstetrics & Gynecology, 59* (5), 624-632.

Williamson, S., Jackson, L., Skeoch, C., Azzim, G., & Anderson, R. (2006). Determination of the prevalence of drug misuse by meconium analysis. *Archives of Disease in Childhood. Fetal and Neonatal Edition, 91* (4). F291-F292.

Wilson, J., DiFiore, J.W., & Peters, C.A. (1993). Experimental fetal tracheal ligation prevents the pulmonary hypoplasia associated with fetal nephrectomy: possible application for congenital diaphragmatic hernia. *Journal of Pediatric Surgery, 28*, 1433–1439.

Wilson, J.G., & Warkany, J. (1985). The history of organized teratology in North America. *Teratology, 31*, 285–296.

Windle, W.F. (1971). *Physiology of the fetus*. Springfield, Ill.: Charles C. Thomas.

Winick, M. (1976). *Malnutrition and brain development*. NY: Oxford Univ Press.

Winnicott, D.W. (1957) *Mother and child: A primer of first relationships*. NY: Basic Books.

Winnicott, D.W. (1958). *Collected papers: Through pediatrics to psycho-analysis*. New York: Basic Books.

Winnicott, D.W. (1972). *The maturational processes and the facilitating environment*. London: Hogarth Press.

Wolfe, L.A., Lowe-Wylde, S.J., Tranmer, J.E., (1988). Fetal heart rate during maternal static exercise. *Canadian Journal of Sport Sciences, 13*, 95P–96P.

Wolff, P.H. (1978). The natural history of crying and other vocalizations in early infancy. In *Determinants of infant behavior*. (vol. 4). B.M. Foss (Ed.). London: Methuen.

Wolff, P.H., & White, L.W. (1965). Visual pursuit and attention in young infants. *Journal of the American Academy of Child Psychiatry 4*, 437-484.

Wolkind, S. (1981). Pre-natal emotional stress-- Effects on the fetus. In *Pregnancy: A psychological and social study*. S. Wolkind (Ed.). 177-194. London: Academic Press.

Woo, J. (2006) A short history of amniocentesis, fetoscopy and chorionic villus sampling. Obstetric Ultrasound.com. Retrieved October 28, 2006 from http://www.ob-ultrasound.net/history.html.

Wood, N., Marlow, N., Costeloe, K., Gibson, A., & Wilkinson, A. (2000). Neurologic and developmental disability after extremely preterm birth. *New England Journal of Medicine, 343*, 378-384.

Woods, C.R. (2005). Syphilis in children: congenital and acquired. *Seminars in Pediatric Infectious Diseases, 16* (4), 245-257.

Wu, J.H., & Eichmann, M.A. (1988). Fetal sex identification and prenatal bonding. *Psychological Reports 63*, 199-202.

Wucherer-Huldenfeld, A.K. (1973). Ursprung und Anfang des menschlichen Lebens. In *Vorgeburtliches Seelenleben*. G.H. Graber & F. Kruse (Eds.). München: Goldmann.

Wynne-Edwards, E. (2001). Hormonal changes in mammalian fathers. *Hormones & Behavior, 40*, 139-145.

Wynne-Edwards, E., & Reburn, C. (2000) Behavioural endocrinology of mammalian fatherhood. *Trends in Ecology & Evolution, 15*, 464-468.

Y

Yanai, J., & Pick, C.G. (1988). Neuron transplantation reverses phenobarbital-induced behavioral birth defects in mice. *International Journal of Developmental Neuroscience 6*, 409-416.

Yandow, V. (1989). Alcoholism in Women. *Psychiatric Annals 19*, 243-247.

Yang, E.Y., & Adzick, N.S. (1998). Fetoscopy. *Seminars in Laparoscopic Surgery, 5* (1), 31–39.

Yeh, H.C., & Rabinowitz, J.G. (1988). Amniotic sac development: ultrasound features of early pregnancy--the double bleb sign. *Radiology, 166*, 97-103.

Yoshida, K., Smith, B., Craggs, M. & Kumar, R.C. (1998). Fluoxetine in breastmilk and developmental outcome of breastfed infants. *British Journal of Psychiatry, 172*, 175-178.

Yost, N.P., Owen, J., Berghella, V., Thom, E., Swain, M., Dildy, G.A., Miodovnik, M., Langer, O., Sibai, B, & National Institute of Child Health and Human Development, Maternal-Fetal Medicine Units Network. (2006). Effect of coitus on recurrent preterm birth. *Obstetrics & Gynecology, 107* (4), 793-797.

Youngerman-Cole, S. (2006). Fetoscopy. WebMD. Retrieved October 28, 2006 from http://www.webmd.com/hw/being_pregnant/hw4744.asp.

Younglai, E., Holloway, A.C., & Foster, W.G. (2005). Environmental and occupational factors affecting fertility and IVF success. *Human Reproduction Update, 11* (1), 43-57.

Z

Zaret, B.L., Jatlow, P.I., & Katz, L.D. (1997). *The Patient's Guide to Medical Tests.* New York: Houghton Mifflin.

Zeskind P.S., & Lester, B.M. (1978). Acoustic features and auditory perceptions of the cries of newborns with prenatal and perinatal complications. *Child Development 49,* 580-589.

Zoloft & Pregnancy (2006). Organization of Teratology Information Services. Retreived on December 11, 2006 from http://otispregnancy.org/pdf/zoloft.pdf.

Zysk, K. (1991). Asceticism and Healing in Ancient India. New York: Oxford Univ Press .

Made in United States
North Haven, CT
10 March 2025

66612814R00109